BAG O' T

�❀

BAG O' TALES

A Source Book for Story-Tellers

by

EFFIE POWER, A. M.

Assistant Professor School of Library Science
Western Reserve University
Director Work with Children
Cleveland Public Library

Illustrated by Corydon Bell

E. P. DUTTON AND CO., INC.
NEW YORK · 1934

Now Reissued by
Singing Tree Press
1249 Washington Blvd., Detroit, Michigan 1968

TO MOTHER

"Our finest hope is finest memory."

GEORGE ELIOT

ACKNOWLEDGMENTS

FOR the most part the selections quoted in this volume are from folk literature. Where it has proved possible to trace versions to definite sources credit has been given to editors.

My thanks are gratefully extended to Thomas Nelson and Sons for permission to use Arthur Ransome's "The Stolen Turnips" from *Old Peter's Russian Fairy Tales;* Row, Peterson and Co. for Mrs. Thorne Thomsen's version of *East O' the Sun and West O' the Moon;* the Frederick A. Stokes Co. for "The Old Woman and the Tramp" from *Fairy Tales from the Swedish* edited by G. Djurklo; G. P. Putnam's Sons for "Lambikin" and "The Farmer and the Money Lender" from *Indian Fairy Tales* edited by Joseph Jacobs, "The Pancake" and "The Sheep and the Pig Who Set Up House" from Asbjornsen's *Tales of the Fjeld,* translated by Dasent; the University of Chicago Press for "Hundred-Wit, Thousand-Wit and Single-Wit" from The *Panchatantra* edited by G. W. Ryder; the A. Flanagan Co. for Flora Cooke's "Clytie" from her *Nature Myths;* The Macmillan Company for Alfred Church's "Death of Hector" from *The Iliad for Boys and Girls,* and "The Cyclops" from *The Odyssey for Boys and Girls;* E. P. Dutton & Co., Inc., for three stories from the *Adventures of Odysseus* by Marvin, Mayor and Stawell, Henrietta Marshall's "How Beowulf Came to Daneland," from her *Stories of Beowulf* and "Death of Roland" from her *Stories of Roland,* "The Pies of the Princess" from Arthur B. Chrisman's *Shen of the Sea,* "The Silver Arrow" from F. C. Tilney's *Robin Hood and His Merry Outlaws;* Houghton Mifflin Co. for Eva March Tappan's versions of "Saddle to Rags" and "Forester Etin" from her *Old Ballads in Prose;* Thomas Y. Crowell Co. for the E. M. Wilmot-Buxton's versions of "The Apples of Youth," "How Thor's Hammer Was Lost and Found" and "How Sigurd Won the Hand of Brynhild" from her *Stories of*

ACKNOWLEDGMENTS

Norse Heroes and "Cuchulain's Wooing" from Eleanor Hull's *Boys' Cuchulain*.

Thanks are given also to Alice Hatch for her kindness in allowing me to use her manuscript version of "Frithiof's Journey to the Orkneys," and to Katherine Moorhead for her adaptation of "Zal, the White-Haired."

E. P.

CONTENTS

INTRODUCTION

IN THE days when the world was young, the story-teller held an honored place in cottage and hall. As a living voice he moved down the centuries, amusing, warning, cheering the people; transmitting language and thought; preserving literature. Thus the charm of story-telling became proverbial.

Then came the printing of many books, emphasis on reading, and widespread education following new methods. For a time the story-teller was forgotten by all but a few simple peoples in remote places, but it was inevitable that so popular a form of human appeal should not be lost. As was to be expected, the educational program based on a fuller knowledge of child psychology which was formed to meet the modern needs of our century, reinstated story-telling, at least for children. In homes, schools, libraries, playgrounds and camps, the story-teller is again a person of influence.

"Please tell a story about a most high princess, because I like to pretend I am the princess while you are telling it," said a pale-faced little girl in shabby clothes. And the children's librarian, remembering the master-story-teller who was himself an ugly duckling, repeated the old story of the princess who stood outside the town gate and knocked.

INTRODUCTION

"But mercy! how she looked from the rain and the rough weather! The water ran down from her hair and her clothes, it ran in at the points of her shoes and out at the heels: and yet she declared she was a real princess.

" 'Yes, we will soon find that out,' thought the Queen."

My earliest recollections of story-telling are associated with an old Pennsylvania farmhouse; a warm corner in the upper hall near a drum in a stovepipe that extended through an opening from the room below to the low ceiling above; the large lap and long protecting arms of Maggie, the hired girl; her low open chair with short rockers that creaked to the rhythm of—

> "See by the moonlight
> 'Tis long past midnight,
> Time Kid and I were home
> An hour ago."

Maggie was Scotch and resourceful in improvising. On some evenings "Kid and I" were woefully late and the one hour was lengthened to many. But one point in the story never varied and to this day I cannot be persuaded, many versions to the contrary notwithstanding, that it was a pig, not a kid, that behaved so contrarily.

Since that time other story-telling pictures have become etched on my memory. One, a playground scene in Pittsburgh; a horde of ragged children running gleefully to meet a library story-teller and calling out, "Here comes the Rat Lady! The Rat Lady!" (Her last story having been Browning's "Pied Piper.")

Another, a dingy, open space beneath elevated railroad tracks in St. Louis, where, surrounded by smoke, cinders, and the noise of trains, a group of children listened spellbound to "Nanny Who Wouldn't Go Home To Supper," told by a young negro woman.

It is the remembrance of these scenes, and similar impressions gained in telling stories to intimate groups in public libraries, that have convinced me that the secret of story-telling is having a story to tell, one that is worth telling, one that lives vividly in the memory.

INTRODUCTION

This Bag o' Tales is intended for those mothers, fathers, aunts, uncles, teachers and children's librarians who, regardless of talent, want to tell stories which will give joy to children and lead them to love good books. To do this requires time and effort in selection and preparation, but a well-chosen story, made one's own, is a lifelong possession that adds luster with years and is never out of fashion.

As to the manner of telling, it is probably true that the greatest story-tellers are born with the gift. But the average person gets a great deal of pleasure from the responses which children give to any sincere presentation of what they consider is a real story, and in turn, children's appreciative reactions often bring out undreamed-of talent from the story-teller.

A natural approach to the art of story-telling is through the use of traditional material which is already in form for telling and which is an accepted part of children's literature. This comprises familiar folk tales, myths and parts of epics, sagas, legends and chronicles.

For the most part, this world literature is simple in style, direct in appeal and objectively heroic. Some of it emphasizes as virtues certain attributes which children of the present day should not emulate, but there is no need to consider debatable stories when so large a number which have been judged for ethical content, beauty of style and associations with literature and art are available. It is chiefly from the historic traditional sources which form the basis of imaginative literature for children that the stories in this collection have been drawn, but the best of modern writing for children is represented.

Telling stories to children may become a rich personal experience for the story-teller. Also, in view of the present-day emphasis on learning through activities, some means must be found to train the listening ear that is so necessary to your child or mine if he is to develop culture, physical repose and spiritual vision.

EFFIE POWER

Cleveland, Ohio
June, 1934

BAG O' TALES

STORIES FOR LITTLE CHILDREN

STORIES FOR LITTLE CHILDREN

THE simplest form of traditional story for little children is the nonsense tale which develops its theme by reiteration of words and phrases according to a pattern. Its conclusions usually depend upon a contest of wit, or physical strength, or both. The final situation is intended to be humorous although the details may be gruesome, rollicking, or merely silly.

One form of this nonsense tale is illustrated by "The Pancake," in which the same incident occurs in succession but with a different actor until a climax is reached suddenly, and in a manner unexpected, at the end.

The familiar "The Old Dame and Her Silver Sixpence," also known as "The Old Woman and Her Pig," found in Mother Goose collections, illustrates a better literary form and one which is more satisfactory to young children because the transitions are more easily comprehended by them. In this story the narrative follows the repetitive pattern of "The Pancake" to a climax and closes gradually by reversing the situations created.

These repetitive folk tales are chimney-corner stories intended to be told informally, in a playful mood, but with a pretense of credence.

17

It is very important that their rhythmic quality and humor should be preserved since these elements constitute their main appeal to little children.

In testing folk tales for weakness it is sometimes helpful to try to discover the editor in the background introducing irrelevant comments which hinder the action. Sometimes aside remarks add humor or pathos to situations, but as a rule, true tales from the mind of the folk are impersonal. Remembering this, the creative story-teller adds the warmth of her own personality to each tale as she tells it without moralizing or otherwise intruding her own ideas. She respects her story and allows it to speak for itself through her.

In preparing nursery stories for telling, it is necessary to memorize the sequence of events and the repetitive parts. They are the type of story which children require to be told "Just so."

The stories which follow are mainly folk tales of which there are many variants. The versions given have been selected for their adherence to original sources, beauty and vigor in style and characterization, and appeal to children.

Other types of stories for little children are considered in the chapter "Fanciful Stories and Family Books."

✺

The Old Dame and Her Silver Sixpence

ONCE upon a time an old Dame was sweeping out her cottage when to her great joy she found a silver sixpence, so she sat down to think what she should do with such a good piece of luck.

First of all she thought she would buy a fat duck, and then she thought she would buy a hen that laid eggs well, but after thinking and thinking for a long, long time, she thought she would buy a pig. So she put up her broom in the closet, and got out her best high-heeled shoes, and her steeple-crowned hat, and taking her good old stick, she set out for the market town close by.

The way to the town was through green lanes and across large meadows, and as the good old Dame clambered over the stile at the

18

end of the meadow, she sat on the top to rest herself, and to think again on her good luck. Then she went on again till she came to the town.

She went straight to the market-place, and there she found a boy with a nice, white pig to sell; so, after a little bargaining, she gave the boy the silver sixpence for the white pig, and then she tied a piece of string to one of the pig's hind legs, and began to drive him home.

Piggy went through the streets very well, only grunting sometimes and running into the gutter when he saw anything he could eat, until at last they came to the stile into the meadow. The good Dame tried to lift the pig over the lower bar of the stile, but he squeaked, and grunted, and wriggled about, till she was quite tired, and after that, piggy laid down and would not stir.

Just then a little dog came trotting up, so the Dame said to him,

"Good dog, bite pig; pig will not get over the stile, and I shall not get home tonight."

But the dog would not.

So the Dame held up her stick and said,

"Good stick, beat dog; dog will not bite pig; pig will not get over the stile—and I shall not get home tonight."

But the stick would not.

So the Dame gathered some bits of wood together and set them into the fire, and said,

"Good fire, burn stick; stick will not beat dog; dog will not bite pig; pig will not get over the stile—and I shall not get home tonight."

But the fire would not.

So the Dame fetched a pail of water that was standing near, and said,

"Good water, quench fire; fire will not burn stick; stick will not beat dog; dog will not bite pig; pig will not get over the stile—and I shall not get home tonight."

But the water would not.

So the Dame turned round in a passion, and then she saw an ox coming; and so she said,

"Good ox, drink water; water will not quench fire; fire will not burn stick; stick will not beat dog; dog will not bite pig; pig will not get over the stile—and I shall not get home tonight."

But the ox would not.

So the Dame turned round to the stile again, and then she saw a jolly butcher leaning on the stile; so she said to him,

"Good butcher, kill ox; ox will not drink water; water will not quench fire; fire will not burn stick; stick will not beat dog; dog will not bite pig; pig will not get over the stile—and I shall not get home tonight."

But the butcher would not.

So the Dame took a rope out of her pocket, and said,

"Good rope, hang butcher; butcher will not kill ox; ox will not drink water; water will not quench fire; fire will not burn stick; stick will not beat dog; dog will not bite pig; pig will not get over the stile —and I shall not get home tonight."

But the rope would not.

So the Dame was in despair; but just then a large brown mouse ran across the meadow, and she said,

"Good mouse, gnaw rope; rope will not hang butcher; butcher will not kill ox; ox will not drink water; water will not quench fire; fire will not burn stick; stick will not beat dog; dog will not bite pig; pig will not get over the stile—and I shall not get home tonight."

"Yes," said the mouse, "I will, if you will give me some cheese."

So the Dame put her hand in her pocket and brought out a nice piece of cheese; and when the mouse had eaten it—

The mouse began to gnaw the rope; the rope began to hang the butcher; the butcher began to kill the ox; the ox began to drink the water; the water began to quench the fire; the fire began to burn the stick; the stick began to beat the dog; the dog began to bite the pig— the pig rushed right through the stile,—

And so the good Dame got home in time to boil her apple-dumplings.

OLD FOLK TALE

Old Mother Hubbard and Her Wonderful Dog

OLD Mother Hubbard
Went to the cupboard
To get her poor dog a bone;
But when she came there
The cupboard was bare,
And so the poor dog had none.

She went to the baker's
To buy him some bread;
But when she came back
The poor dog was dead.

She went to the joiner's
To buy him a coffin;
But when she came back
The poor dog was laughing.

She took a clean dish
To get him some tripe;
But when she came back
He was smoking a pipe.

She went to the ale-house
To get him some beer;
But when she came back
The dog sat in a chair.

She went to the tavern
For white wine and red;
But when she came back
The dog stood on his head.

She went to the hatter's
To buy him a hat;
But when she came back
He was feeding the cat.

21

She went to the barber's
To buy him a wig
But when she came back
He was dancing a jig.

She went to the fruiterer's
To buy him some fruit;
But when she came back
He was playing the flute.

She went to the tailor's
To buy him a coat;
But when she came back
He was riding a goat.

She went to the cobbler's
To buy him some shoes;
But when she came back
He was reading the news.

She went to the seamstress
To buy him some linen;
But when she came back
The dog was spinning.

She went to the hosier's
To buy him some hose;
But when she came back
He was dressed in his clothes.

The dame made a curtsey
The dog made a bow;
The dame said, "Your servant,"
The dog said, "Bow, wow!"

This wonderful dog
Was Dame Hubbard's delight;
He could sing, he could dance,
He could read, he could write.

She gave him rich dainties
Whenever he fed,
And erected a monument
When he was dead.

From "Mother Goose's Book of Nursery Rhymes and Songs."

The Story of Chicken-Licken

As CHICKEN-LICKEN went one day to the wood, an acorn fell upon her poor bald pate, and she thought the sky had fallen.

So she said she would go and tell the King the sky had fallen.

So Chicken-licken turned back, and met Hen-len. "Well, Hen-len, where are you going?"

And Hen-len said, "I'm going to the wood for some meat."

And Chicken-licken said, "Oh! Hen-len, don't go, for I was going, and the sky fell upon my poor bald pate, and I'm going to tell the King."

So Hen-len turned back with Chicken-licken, and met Cock-lock. "Oh! Cock-lock, where are you going?"

And Cock-lock said, "I'm going to the wood for some meat."

Then Hen-len said, "Oh! Cock-lock, don't go, for I was going, and I met Chicken-licken, and Chicken-licken had been at the wood, and the sky had fallen on her poor bald pate, and we are going to tell the King."

So Cock-lock turned back, and met Duck-luck. "Well, Duck-luck, where are you going?"

And Duck-luck said, "I'm going to the wood for some meat."

Then Cock-lock said, "Oh! Duck-luck, don't go, for I was going, and I met Hen-len, and Hen-len met Chicken-licken, and Chicken-licken had been at the wood, and the sky had fallen on her poor bald pate, and we are going to tell the King."

23

So Duck-luck turned back, and met Drake-lake. "Well, Drake-lake, where are you going?"

And Drake-lake said, "I'm going to the wood for some meat."

Then Duck-luck said, "Oh! Drake-lake, don't go, for I was going, and I met Cock-lock, and Cock-lock met Hen-len, and Hen-len met Chicken-licken, and Chicken-licken had been at the wood, and the sky had fallen on her poor bald pate, and we are going to tell the King."

So Drake-lake turned back, and met Goose-loose. "Well, Goose-loose, where are going?"

And Goose-loose said, "I'm going to the wood for some meat."

Then Drake-lake said, "Oh! Goose-loose, don't go, for I was going, and I met Duck-luck, and Duck-luck met Cock-lock, and Cock-lock met Hen-len, and Hen-len met Chicken-licken, and Chicken-licken had been at the wood, and the sky had fallen on her poor bald pate, and we are going to tell the King."

So Goose-loose turned back, and met Gander-lander. "Well, Gander-lander, where are you going?"

And Gander-lander said, "I'm going to the wood for some meat."

Then Goose-loose said, "Oh! Gander-lander, don't go, for I was going, and I met Drake-lake, and Drake-lake met Duck-luck, and Duck-luck met Cock-lock, and Cock-lock met Hen-len, and Hen-len met Chicken-licken, and Chicken-licken had been at the wood, and the sky had fallen on her poor bald pate, and we are going to tell the King."

So Gander-lander turned back, and met Turkey-lurkey. "Well, Turkey-lurkey, where are you going?"

And Turkey-lurkey said, "I'm going to the wood for some meat."

Then Gander-lander said, "Oh! Turkey-lurkey, don't go, for I was going, and I met Goose-loose, and Goose-loose met Drake-lake, and Drake-lake met Duck-luck, and Duck-luck met Cock-lock, and Cock-lock met Hen-len, and Hen-len met Chicken-licken, and Chicken-licken had been at the wood, and the sky had fallen on her poor bald pate, and we are going to tell the King."

So Turkey-lurkey turned back, and walked with Gander-lander, Goose-loose, Drake-lake, Duck-luck, Cock-lock, Hen-len, and

Chicken-licken. And as they were going along, they met Fox-lox. And Fox-lox said, "Where are you going, my pretty maids?"

And they said, "Chicken-licken went to the wood, and the sky fell upon her poor bald pate, and we are going to tell the King."

And Fox-lox said, "Come along with me, and I will show you the way."

But Fox-lox took them into the fox's hole, and he and his young ones soon ate up poor Chicken-licken, Hen-len, Cock-lock, Duck-luck, Drake-lake, Goose-loose, Gander-lander, and Turkey-lurkey, and they never saw the King to tell him that the sky had fallen.

From "Mother Goose's Book of Nursery Rhymes and Songs."

Nanny Who Wouldn't Go Home to Supper

THERE was once a woman who had a son and a goat. The son was called Espen and the goat was called Nanny.

Now you must know that Espen and Nanny were not good friends because Nanny was wayward, as goats will be, and she would never go home at the right time for her supper.

It happened one evening that Espen went to fetch her and when he had been looking awhile he saw her high, high up on a crag. "My dear Nanny," he called, "you should come home at once, it is supper time and I am so hungry."

"No," said Nanny, tossing her head, "not before I have finished the grass on this tussock, and that tussock, and this and that tussock."

"Then I shall go and tell Mother," said the lad.

"That you may and then I shall be left to eat in peace," said Nanny.

So Espen went to his mother. "Go to the fox and ask him to bite Nanny," she said.

The lad went to the fox. "My dear fox, bite Nanny, for Nanny won't go home in time. I am so hungry and I want my supper," said Espen.

"Indeed, I'll not spoil my snout on a goat's bristles," said the fox.

So the lad went to his mother. "Go to the wolf," she said, "and ask him to tear the fox."

The lad went to the wolf and said: "My dear wolf, tear the fox, for the fox won't bite Nanny and Nanny won't go home in time. I am so hungry and I want my supper."

"No," said the wolf, "I can't wear out my claws and teeth on a skinny fox."

When the lad told his mother she said, "Go to the hunter and ask him to shoot the wolf."

The lad went to the hunter. "My dear hunter, shoot the wolf, for the wolf won't tear the fox, the fox won't bite Nanny, and Nanny won't go home in time. I am so hungry and I want my supper," said Espen.

"No," said the hunter, "I am not going to shoot away my bullets for that."

So the lad went to his mother. "Go to the fir tree and ask it to crush the hunter," she said.

The lad went to the fir tree. "My dear fir, crush the hunter, for the hunter won't shoot the wolf, the wolf won't tear the fox, the fox won't bite Nanny, and Nanny won't go home in time. I am so hungry and I want my supper," said Espen.

"No," said the fir tree, "I am not going to break my boughs for that."

The lad went to his mother. "Go to the fire and ask it to burn the fir," she said.

The lad went to the fire. "My dear fire, burn the fir, for the fir won't crush the hunter, the hunter won't shoot the wolf, the wolf won't tear the fox, the fox won't bite Nanny, and Nanny won't go home in time. I am so hungry and I want my supper," said Espen.

"No," said the fire, "I am not going to burn myself out for that."

So the lad went to his mother. "Go to the water, and ask it to quench the fire," she said.

The lad went to the water. "My dear water, quench the fire, for the fire won't burn the fir, the fir won't crush the hunter, the hunter won't shoot the wolf, the wolf won't tear the fox, the fox won't bite Nanny, and Nanny won't go home in time. I am so hungry and I want my supper," said Espen.

"No," said the water, "I am not going to waste myself for that."

So the lad went to his mother. "Go to the ox," she said, "and ask him to drink the water."

The lad went to the ox. "My dear ox, drink the water, for the water won't quench the fire, the fire won't burn the fir, the fir won't crush the hunter, the hunter won't shoot the wolf, the wolf won't tear the fox, the fox won't bite Nanny, and Nanny won't go home in time. I am so hungry and I want my supper," said Espen.

"No," said the ox, "I am not going to burst myself for that."

When the lad told his mother, she said, "Go to the rope and ask it to bind the ox."

The lad went to the rope. "My dear rope, bind the ox, for the ox won't drink the water, the water won't quench the fire, the fire won't burn the fir, the fir won't crush the hunter, the hunter won't shoot the wolf, the wolf won't tear the fox, the fox won't bite Nanny, and Nanny won't go home in time. I am so hungry and I want my supper," said Espen.

"No," said the rope, "I am not going to break in two for that."

So the lad went to his mother. "Go to the mouse," she said, "and ask her to gnaw the rope."

"No," said the mouse, "I am not going to wear out my teeth for that."

So the lad went again to his mother. "Go to the cat," she said, "and ask her to catch the mouse."

The lad went to the cat. "My dear cat, catch the mouse for the mouse won't gnaw the rope, the rope won't bind the ox, the ox won't drink the water, the water won't quench the fire, the fire won't burn the fir, the fir won't crush the hunter, the hunter won't shoot the wolf, the wolf won't tear the fox, the fox won't bite Nanny, and Nanny won't go home in time. I am so hungry and I want my supper," said Espen.

"Yes, if you will give me some milk for my kittens," said the cat. Yes, that she should have.

So the cat caught the mouse, the mouse gnawed the rope, the rope bound the ox, the ox drank the water, the water quenched the fire, the fire burned the fir, the fir crushed the hunter, the hunter shot the wolf, the wolf tore the fox, the fox bit Nanny, and Nanny took to her heels and scampered home.

Espen gave some of Nanny's milk to the cat and they all had their supper. But Nanny was already so full of grass from this tussock, and that tussock, and this and that tussock, that when Espen scolded her she could only bleat "M-a-h-a-h."

Freely adapted from version in "Fairy Tales from the Far North," by P. C. Asbjornsen, tr. from the Norwegian by H. L. Braekstad. n. d. The A. L. Burt Co.

The Story of the Three Little Pigs

THERE was an old sow with three little pigs, and as she had not enough to keep them, she sent them out to seek their fortune. The first met a man with a bundle of straw, and said to him:

"Please, man, give me that straw to build me a house."

Which the man did, and the little pig built a house with it. Presently along came a wolf, and knocked at the door, and said:

"Little pig, little pig, let me come in."

The pig answered: "No, no, by the hair of my chinny chin chin."

Said the wolf: "Then I'll huff, and I'll puff, and I'll blow your house in."

So he huffed, and he puffed, and he blew the house in, and ate up the little pig.

The second little pig met a man with a bundle of furze and said:

"Please, man, give me that furze to build a house."

Which the man did, and the pig built his house. Then along came the wolf, and said:

"Little pig, little pig, let me come in."

"No, no, by the hair of my chinny chin chin."

"Then I'll huff, and I'll puff, and I'll blow your house in."

So he huffed, and he puffed, and he puffed, and he huffed, and at last he blew the house down. Then he ate up the second little pig.

The third little pig met a man with a load of bricks, and said:

"Please, man, will you give me those bricks to build a house."

And the man gave him the bricks, and he built his house with them. So the wolf came, as he did to the other little pigs, and said:

"Little pig, little pig, let me come in."

"No, no, by the hair on my chinny chin chin."

"Then I'll huff, and I'll puff, and I'll blow your house in."

Well, he huffed, and he puffed, and he huffed and he puffed, and he puffed and huffed; but he could not get the house down. So the wolf said:

"Little pig, I know where there is a nice field of turnips."

"Where?" said the little pig.

"Oh, in Mr. Smith's Home-field, and if you will be ready to-morrow morning I will call for you, and we will go together, and get some for dinner."

"Very well," said the little pig. "What time do you mean to go?"

"Oh, at six o'clock."

Well, the little pig got up at five, and got the turnips, and brought them home. When the wolf came about six, he said:

"Little pig, are you ready?"

The little pig said: "Ready! I have been and come back again, and have a nice potful for dinner."

The wolf felt very angry at this, but thought that he would be up to the little pig somehow or other, so he said:

"Little pig, I know where there is a nice apple tree."

"Where?" said the pig.

"Down at Merry-garden," replied the wolf, "and if you will not

29

deceive me I will come for you at five o'clock tomorrow and get some apples."

Well, the little pig bustled up the next morning at four o'clock, and went off for the apples, hoping to get back before the wolf came; but he had further to go, and had to climb the tree, so that just as he was coming down from it, he saw the wolf coming, which, as you may suppose, frightened him very much. When the wolf came up he said:

"Little pig, what! are you here before me? Are they nice apples?"

"Yes, very," said the little pig. "I will throw you down one."

And he threw it so far, that, while the wolf was gone to pick it up, the little pig jumped down and ran home.

The next day the wolf came again, and said to the little pig:

"Little pig, there is a fair at Shanklin this afternoon, will you go?"

"Oh, yes," said the pig, "I will go; what time shall you be ready?"

"At three," said the wolf. So the little pig went off before time as usual, and got to the fair, and bought a butter-churn, which he was taking home, when he saw the wolf coming. Then he could not tell what to do. So he got into the churn to hide, and by so doing turned it round, and it rolled down the hill with the pig in it, which frightened the wolf so much, that he ran home without going to the fair.

Then the wolf went to the little pig's house, and told him how frightened he had been by a great round thing which came down the hill past him. But the little pig said: "Ha! I frightened you, then. I had been to the fair and bought a butter-churn, and when I saw you, I got into it, and rolled down the hill."

Then the wolf was very angry indeed, and declared he would eat up the little pig, and that he would get down the chimney after him. When the little pig saw what the wolf was about, he hung on the pot full of water, and made up a blazing fire, and, just as he was coming down, took off the cover, and in fell the wolf; so the little pig put on the cover again in an instant, boiled him up, and ate him for supper, and lived happy ever afterwards.

OLD FOLK TALE

The Cat and the Mouse

> The cat and the mouse
> Played in the malt-house:

THE cat bit the mouse's tail off. "Pray, puss, give me my tail." "No," says the cat, "I'll not give you your tail, till you go to the cow, and fetch me some milk."

> First she leapt, and then she ran,
> Till she came to the cow, and so began,—

"Pray, cow, give me milk, that I may give cat milk, that cat may give me my own tail again." "No," said the cow, "I will give y u no milk, till you go to the farmer, and get me some hay."

> First she leapt, and then she ran,
> Till she came to the farmer, and so began,—

"Pray, farmer, give me hay, that I may give cow hay, that cow may give me milk, that I may give cat milk, that cat may give me my own tail again."
"No," says the farmer, "I'll give you no hay, till you go to the butcher and fetch me some meat."

> First she leapt, and then she ran,
> Till she came to the butcher, and so began,—

"Pray, butcher, give me meat, that I may give farmer meat, that farmer may give me hay, that I may give cow hay, that cow may give me milk, that I may give cat milk, that cat may give me my own tail again." "No," says the butcher, "I'll give you no meat, till you go to the baker and fetch me some bread."

> First she leapt, and then she ran,
> Till she came to the baker, and so began,—

31

"Pray, baker, give me bread, that I may give butcher bread, that butcher may give me meat, that I may give farmer meat, that farmer may give me hay, that I may give cow hay, that cow may give me milk, that I may give cat milk, that cat may give me my own tail again."

"Yes," says the baker, "I'll give you some bread,
But if you eat my meal, I'll cut off your head."

Then the baker gave mouse bread, and the mouse gave butcher bread, and butcher gave mouse meat, and mouse gave farmer meat, and farmer gave mouse hay, and mouse gave cow hay, and cow gave mouse milk, and mouse gave cat milk, and cat gave mouse her own tail again!

And so she leapt, and so she ran,
For the mouse had her own tail again.

From "Mother Goose's Book of Nursery Rhymes and Songs."

Cock Robin

WHO killed Cock Robin?
I, said the Sparrow,
With my bow and arrow
I killed Cock Robin.

Who saw him die?
I, said the Magpie,
With my little eye
I saw him die.

Who caught his blood?
I, said the Fish,
With my little dish
I caught his blood.

Who made his shroud?
I, said the Eagle,
With my thread and needle
I made his shroud.

Who'll dig his grave?
The Owl, with aid,
But mattock and spade,
Will dig Robin's grave.

Who'll be the parson,
I, said the Rook,
With my little book
I'll be the parson.

Who'll be the clerk?
I, said the Lark,
If not in the dark,
I'll be the clerk.

Who'll carry him to the grave?
I, said the Kite,
If not in the night,
I'll carry him to the grave.

Who'll be chief mourner?
I, said the Swan,
I'm sorry he's gone,
I'll be chief mourner.

Who'll bear the pall?
We, said the Wren,
Both the Cock and the Hen,
We'll bear the pall.

Who'll toll the bell?
   I, said the Bull,
   Because I can pull,
And I'll pull the bell.

Who'll lead the way?
   I, said the Martin,
   When ready for starting,
And I'll lead the way.

All the birds in the air
   Began sighing and sobbing,
When they heard the bell toll
   For poor Cock Robin.

To all it concerns,
   This notice apprises,
The Sparrow's for trial
   At next bird assizes.

From "Mother Goose's Book of Nursery Rhymes and Songs."

The Lambikin

ONCE upon a time there was a wee wee Lambikin, who frolicked about on his little tottery legs, and enjoyed himself amazingly.

Now one day he set off to visit his Granny, and was jumping with joy to think of all the good things he should get from her, when whom should he meet but a Jackal, who looked at the tender young morsel and said: "Lambikin! Lambikin! I'll eat YOU!"

But Lambikin only gave a little frisk and said:

> "To Granny's house I go,
> Where I shall fatter grow,
> Then you can eat me so."

The Jackal thought this reasonable, and let Lambikin pass.

By and by he met a Vulture, and the Vulture looking hungrily at the tender morsel before him, said: "Lambikin! Lambikin! I'll eat YOU!"

But Lambikin only gave a little frisk, and said:

> "To Granny's house I go,
> Where I shall fatter grow,
> Then you can eat me so."

The Vulture thought this reasonable, and let Lambikin pass.

And by and by he met a Tiger, and then a Wolf, and a Dog, and an Eagle, and all these, when they saw the tender little morsel, said: "Lambikin! Lambikin! I'll eat YOU!"

But to all of them Lambikin replied, with a little frisk:

> "To Granny's house I go,
> Where I shall fatter grow,
> Then you can eat me so."

At last he reached his Granny's house, and said, all in a great hurry, "Granny, dear, I've promised to get very fat; so, as people ought to keep their promises, please put me into the corn-bin at once."

So his Granny said he was a good boy, and put him into the corn-bin, and there the greedy little Lambikin stayed for seven days, and ate, and ate, and ate, until he could scarcely waddle, and his Granny said he was fat enough for anything, and must go home. But cunning little Lambikin said that would never do, for some animal would be sure to eat him on the way back, he was so plump and tender.

"I'll tell you what you must do," said Master Lambikin, "you must make a little drumikin out of the skin of my little brother who died, and then I can sit inside and trundle along nicely, for I'm as tight as a drum myself."

So his Granny made a nice little drumikin out of his brother's skin, with the wool inside, and Lambikin curled himself up snug and warm in the middle, and trundled away gayly. Soon he met with the Eagle, who called out:

> "Drumikin! Drumikin!
> Have you seen Lambikin?"

And Mr. Lambikin, curled up in his soft warm nest, replied:

> "Fallen into the fire, and so will you
> On little Drumikin. Tum-pa, tum-too!"

"How very annoying!" sighed the Eagle, thinking regretfully of the tender morsel he had let slip.

Meanwhile Lambikin trundled along, laughing to himself, and singing:

> "Tum-pa, tum-too;
> Tum-pa, tum-too!"

Every animal and bird he met asked him the same question:

> "Drumikin! Drumikin!
> Have you seen Lambikin?"

And to each of them the little slyboots replied:

> "Fallen into the fire, and so will you
> On little Drumikin. Tum-pa, tum-too;
> Tum-pa, tum-too; Tum-pa, tum-too!"

Then they all sighed to think of the tender little morsel they had let slip.

At last the Jackal came limping along, for all his sorry looks as sharp as a needle, and he called out:

> "Drumikin! Drumikin!
> Have you seen Lambikin?"

And Lambikin, curled up in his snug little nest, replied gayly:

"Fallen into the fire, and so will you
On little Drumikin! Tum-pa———"

But he never got any further, for the Jackal recognized his voice at once, and cried: "Hullo! you've turned yourself inside out, have you? Just you come out of that!"

Whereupon he tore open Drumikin and gobbled up Lambikin.

*From "Indian Fairy Tales," ed. by Joseph Jacobs.
n. d., G. P. Putnam's Sons. Reprinted by permission
of the publishers.*

Scrapefoot

ONCE upon a time, there were three bears who lived in a castle in a great wood. One of them was a great big bear, one was a middling bear, and one was a little bear. And in the same wood there was a fox who lived all alone. His name was Scrapefoot.

Now Scrapefoot was very much afraid of the three bears, but for all that he wanted very much to know about them. One day as he went through the wood he found himself near the bears' castle, and he became more and more curious. First he looked all about him and he could not see anyone, then he came up to the door of the castle, and tried to open it. Yes! the door was not locked. He opened the door a little way, and put his nose in and looked and looked and still he could not see anyone. So he opened it a little way farther, and put one paw in, and then another paw, and another, and another, and then he was all in the bears' castle.

Scrapefoot found he was in a great hall with three chairs in it; one big, one middling, and one little chair, and he thought he would like to sit down and rest, and look about him. He sat down on the big chair but he found it so hard and uncomfortable that it made his

37

bones ache, so he jumped down at once and got into the middling chair. He turned round and round in the middling chair but he couldn't make himself comfortable, so then he went to the little chair and sat down in it. Now the little chair was so soft and warm and comfortable that Scrapefoot was quite happy; but all at once it broke to pieces under him and he couldn't put it together again!

So Scrapefoot got up and began to look about him, and on one table he saw three saucers, of which one was very big, one was middling, and one was quite a little saucer. He was very thirsty, and he began to drink out of the big saucer. But he only just tasted the milk in the big saucer; it was sour and horrid. Then he tried two or three mouthfuls from the middling saucer but it was not nice, and he left it and went to the little saucer. The milk in the little saucer was so sweet and so nice that he went on drinking it till it was all gone.

Then Scrapefoot thought he would like to go upstairs. So upstairs he went, and he found a great room with three beds in it; one was a big bed, one was a middling bed, and one was a little bed. He climbed up into the big bed, but it was so hard and lumpy and uncomfortable that he jumped down at once, and tried the middling bed. That was rather better, but he could not lie comfortably in it, and after turning about and over a little while he got up and went to the little bed. That was so soft and so warm and so nice that he fell fast asleep.

After a time the bears came home. When they got into the great hall the big bear went to his chair and said: "Who's been sitting in my chair?" and the middling bear said: "Who's been sitting in my chair?" and the little bear said: "Who's been sitting in my chair and has broken it all to pieces?"

And then they went to have their milk, and the big bear said: "Who's been drinking my milk?" and the middling bear said: "Who's been drinking my milk?" and the little bear said: "Who's been drinking my milk and has drunk it all up?"

Then they went upstairs and into the bedroom, and the big bear said: "Who's been sleeping in my bed?" and the middling bear said: "Who's been sleeping in my bed?" and the little bear said: "Who's been sleeping in my bed?—and see, here he is!"

So then the bears came and wondered what they should do with

Scrapefoot and the big bear said: "Let's hang him!" and the middling bear said: "Let's drown him!" and the little bear said: "Let's throw him out of the window." So the bears took him to the window, and the big bear took two legs on one side and the middling bear took two legs on the other side, and they swung him backward and forward, backward and forward, and out of the window.

Poor Scrapefoot was very frightened, and he thought every bone in his body must be broken. But he got up and first shook one leg— no, that was not broken; then he shook another leg, and another and another, then he wagged his tail and found there were no bones broken. He galloped off home as fast as he could go, and never went near the bears' castle again.

OLD FOLK TALE

The Three Billy-Goats Gruff

ONCE on a time there were three Billy-goats, who were to go up to the hillside to make themselves fat, and the name of all three was "Gruff."

On the way up was a bridge over a burn they had to cross; and under the bridge lived a great ugly Troll, with eyes as big as saucers, and a nose as long as a poker.

So first of all came the youngest billy-goat Gruff to cross the bridge.

"Trip, trap; trip, trap!" went the bridge.

"Who's that tripping over my bridge?" roared the Troll.

"Oh! it is only I, the tiniest billy-goat Gruff; and I'm going up to the hillside to make myself fat," said the billy-goat, with such a small voice.

"Now, I'm coming to gobble you up!" said the Troll.

"Oh, no! pray don't take me. I'm too little, that I am," said the billy-goat; "wait a bit till the second billy-goat Gruff comes, he's much bigger."

"Well, be off with you!" said the Troll.

A little while after came the second billy-goat Gruff to cross the bridge.

"Trip, trap! trip, trap! trip, trap!" went the bridge.

"WHO'S THAT tripping over my bridge?" roared the Troll.

"Oh! it's the second billy-goat Gruff, and I'm going up to the hill-side to make myself fat," said the billy-goat, who hadn't such a small voice.

"Now, I'm coming to gobble you up," said the Troll.

"Oh, no! don't take me, wait a little till the big billy-goat Gruff comes, he's much bigger."

"Very well, be off with you!" said the Troll.

But just then up came the big billy-goat Gruff.

"TRIP, TRAP! TRIP, TRAP! TRIP, TRAP!" went the bridge, for the billy-goat was so heavy that the bridge creaked and groaned under him.

"WHO'S THAT tramping over my bridge?" roared the Troll.

"IT'S I! THE BIG BILLY-GOAT GRUFF," said the billy-goat, who had an ugly hoarse voice of his own.

"Now I'm coming to gobble you up!" roared the Troll.

> "Well, come along! I've got two spears,
>   And I'll poke your eyeballs out at your ears;
> I've got besides two curling stones,
>   And I'll crush you to bits, body and bones."

That was what the big billy-goat said; and so he flew at the Troll and poked his eyes out with his horns, and crushed him to bits, body and bones, and tossed him out into the burn, and after that he went up to the hillside. There the billy-goats got so fat they were scarce able to walk home again; and if the fat hasn't fallen off them, why they're still fat; and so,—

"Snip, snap, snout,
This tale's told out."

From "Tales from the Norse," by Sir George William Dasent. n. d. E. P. Dutton & Co., Inc., and reprinted by permission of the publishers.

Wee Robin's Yule Song

THERE was once a gray Pussy who went down by the water side, and there she saw wee Robin Redbreast hopping on a brier. Pussy says, "Where are you going, wee Robin?" And Robin says, "I'm going to the King to sing him a song this good Yule morning." And Pussy says, "Come here, wee Robin, and I'll let you see a bonny white ring around my neck." But wee Robin says, "No, no, gray Pussy, you worried the wee mousie but not me."

So Robin flew away till he came to a turf wall and there he saw a gray, greedy Hawk sitting. And the Hawk says, "Where are you going, wee Robin?" And Robin says, "I'm going to the King to sing him a song this fine Yule morning." And the gray, greedy Hawk says, "Come here, wee Robin, and I'll let you see a bonny feather in my wing." But Robin says, "No, no, gray, greedy Hawk, you pecked at the Linnet but not at me."

So Robin flew away till he came to the side of a rock and there he saw a sly Fox sitting. And the sly Fox says, "Where are you going, wee Robin?" And Robin says, "I'm going to the King to sing him a song this fine Yule morning." And the sly Fox says, "Come, wee Robin, and I'll let you see a bonny spot on the top of my tail." But Robin says, "No, no, sly Fox, you caught the wee lamb but not me."

So Robin flew on till he came to the King's palace and there he sat on the window sill and sang the King a bonny song. And the King says to the Queen, "What shall we give wee Robin for singing us this bonny song?" And the Queen says, "We'll give him the wee Wren to be his bride." So wee Robin and the wee Wren were married and the King and Queen and all the court danced at the wedding and afterwards wee Robin flew away home alone to his own water side and hopped on a brier.

OLD FOLK TALE

The Pancake

ONCE on a time there was a goody who had seven hungry bairns, and she was frying a pancake for them. It was a sweet-milk pancake, and there it lay in the pan bubbling and frizzling so thick and good, it was a sight for sore eyes to look at. And the bairns stood round about, and the goodman sat by and looked on.

"Oh, give me a bit of pancake, Mother, dear; I am so hungry," said one bairn.

"Oh, darling Mother," said the second.

"Oh, darling, good Mother," said the third.

"Oh, darling, good, nice Mother," said the fourth.

"Oh, darling, pretty, good, nice Mother," said the fifth.

"Oh, darling, pretty, good, nice, clever Mother," said the sixth.

"Oh, darling, pretty, good, nice, clever, sweet Mother," said the seventh.

So they begged for the pancake all round, the one more prettily than the other; for they were so hungry and so good.

"Yes, yes, bairns, only bide a bit till it turns itself,"—she ought to have said, "till I can get it turned,"—"and then you shall all have some—a lovely sweet-milk pancake; only look how fat and happy it lies there."

When the pancake heard that it got afraid, and in a trice it turned itself all of itself, and tried to jump out of the pan; but it fell back

42

into it again t'other side up, and so when it had been fried a little on the other side too, till it got firmer in its flesh, it sprang out on the floor, and rolled off like a wheel through the door and down the hill.

"Holloa! Stop, pancake!" and away went the goody after it, with the frying-pan in one hand and the ladle in the other, as fast as she could, and her bairns behind her, while the goodman limped after them last of all.

"Hi! won't you stop? Seize it. Stop, pancake," they all screamed out, one after the other, and tried to catch it on the run and hold it; but the pancake rolled on and on, and in the twinkling of an eye it was so far ahead that they couldn't see it, for the pancake was faster on its feet than any of them.

So when it had rolled awhile it met a man.

"Good day, pancake," said the man.

"God bless you, Manny Panny!" said the pancake.

"Dear pancake," said the man, "don't roll so fast; stop a little and let me eat you."

"When I have given the slip to Goody Poody, and the goodman, and seven squalling children, I may well slip through your fingers, Manny Panny," said the pancake, and rolled on and on till it met a hen.

"Good day, pancake," said the hen.

"The same to you, Henny Penny," said the pancake.

"Pancake, dear, don't roll so fast; bide a bit and let me eat you up," said the hen.

"When I have given the slip to Goody Poody, and the goodman, and seven squalling children, and Manny Panny, I may well slip through your claws, Henny Penny," said the pancake, and so it rolled on like a wheel down the road.

Just then it met a cock.

"Good day, pancake," said the cock.

"The same to you, Cocky Locky," said the pancake.

"Pancake, dear, don't roll so fast, but bide a bit and let me eat you up."

"When I have given the slip to Goody Poody, and the goodman, and seven squalling children, and to Manny Panny, and Henny

Penny, I may well slip through your claws, Cocky Locky," said the pancake, and off it set rolling away as fast as it could; and when it had rolled a long way it met a duck.

"Good day, pancake," said the duck.

"The same to you, Ducky Lucky."

"Pancake, dear, don't roll away so fast; bide a bit and let me eat you up."

"When I have given the slip to Goody Poody, and the goodman, and seven squalling children, and Manny Panny, and Henny Penny, and Cocky Locky, I may well slip through your fingers, Ducky Lucky," said the pancake, and with that it took to rolling and rolling faster than ever; and when it had rolled a long, long while, it met a goose.

"Good day, pancake," said the goose.

"The same to you, Goosey Poosey."

"Pancake, dear, don't roll so fast; bide a bit and let me eat you up."

"When I have given the slip to Goody Poody, and the goodman, and seven squalling children, and Manny Panny, and Henny Penny, and Cocky Locky, and Ducky Lucky, I can well slip through your feet, Goosey Poosey," said the pancake, and off it rolled.

So when it had rolled a long, long way farther, it met a gander.

"Good day, pancake," said the gander.

"The same to you, Gander Pander," said the pancake.

"Pancake, dear, don't roll so fast; bide a bit and let me eat you up."

"When I have given the slip to Goody Poody, and the goodman, and seven squalling children, and Manny Panny, and Henny Penny, and Cocky Locky, and Ducky Lucky, and Goosey Poosey, I may well slip through your feet, Gander Pander," said the pancake, which rolled off as fast as ever.

So when it had rolled a long, long time, it met a pig.

"Good day, pancake," said the pig.

"The same to you, Piggy Wiggy," said the pancake, which, without a word more, began to roll and roll like mad.

"Nay, nay," said the pig, "you needn't be in such a hurry; we two can then go side-by-side and see one another over the wood; they say it is not too safe in there."

The pancake thought there might be something in that, and so they kept company. But when they had gone awhile, they came to a brook. As for Piggy, he was so fat he swam safe across, it was nothing to him; but the poor pancake couldn't get over.

"Seat yourself on my snout," said the pig, "and I'll carry you over."

So the pancake did that.

"Ouf, ouf," said the pig, and swallowed the pancake at one gulp; and then, as the poor pancake could go no farther, why—this story can go no farther either.

> *From "Tales from the Fjeld," by P. Ch. Asbjorn-sen, tr. by Sir George Dasent. n. d. G. P. Putnam's Sons. Reprinted by permission of the publishers.*

The Sheep and the Pig Who Set Up House

ONCE on a time, there was a sheep who stood in the pen to be fattened; so he lived well, and was stuffed and crammed with everything that was good. So it went on, till one day the dairymaid came and gave him still more food, and then she said, "Eat away, sheep; you won't be much longer here; we are going to kill you tomorrow."

It is an old saying, that women's counsel is always worth having, and that there is a cure and physic for everything but death. "But after all," said the sheep to himself, "there may be a cure even for death this time."

So he ate till he was ready to burst; and when he was crammed full, he butted out the door of the pen, and took his way to the neighboring farm. There he went to the pigsty to a pig whom he had known out on the common, and ever since had been the best friends with.

45

"Good day," said the sheep, "and thanks for our last merry meeting."

"Good day," answered the pig, "and the same to you."

"Do you know," said the sheep, "why it is you are so well off, and why it is they fatten you, and take such pains with you?"

"No, I don't," said the pig.

"Many a flask empties the cask; I suppose you know that," said the sheep. "They are going to kill and eat you."

"Are they?" said the pig; "well, I hope they'll say grace after meat."

"If you will do as I do," said the sheep, "we'll go off to the wood, build us a house, and set up for ourselves. A home is a home, be it ever so homely."

Yes, the pig was willing enough. "Good company is such a comfort," he said, and so the two set off.

So when they had gone a bit they met a goose.

"Good day, good sirs, and thanks for our last merry meeting," said the goose; "whither away so fast today?"

"Good day, and the same to you," said the sheep; "you must know we were too well off at home, and so we are going to set up for ourselves in the wood, for you know every man's house is his castle."

"Well," said the goose, "it's much the same with me where I am. Can't I go with you too? for it's child's play when three share the day."

"With gossip and gabble is built neither house nor stable," said the pig; "let us know what you can do."

"By cunning and skill a cripple can do what he will," said the goose. "I can pluck moss and stuff it into the seams of the planks, and your house will be tight and warm."

Yes, they would give him leave, for, above all things, piggy wished to be warm and comfortable.

So when they had gone a bit farther—the goose had hard work to walk so fast—they met a hare, who came frisking out of the wood.

"Good day, good sirs, and thanks for our last merry meeting," she said; "how far are you trotting today?"

"Good day, and the same to you," said the sheep; "we were far

46

too well off at home, and so we're going to the wood to build us a house, and set up for ourselves, for you know, try all the world round, there's nothing like home."

"As for that," said the hare, "I have a house in every bush—yes, a house in every bush; but yet, I have often said in winter, 'If I only live till summer, I'll build me a house'; and so I have half a mind to go with you and build one up, after all."

"Yes," said the pig, "if we ever get into a scrape, we might use you to scare away the dogs, for you don't fancy you could help us in house-building."

"He who lives long enough always finds work enough to do," said the hare. "I have teeth to gnaw pegs, and paws to drive them into the wall, so I can very well set up to be a carpenter; for 'Good tools make good work,' as the man said when he flayed the mare with a gimlet."

Yes, he too got leave to go with them and build their house; there was nothing more to be said about it.

When they had gone a bit farther they met a cock.

"Good day, good sirs," said the cock, "and thanks for our last merry meeting; whither are ye going today, gentlemen?"

"Good day, and the same to you," said the sheep; "at home we were too well off, and so we are going off to the wood to build us a house, and set up for ourselves; for he who out-of-doors shall bake, loses at last both coal and cake."

"Well," said the cock, "that's just my case; but it's better to sit on one's own perch, for then one can never be left in the lurch, and besides, all cocks crow loudest at home. Now, if I might have leave to join such a gallant company, I also would like to go to the wood and build a house."

"Ay, ay!" said the pig; "flapping and crowing sets tongues a-going, but a jaw on a stick never yet laid a brick. How can you ever help us to build a house?"

"Oh," said the cock, "that house will never have a clock where there is neither dog nor cock. I am up early, and I wake every one."

"Very true," said the pig; "the morning hour has a golden dower; let him come with us"; for, you must know, piggy was always the soundest sleeper. "Sleep is the biggest thief," he said; "he thinks nothing of stealing half one's life."

So they all set off to the wood as a band and brotherhood, and built the house. The pig hewed the timber, and the sheep drew it home; the hare was carpenter, and gnawed pegs and bolts, and hammered them into the walls and roof; the goose plucked moss, and stuffed it into the seams; the cock crew, and looked out that they did not oversleep themselves in the morning; and when the house was ready, and the roof lined with birch bark and thatched with turf, there they lived by themselves, and were merry and well. " 'Tis good to travel east and west," said the sheep, "but after all a home is best."

But you must know that a bit farther on in the wood was a wolf's den, and there lived two graylegs. So when they saw that a new house had risen up hard by, they wanted to know what sort of folk their neighbors were, for they thought to themselves that a good neighbor was better than a brother in a foreign land, and that it was better to live in a good neighborhood than to know many people miles and miles off.

So one of them made up an errand, and went into the new house and asked for a light for his pipe. But as soon as ever he got inside the door, the sheep gave him such a butt that he fell head foremost into the stove. Then the pig began to gore and bite him, the goose to nip and peck him, the cock upon the roost to crow and chatter; and as for the hare, he was so frightened out of his wits, that he ran about aloft and on the floor, and scratched and scrambled in every corner of the house.

So after a long time the wolf came out.

"Well," said the one who waited for him outside, "neighborhood makes brotherhood. You must have come into a perfect paradise on bare earth since you stayed so long. But what became of the light, for you have neither pipe nor smoke?"

"Yes, yes," said the other; "it was just a nice light, and a pleasant company. Such manners I never saw in all my life. But then you know we can't pick and choose in this wicked world, and an unbidden guest gets bad treatment. As soon as I got inside the door, the shoemaker let fly at me with his last, so that I fell head foremost into the

48

stithy fire; and there sat two smiths, who blew the bellows and made the sparks fly, and beat and punched me with red-hot tongs and pincers, so that they tore whole pieces out of my body. As for the hunter, he went scrambling about looking for his gun, and it was good luck he did not find it. And all the while there was another who sat up under the roof, and slapped his arms, and sang out, 'Put a hook into him and drag him hither, drag him hither.' That was what he screamed, and if he had only got hold of me, I should never have come out alive."

> From "Tales from the Fjeld," by P. Ch. Asbjorn-sen, tr. by Sir George Dasent. n. d. G. P. Putnam's Sons. Reprinted by permission of the publishers.

The Princess on the Pea

THERE was once a Prince who wanted to marry a Princess; but she was to be a real princess. So he traveled about, all through the world, to find a real one, but everywhere there was something in the way. There were princesses enough, but whether they were real princesses he could not quite make out: there was always something that did not seem quite right. So he came home again, and was quite sad: for he wished so much to have a real princess.

One evening a terrible storm came on. It lightened and thundered, the rain streamed down; it was quite fearful! Then there was a knocking at the town gate, and the old King went out to open it.

It was a Princess who stood outside the gate. But, mercy! how she looked, from the rain and the rough weather! The water ran down from her hair and her clothes; it ran in at the points of her shoes, and out at the heels; and yet she declared that she was a real princess.

"Yes, we will soon find that out," thought the old Queen. But she said nothing, only went into the bedchamber, took all the bedding off, and put a pea on the flooring of the bedstead; then she took

49

twenty mattresses and laid them upon the pea, and then twenty eider-down beds upon the mattresses. On this the Princess had to lie all night. In the morning she was asked how she had slept.

"Oh, miserably!" said the Princess. "I scarcely closed my eyes all night long. Goodness knows what was in my bed. I lay upon something hard, so that I am black and blue all over. It is quite dreadful!"

Now they saw that she was a real princess, for through the twenty mattresses and the twenty eider-down beds she had felt the pea. No one but a real princess could be so delicate.

So the Prince took her for his wife, for now he knew that he had a true princess; and the pea was put in the museum, and it is there now, unless somebody has carried it off.

Look you, this is a true story.

From "Fairy Tales," by Hans Christian Andersen.

Collections of Nursery Stories and Rhymes for Little Children

Baldwin, James. *Fairy Stories and Fables.* American Book Co.
Brooke, Leslie. *The Golden Goose Book.* Frederick Warne & Co., Ltd.
Carrick, Valery. *Tales of Wise and Foolish Animals.* Frederick A. Stokes Co.
De la Mare, Walter. *Peacock Pie.* Henry Holt & Co.
Free and Treadwell.
    Primer. Row, Peterson & Co.
    First Reader. Row, Peterson & Co.
    Second Reader. Row, Peterson & Co.
Hutchinson, Veronica.
    Candle-light Stories. Minton Balch & Co.
    Fireside Stories. Minton Balch & Co.
Jacobs, Joseph.
    English Fairy Tales. G. P. Putnam's Sons.
    More English Fairy Tales. G. P. Putnam's Sons.

STORIES FOR LITTLE CHILDREN

Johnson, Clifton. *Oak-tree Fairy Book.* Little, Brown & Company.

Lansing. *Rhymes and Stories.* Ginn and Company.

Lindsay, Maud. *Story Garden.* Lothrop, Lee & Shepard.

Mother Goose.
   Little Mother Goose. Dodd, Mead and Company.
   Real Mother Goose. Rand McNally & Co.

Rossetti, Christina. *Sing-Song.* The Macmillan Company.

Ruskin, John, ed. *Dame Wiggins of Lee and Her Seven Wonderful Cats.*
   E. P. Dutton & Co., Inc.

Scudder, H. E. *Book of Fables and Folk Stories.* Houghton Mifflin Co.

Thorne-Thomsen, Mrs. Gudrun, tr.
   The Birch and the Star and Other Stories. Row, Peterson & Co.
   East O' the Sun and West O' the Moon. Row, Peterson & Co.

Whiteman, Edna. *Playmates in Print.* Thomas Nelson & Sons.

Wiggin and Smith. *Tales of Laughter.* Doubleday, Doran & Co.

FOLK TALES AND FABLES

FOLK TALES AND FABLES

OTHER types of folk tales suited to children of six years and older are realistic beast tales, humorous folk tales called drolls, and realistic and romantic fairy tales. This distinction is not altogether definite, as any classification is bound to result in some overlapping of groups. Many beast tales are drolls but not all drolls are beast tales, and few of the so-called fairy tales actually introduce fairies although most of them have a preternatural element.

The number of stories in these groups which are suitable for oral presentation is large. Enough of a selection to offer variety is given, and attention is called to the story sources listed at the end of the chapter.

The animal fables included have been chosen for story content. Literary versions, in preference to historical, are given.

The drolls are tales of the common folk which were passed along from generation to generation, orally. They are in the same colloquial language as the repetitive nursery tales, but their humor is broader and more sophisticated.

Both the drolls and the beast tales may be used singly, or to open story hour programs. They are adapted to large audiences and do not require a high degree of skill for telling. Because this type of rollicking, humorous story is popular and easy to tell, it should not be allowed to crowd out the more imaginative story of greater beauty that requires longer preparation and greater concentration from the children who listen.

The realistic fairy tale is illustrated by "The Brave Little Tailor," a primitive type of hero tale that appeals to the child's love for adventure, and by "The Squire's Bride," that savors of the droll, and is crude, but not coarse.

The romantic fairy tales such as "Sleeping Beauty" and "East O' the Sun and West O' the Moon," interpret life idealistically. They gain their best response when told to intimate groups of not more than thirty children.

Preparation for telling the longer and more varied fairy tales is more difficult than that required for nursery tales. One simple method which has met with success is offered for the amateur:

Read the story to be told for sheer pleasure; re-read for plot and if the incidents are many, or complicated, make a written outline and memorize it; re-read for descriptive parts and for general atmosphere.

When this has been done, put aside the text and visualize the story imaginatively. If there is time to dwell on the story during several days, so much the better. Parts to be memorized may require further reading.

Finally, with your audience in mind, repeat the story aloud, as you expect to tell it. This will aid your memory, give facility in diction and acquaint you with the sound of your own voice, all of which are important points in developing ease in story-telling.

No matter how familiar a story may become, it should be reviewed, to some extent, before re-telling, in order to recapture its mood.

A genuine liking for fairy tales may be stimulated by observing children's response to them and by recalling one's own childhood feeling for favorite tales.

Comparing variants of an old tale and seeking out reasons for differences may add to interest. The many collections of folk tales made by Joseph Jacobs contain stimulating bibliographic notes on original forms of tales and the changes which have occurred in their migration. Perrault's literary versions of popular tales may be compared with folklore versions; La Fontaine's *Fables* in literary verse may be read in connection with earlier folklore versions of fables found in *The Panchatantra,* edited by Ryder, or The *Fables of Æsop.*

Reading the attractive beginning and closing sentences in the German folk tales collected by the Brothers Grimm, and the more modern stories of Hans Christian Andersen, will help to create the right mood for telling other stories of similar nature.

The Brave Little Tailor

ONE summer morning a little tailor was sitting on his board near the window, and working cheerfully with all his might, when an old woman came down the street crying:

"Good jelly to sell! Good jelly to sell!"

The cry sounded pleasant in the little tailor's ears, so he put his head out of the window, and called out:

"Here, my good woman—come here, if you want a customer."

So the poor woman climbed the steps with her heavy basket, and was obliged to unpack and display all her pots to the tailor. He looked at every one of them, and lifting all the lids, applied his nose to each, and said at last:

"The jelly seems pretty good; you may weigh me out four half ounces, or I don't mind having a quarter of a pound."

The woman, who had expected to find a good customer, gave him what he asked for, but went off angry and grumbling.

"This jelly is the very thing for me," cried the little tailor; "it will give me strength and cunning"; and he took down the bread from the cupboard, cut a whole round of the loaf, and spread the jelly on it, laid it near him, and went on stitching more gallantly than ever. All the while the scent of the sweet jelly was spreading throughout the room, where there were quantities of flies, who were attracted by it and flew to partake.

"Now, then, who asked you to come?" said the tailor, and drove the unbidden guests away. But the flies, not understanding his language, were not to be got rid of like that, and returned in larger numbers than before. Then the tailor, not being able to stand it any longer, took from his chimney-corner a ragged cloth, and saying,

"Now, I'll let you have it!" beat it among them unmercifully. When he ceased, and counted the slain, he found seven lying dead before him.

"This is indeed somewhat," he said, wondering at his own gallantry; "the whole town shall know this."

So he hastened to cut out a belt, and he stitched it, and put on it in large capitals, "Seven at one blow!"

"—The town, did I say!" said the little tailor; "the whole world shall know it!" And his heart quivered with joy, like a lamb's tail.

The tailor fastened the belt round him, and began to think of going out into the world, for his workshop seemed too small for his worship. So he looked about in all the house for something that would be useful to take with him, but he found nothing but an old cheese, which he put in his pocket. Outside the door he noticed that a bird had got caught in the bushes, so he took that and put it in his pocket with the cheese. Then he set out gallantly on his way, and as he was light and active he felt no fatigue. The way led over a mountain, and when he reached the topmost peak he saw a terrible giant sitting there, and looking about him at his ease. The tailor went bravely up to him, called out to him, and said,

"Comrade, good day! there you sit looking over the wide world! I am on the way thither to seek my fortune: have you a fancy to go with me?"

The giant looked at the tailor contemptuously, and said:

"You little rascal! you miserable fellow!"

"That may be!" answered the little tailor, and undoing his coat he showed the giant his belt; "you can read there whether I am a man or not!"

The giant read: "Seven at one blow!" and thinking it meant men that the tailor had killed, felt at once more respect for the little fellow. But as he wanted to prove him, he took up a stone and squeezed it so hard that water came out of it.

"Now you can do that," said the giant, "—that is, if you have the strength for it."

"That's not much," said the little tailor, "I call that play," and he put his hand in his pocket and took out the cheese and squeezed it, so that the whey ran out of it.

"Well," said he, "what do you think of that?"

The giant did not know what to say to it, for he could not have believed it of the little man. Then the giant took up a stone and threw it so high that it was nearly out of sight.

"Now, little fellow, suppose you do that!"

"Well thrown," said the tailor; "but the stone fell back to earth again,—I will throw you one that will never come back." So he felt in his pocket, took out the bird, and threw it into the air. And the bird, when it found itself at liberty, took wing, flew off, and returned no more.

"What do you think of that, comrade?" asked the tailor.

"There is no doubt that you can throw," said the giant; "but we will see if you can carry."

He led the little tailor to a mighty oak tree which had been felled, and was lying on the ground, and said:

"Now, if you are strong enough, help me to carry this tree out of the wood."

"Willingly," answered the little man; "you take the trunk on your shoulders, I will take the branches with all their foliage, that is much the most difficult."

So the giant took the trunk on his shoulders, and the tailor seated himself on a branch, and the giant, who could not see what he was doing, had the whole tree to carry, and the little man on it as well. And the little man was very cheerful and merry, and whistled the tune: "There were three tailors riding by," as if carrying the tree was mere child's play. The giant, when he had struggled on under his heavy load a part of the way, was tired out, and cried:

"Look here, I must let go the tree!"

The tailor jumped off quickly, and taking hold of the tree with both arms, as if he were carrying it, said to the giant:

"You see you can't carry the tree though you are such a big fellow!"

They went on together a little farther, and presently they came to a cherry tree, and the giant took hold of the topmost branches, where the ripest fruit hung, and pulling them downwards, gave them to the tailor to hold, bidding him eat. But the little tailor was much too weak to hold the tree, and as the giant let go, the tree sprang back, and the tailor was caught up into the air. And when he dropped down again without any damage, the giant said to him,

"How is this? Haven't you strength enough to hold such a weak sprig as that?"

"It is not strength that is lacking," answered the little tailor; "how should it to one who has slain seven at one blow! I just jumped over the tree because the hunters are shooting down there in the bushes. You jump it too, if you can."

The giant made the attempt, and not being able to vault the tree, he remained hanging in the branches, so that once more the little tailor got the better of him. Then said the giant:

"As you are such a gallant fellow, suppose you come with me to our den, and stay the night."

The tailor was quite willing, and he followed him. When they reached the den there sat some other giants by the fire, and all gladly welcomed him. The little tailor looked round and thought:

"There is more elbow-room here than in my workshop."

And the giant showed him a bed, and told him he had better lie down upon it and go to sleep. The bed was, however, too big for the tailor, so he did not stay in it, but crept into a corner to sleep. As soon as it was midnight the giant got up, took a great staff of iron and beat the bed through with one stroke, and supposed he had made an end of that grasshopper of a tailor. Very early in the morning the giants went into the wood and forgot all about the little tailor, and when they saw him coming after them alive and merry, they were terribly frightened, and, thinking he was going to kill them, they ran away in all haste.

So the little tailor marched on, always following his nose. And after he had gone a great way he entered the courtyard belonging to a king's palace, and there he felt so overpowered with fatigue that he lay down and fell asleep. In the meanwhile came various people, who looked at him very curiously, and read on his belt, "Seven at one blow!"

"Oh!" said they, "why should this great lord come here in time of peace? What a mighty champion he must be."

Then they went and told the King about him, and they thought that if war should break out, what a worthy and useful man he would be, and that he ought not to be allowed to depart at any price. The King then summoned his council, and sent one of his courtiers to the little tailor to beg him, so soon as he should wake up, to consent to serve in the King's army. So the messenger stood and waited at the sleeper's side until his limbs began to stretch, and his eyes to open, and then he carried his answer back. And the answer was:

"That was the reason for which I came," said the little tailor. "I am ready to enter the King's service."

So he was received into it very honorably, and a separate dwelling set apart for him.

But the rest of the soldiers were very much set against the little tailor, and they wished him a thousand miles away.

"What shall be done about it?" they said among themselves; "If we pick a quarrel and fight with him then seven of us will fall at each blow. That will be of no good to us."

So they came to a resolution, and went all together to the King to ask for their discharge.

"We never intended," said they, "to serve with a man who kills seven at a blow."

The King felt sorry to lose all his faithful servants because of one man, and he wished that he had never seen him, and would willingly get rid of him if he might. But he did not dare to dismiss the little tailor for fear he should kill all the King's people, and place himself upon the throne. He thought a long while about it, and at last made up his mind what to do. He sent for the little tailor, and told him that as he was so great a warrior he had a proposal to make to him. He

61

told him that in a wood in his dominions dwelt two giants, who did great damage by robbery, murder, and fire, and that no man durst go near them for fear of his life. But that if the tailor should overcome and slay both these giants the King would give him his only daughter in marriage, and half his kingdom as dowry, and that a hundred horsemen should go with him to give him assistance.

"That would be something for a man like me!" thought the little tailor, "a beautiful princess and half a kingdom are not to be had every day," and he said to the King:

"Oh, yes, I can soon overcome the giants, and yet have no need of the hundred horsemen; he who can kill seven at one blow has no need to be afraid of two."

So the little tailor set out, and the hundred horsemen followed him. When he came to the border of the wood he said to his escort:

"Stay here while I go to attack the giants."

Then he sprang into the wood, and looked about him right and left. After a while he caught sight of the two giants; they were lying down under a tree asleep, and snoring so that all the branches shook. The little tailor, all alive, filled both his pockets with stones and climbed up into the tree, and made his way to an overhanging bough, so that he could seat himself just above the sleepers; and from there he let one stone after another fall on the chest of one of the giants. For a long time the giant was quite unaware of this, but at last he waked up and pushed his comrade, and said:

"What are you hitting me for?"

"You are dreaming," said the other, "I am not touching you." And they composed themselves again to sleep, and the tailor let fall a stone on the other giant.

"What can that be?" cried he. "What are you casting at me?"

"I am casting nothing at you," answered the first, grumbling.

They disputed about it for a while, but as they were tired, they gave it up at last, and their eyes closed once more. Then the little tailor began his game anew, picked out a heavier stone and threw it down with force upon the first giant's chest.

"This is too much!" cried he, and sprang up like a madman and struck his companion such a blow that the tree shook above them. The other paid him back with ready coin, and they fought with such fury that they tore up trees by their roots to use for weapons against each other, so that at last they both of them lay dead upon the ground. And now the little tailor got down.

"Another piece of luck!" said he, "that the tree I was sitting in did not get torn up too, or else I should have had to jump like a squirrel from one tree to another."

Then he drew his sword and gave each of the giants a few hacks in the breast, and went back to the horsemen and said,

"The deed is done, I have made an end of both of them: but it went hard with me, in the struggle they rooted up trees to defend themselves, but it was of no use, they had to do with a man who can kill seven at one blow."

"Then are you not wounded?" asked the horsemen.

"Nothing of the sort!" answered the tailor, "I have not turned a hair."

The horsemen still would not believe it, and rode into the wood to see, and there they found the giants wallowing in their blood, and all about them lying the uprooted trees.

The little tailor then claimed the promised boon, but the King repented him of his offer, and he sought again how to rid himself of the hero.

"Before you can possess my daughter and the half of my kingdom," said he to the tailor, "you must perform another heroic act. In the wood lives a unicorn who does great damage; you must secure him."

"A unicorn does not strike more terror into me than two giants. Seven at one blow!—that is my way," was the tailor's answer.

So, taking a rope and an ax with him, he went out into the wood, and told those who were ordered to attend him to wait outside. He had not far to seek, the unicorn soon came out and sprang at him, as if he would make an end of him without delay. "Softly, softly," said he, "most haste, worst speed," and remained standing until the animal came quite near, then he slipped quietly behind a tree. The unicorn ran with all his might against the tree and stuck his horn so deep into the trunk that he could not get it out again, and so was taken.

63

"Now I have you," said the tailor, coming out from behind the tree, and, putting the rope round the unicorn's neck, he took the ax, set free the horn, and when all his party were assembled he led forth the animal and brought it to the King.

The King did not yet wish to give him the promised reward, and set him a third task to do. Before the wedding could take place the tailor was to secure a wild boar which had done a great deal of damage in the wood.

The huntsmen were to accompany him.

"All right," said the tailor, "this is child's play."

But he did not take the huntsmen into the wood, and they were all the better pleased, for the wild boar had many a time before received them in such a way that they had no fancy to disturb him. When the boar caught sight of the tailor he ran at him with foaming mouth and gleaming tusks to bear him to the ground, but the nimble hero rushed into a chapel which chanced to be near, and jumped quickly out of a window on the other side. The boar ran after him, and when he got inside the door shut after him, and there he was imprisoned, for the creature was too big and unwieldy to jump out of the window too. Then the little tailor called the huntsmen that they might see the prisoner with their own eyes; and then he betook himself to the King, who now, whether he liked it or not, was obliged to fulfill his promise, and give him his daughter and the half of his kingdom. But if he had known that the great warrior was only a little tailor he would have taken it still more to heart. So the wedding was celebrated with great splendor and little joy, and the tailor was made into a king.

One night the young queen heard her husband talking in his sleep and saying,

"Now, boy, make me that waistcoat and patch me those breeches, or I will lay my yard measure about your shoulders!"

And so, as she perceived of what low birth her husband was, she went to her father the next morning and told him all, and begged him to set her free from a man who was nothing better than a tailor. The King bade her be comforted, saying,

"Tonight leave your bedroom door open, my guard shall stand

outside, and when he is asleep they shall come in and bind him and carry him off to a ship, and he shall be sent to the other side of the world."

So the wife felt consoled, but the King's water-bearer, who had been listening all the while, went to the little tailor and disclosed to him the whole plan.

"I shall put a stop to all this," said he.

At night he lay down as usual in bed, and when his wife thought that he was asleep, she got up, opened the door and lay down again. The little tailor, who only made believe to be asleep, began to murmur plainly.

"Now, boy, make me that waistcoat and patch me those breeches, or I will lay my yard measure about your shoulders! I have slain seven at one blow, killed two giants, caught a unicorn, and taken a wild boar, and shall I be afraid of those who are standing outside my room door?"

And when they heard the tailor say this, a great fear seized them; they fled away as if they had been wild hares, and none of them would venture to attack him.

And so the little tailor all his lifetime remained a King.

From "Fairy Tales," by Brothers Grimm.

The Elves and the Shoemaker

THERE was once a shoemaker who, through no fault of his own, had become so poor that at last he had only leather enough left for one pair of shoes. At evening he cut out the shoes which he intended to begin upon the next morning, and since he had a good conscience, he lay down quietly, said his prayers, and fell asleep.

In the morning when he had said his prayers, and was preparing to sit down to work, he found the pair of shoes standing finished on his table. He was amazed, and could not understand it in the least.

He took the shoes in his hand to examine them more closely. They were so neatly sewn that not a stitch was out of place, and were as good as the work of a master-hand.

Soon after a purchaser came in, and as he was much pleased with the shoes, he paid more than the ordinary price for them, so that the shoemaker was able to buy leather for two pairs of shoes with the money.

He cut them out in the evening, and next day, with fresh courage, was about to go to work; but he had no need to, for when he got up, the shoes were finished, and buyers were not lacking. These gave him so much money that he was able to buy leather for four pairs of shoes.

Early next morning he found the four pairs finished, and so it went on; what he cut out at evening was finished in the morning, so that he was soon again in comfortable circumstances, and became a well-to-do man.

Now it happened one evening, not long before Christmas, when he had cut out some shoes as usual, that he said to his wife: "How would it be if we were to sit up tonight to see who it is that lends us such a helping hand?"

The wife agreed, lighted a candle, and they hid themselves in the corner of the room behind the clothes which were hanging there.

At midnight came two little naked men who sat down at the shoemaker's table, took up the cut-out work, and began with their tiny fingers to stitch, sew, and hammer so neatly and quickly, that the shoemaker could not believe his eyes. They did not stop till everything was quite finished, and stood complete on the table; then they ran swiftly away.

The next day the wife said: "The little men have made us rich, and we ought to show our gratitude. They were running about with nothing on, and must freeze with cold. Now I will make them little shirts, coats, waistcoats, and hose, and will even knit them a pair of stockings, and you shall make them each a pair of shoes."

The husband agreed, and at evening, when they had everything

66

ready, they laid out the presents on the table, and hid themselves to see how the little men would behave.

At midnight they came skipping in, and were about to set to work; but, instead of the leather ready cut out, they found the charming little clothes.

At first they were surprised, then excessively delighted. With the greatest speed they put on and smoothed down the pretty clothes, singing:

> "Now we're boys so fine and neat,
> Why cobble more for others' feet?"

Then they hopped and danced about, and leapt over chairs and tables and out at the door. Henceforward, they came back no more, but the shoemaker fared well as long as he lived, and had good luck in all his undertakings.

From "Fairy Tales," by Brothers Grimm.

The Princess Whom Nobody Could Silence

THERE was once a king, who had a daughter who would always have the last word; she was so perverse and contrary in her speech that no one could silence her. So the king sent heralds throughout the land announcing that he who could outwit her should have the princess in marriage and half the kingdom besides.

There were plenty of those who wanted to try, I can assure you; for it isn't every day that one may win a princess and half a kingdom. The gate to the king's palace never stood still. The suitors came in swarms and flocks from east and west, both riding and walking. But there was no one who could silence the princess. At last the king announced that those who tried and did not succeed should be branded on both ears with a hot iron; he would not have all this running about the palace for nothing.

Now there were three brothers who had also heard about the princess, and as they were rather badly off at home, they thought they would try their luck. They were good friends and so they agreed to set out together.

When they had traveled a bit on the way, Boots found a dead magpie.

"I have found something! I have found something!" cried he.

"What have you found?" asked the brothers.

"I have found a dead magpie," said he.

"Faugh! throw it away; what can you do with that?" said the other two, who always believed they were the wisest.

"Oh, I've nothing to carry. I may as well take it along," said Boots.

When they had gone on a bit further Boots found a willow twig, which he picked up.

"I have found something! I have found something!" he cried.

"What have you found now?" said the brothers.

"I have found a willow twig," said he.

"Pooh! what are you going to do with that? Throw it away," said the two.

"Oh, I haven't much to carry. I may as well take it along," said he.

When they had gone still further Boots found a broken saucer, which he also picked up.

"Here lads, I have found something! I have found something!" said he.

"Well, what have you found now?" asked the brothers.

"A broken saucer," said he.

"Pshaw! Is it worth while dragging that along with you too? Throw it away!" said the brothers.

"Oh, I haven't much to carry. I may as well take it along," said Boots.

When they had gone a little bit further he came to two crooked goat-horns.

"I have found something! I have found something, lads!" said he.

"What have you found now?" said the others.

"Two goat-horns," answered Boots.

"Well, what are you going to do with them?" said they.

"Oh, I haven't much to carry. I may as well take them along," said Boots.

In a little while he saw a small piece of wood.

"I say, lads, I have found something! I have found something!" he cried.

"You are everlastingly finding something! What have you found now?" asked the two eldest.

"I have found a wedge," he answered.

"Oh, throw it away! What are you going to do with it?" said they.

"Oh, I haven't much to carry. I may as well take it along," said Boots.

As he went across the king's fields, he stooped down and picked up an old boot-sole.

"Hullo, lads! I have found something, I have found something!" said he.

"Heaven grant you may find a little sense before you get to the palace!" said the two. "What is it you have found now?"

"An old boot-sole," said he.

"Is that anything worth picking up? Throw it away! What are you going to do with it?" said the brothers.

"Oh, I haven't much to carry. I may as well take it along. Who knows, it may help me to win the princess and half the kingdom," said Boots.

"Yes, you look a likely one," said the other two.

When they arrived at the palace they went in to the princess, the eldest first.

"Good day!" said he.

"Good day to you!" answered she, with a shrug.

"It's terribly hot here," said he.

"It's hotter over there," said the princess looking at the branding iron that was lying waiting in the fire.

69

When the eldest saw this he was struck speechless, and so it was all over with him.

The second brother fared no better.

"Good day!" said he.

"Good day to you," said she, with a wriggle.

"It's terribly hot here!" said he.

"It's hotter in the fire," said she. With that he lost both speech and wits, and so the iron had to be brought out.

Then came Boots' turn.

"Good day!" said he.

"Good day to you!" said she, with a shrug and a wriggle.

"It is very nice and warm here!" said Boots.

"It's warmer in the fire," she answered. She was in no better humor now she saw the third suitor.

"Then there's a chance for me to roast my magpie," said Boots bringing it out of his pocket.

"I'm afraid the fat will sputter," said the princess.

"No fear of that! I'll tie this willow twig round it," said the lad.

"You can't tie it tight enough," said she.

"Then I'll drive in a wedge," said the lad, and brought out the piece of wood.

"The fat will soon be dripping," said the princess.

"I'll hold this under it," said the lad, and showed her the broken saucer.

"You are crooked in your speech," said the princess.

"No, I am not crooked," answered the lad; "but this is crooked," and he brought out one of the goat-horns.

"Well, I've never seen the like!" cried the princess.

"Here you see the like," said he, and brought out the other horn.

"It seems you have come here to wear out my soul!" she said.

"No, I have not come here to wear out your soul, for I have one which is already worn out," answered the lad, and brought out the old boot-sole.

The princess was so dumfounded at this that she had never a word to say.

"Now you are mine!" said Boots, and so he got her and half the kingdom into the bargain.

Adapted from version in "Fairy Tales from the Far North," by P. C. Asbjornsen, tr. from the Norwegian by H. L. Braekstad. n. d. The A. L. Burt Co.

❈

The Stolen Turnips, the Magic Tablecloth, the Sneezing Goat, and the Wooden Whistle

THIS is the story which old Peter used to tell whenever either Vanya or Maroosia was cross. This did not often happen; but it would be no use to pretend that it never happened at all. Sometimes it was Vanya who scolded Maroosia, and sometimes it was Maroosia who scolded Vanya. Sometimes there were two scoldings going on at once. And old Peter did not like crossness in the hut, whoever did the scolding. He said it spoilt his tobacco and put a sour taste in the tea. And, of course, when the children remembered that they were spoiling their grandfather's tea and tobacco they stopped just as quickly as they could, unless their tongues had run right away with them—which happens sometimes, you know, even to grown-up people. This story used to be told in two ways. It was either the tale of an old man who was bothered by a cross old woman, or the tale of an old woman who was bothered by a cross old man. And the moment old Peter began the story both children would ask at once, "Which is the cross one?"—for then they would know which of them old Peter thought was in the wrong.

"This time it's the old woman," said their grandfather; "but, as like as not, it will be the old man next."

And then any quarreling there was came to an end, and was forgotten before the end of the story. This is the story:

An old man and an old woman lived in a little wooden house.

71

All round the house there was a garden, crammed with flowers, and potatoes, and beetroots, and cabbages. And in one corner of the house there was a narrow wooden stairway which went up and up, twisting and twisting, into a high tower. In the top of the tower was a dovecot, and on the top of the dovecot was a flat roof.

Now, the old woman was never content with the doings of the old man. She scolded all day, and she scolded all night. If there was too much rain, it was the old man's fault; and if there was a drought, and all green things were parched for lack of water, well, the old man was to blame for not altering the weather. And though he was old and tired, it was all the same to her how much work she put on his shoulders. The garden was full. There was no room in it at all, not even for a single pea. And all of a sudden the old woman sets her heart on growing turnips.

"But there is no room in the garden," says the old man.

"Sow them on the top of the dovecot," says the old woman.

"But there is no earth there."

"Carry earth up and put it there," says she.

So the old man labored up and down with his tired old bones, and covered the top of the dovecot with good black earth. He could only take up a very little at a time, because he was old and weak, and because the stairs were so narrow and dangerous that he had to hold on with both hands and carry the earth in a bag which he held in his teeth. His teeth were strong enough, because he had been biting crusts all his life. The old woman left him nothing else, for she took all the crumbs for herself. The old man did his best, and by evening the top of the dovecot was covered with earth, and he had sown it with turnip seed.

Next day, and the day after that and every day, the old woman scolded the old man till he went up to the dovecot to see how those turnip seeds were getting on.

"Are they ready to eat yet?"

"They are not ready to eat."

"Is the green sprouting?"

"The green is sprouting."

And at last there came a day when the old man came down from the dovecot and said: "The turnips are doing finely—quite big they are getting; but all the best ones have been stolen away."

"Stolen away?" cried the old woman, shaking with rage. "And have you lived all these years and not learned how to keep thieves from a turnip-bed, on the top of a dovecot, on the top of a tower, on the top of a house? Out with you, and don't you dare to come back till you have caught the thieves."

The old man did not dare to tell her that the door had been bolted, although he knew it had, because he had bolted it himself. He hurried away out of the house, more because he wanted to get out of earshot of her scolding than because he had any hope of finding the thieves. "They may be birds," thinks he, "or the little brown squirrels. Who else could climb so high without using the stairs? And how is an old man like me to get hold of them, flying through the tops of the high trees and running up and down the branches?"

And so he wandered away without his dinner into the deep forest.

But God is good to old men. Hasn't He given me two little pigeons, who nearly always are as merry as all little pigeons should be? And God led the old man through the forest, though the old man thought he was just wandering on, trying to lose himself and forget the scolding voice of the old woman.

And after he had walked a long way through the dark green forest, he saw a little hut standing under the pine trees. There was no smoke coming from the chimney, but there was such a chattering in the hut you could hear it far away. It was like coming near a rookery at evening, or disturbing a lot of starlings. And as the old man came slowly nearer to the hut, he thought he saw little faces looking at him through the window and peeping through the door. He could not be sure, because they were gone so quickly. And all the time the chattering went on louder and louder, till the old man nearly put his hands to his ears.

And then suddenly the chattering stopped. There was not a sound —no noise at all. The old man stood still. A squirrel dropped a fir cone close by, and the old man was startled by the fall of it, because everything else was so quiet.

"Whatever there is in the hut, it won't be worse than the old

73

woman," says the old man to himself. So he makes the sign of the Holy Cross, and steps up to the little hut and takes a look through the door.

There was no one to be seen. You would have thought the hut was empty.

The old man took a step inside, bending under the little low door. Still he could see nobody, only a great heap of rags and blankets on the sleeping-place on the top of the stove. The hut was as clean as if it had only that minute been swept by Maroosia herself. But in the middle of the floor there was a scrap of green leaf lying, and the old man knew in a moment that it was a scrap of green leaf from the top of a young turnip.

And while the old man looked at it, the heap of blankets and rugs on the stove moved, first in one place and then in another. Then there was a little laugh. Then another. And suddenly there was a great stir in the blankets, and they were all thrown back helter-skelter, and there were dozens and dozens of little queer children, laughing and laughing and laughing, and looking at the old man. And every child had a little turnip, and showed it to the old man and laughed.

Just then the door of the stove flew open, and out tumbled more of the little queer children, dozens and dozens of them. The more they came tumbling out into the hut, the more there seemed to be chattering in the stove and squeezing to get out one over the top of another. The noise of chattering and laughing would have made your head spin. And every one of the children out of the stove had a little turnip like the others, and waved it about and showed it to the old man, and laughed like anything.

"Ho," says the old man, "so you are the thieves who have stolen the turnips from the top of the dovecot?"

"Yes," cried the children, and the chatter rattled as fast as hail-stones on the roof. "Yes! yes! yes! *We* stole the turnips."

"How did you get on to the top of the dovecot when the door into the house was bolted and fast?"

At that the children all burst out laughing, and did not answer a word.

"Laugh you may," said the old man; "but it is I who get the scolding when the turnips fly away in the night."

"Never mind! never mind!" cried the children. "We'll pay for the turnips."

"How can you pay for them?" asks the old man. "You have got nothing to pay with."

All the children chattered together, and looked at the old man and smiled. Then one of them said to the old man, "Are you hungry, Grandfather?"

"Hungry!" says the old man. "Why, yes, of course I am, my dear. I've been looking for you all day, and I had to start without my dinner."

"If you are hungry, open the cupboard behind you."

The old man opened the cupboard.

"Take out the tablecloth."

The old man took out the tablecloth.

"Spread it on the table."

The old man spread the tablecloth on the table.

"Now!" shouted the children, chattering like a thousand nests full of young birds, "we'll all sit down and have dinner."

They pulled out the benches and gave the old man a chair at one end, and all crowded round the table ready to begin.

"But there's no food," said the old man.

How they laughed!

"Grandfather," one of them sings out from the other end of the table, "you just tell the tablecloth to turn inside out."

"How?" says he.

"Tell the tablecloth to turn inside out. That's easy enough."

"There's no harm in doing that," thinks the old man; so he says to the tablecloth as firmly as he could, "Now then you, tablecloth, turn inside out!"

The tablecloth hove itself up into the air, and rolled itself this way and that as if it were in a whirlwind, and then suddenly laid itself flat on the table again. And somehow or other it had covered itself with dishes and plates and wooden spoons with pictures on them, and bowls of soup and mushrooms and kasha, and meat and cakes

75

and fish and ducks, and everything else you could think of, ready for the best dinner in the world.

The chattering and laughing stopped, and the old man and those dozens and dozens of little queer children set to work and ate everything on the table.

"Which of you washes the dishes?" asked the old man, when they had all done.

The children laughed.

"Tell the tablecloth to turn outside in."

"Tablecloth," says the old man, "turn outside in."

Up jumped the tablecloth with all the empty dishes and dirty plates and spoons, whirled itself this way and that in the air, and suddenly spread itself out flat again on the table, as clean and white as when it was taken out of the cupboard. There was not a dish or a bowl, or a spoon or a plate, or a knife to be seen; no, not even a crumb.

"That's a good tablecloth," says the old man.

"See here, Grandfather," shouted the children: "you take the tablecloth along with you, and say no more about those turnips."

"Well, I'm content with that," says the old man. And he folded up the tablecloth very carefully and put it away inside his shirt, and said he must be going.

"Good-by," says he, "and thank you for the dinner and the tablecloth."

"Good-by," say the children, "and thank you for the turnips."

The old man made his way home, singing through the forest in his creaky old voice until he came near the little wooden house where he lived with the old woman. As soon as he came near there he slipped along like any mouse. And as soon as he put his head inside the door the old woman began,—

"Have you found the thieves . . . ?"

"I found the thieves."

"Who were they?"

"They were a whole crowd of little queer children."

"Have you given them a beating they'll remember?"

"No, I have not."

"What? Bring them to me, and I'll teach them to steal my turnips!"

"I haven't got them."

"What have you done with them?"

"I had dinner with them."

Well, at that the old woman flew into such a rage she could hardly speak. But speak she did—yes, and shout too and scream—and it was all the old man could do not to run away out of the cottage. But he stood still and listened, and thought of something else; and when she had done he said, "They paid for the turnips."

"Paid for the turnips!" scolded the old woman. "A lot of children! What did they give you? Mushrooms? We can get them without losing our turnips."

"They gave me a tablecloth," said the old man; "it's a very good tablecloth."

He pulled it out of his shirt and spread it on the table; and as quickly as he could, before she began again, he said, "Tablecloth, turn inside out!"

The old woman stopped short, just when she was taking breath to scold with, when the tablecloth jumped up and danced in the air and settled on the table again, covered with things to eat and to drink. She smelt the meat, took a spoonful of the soup, and tried all the other dishes.

"Look at all the washing up it will mean," says she.

"Tablecloth, turn outside in!" says the old man; and there was a whirl of white cloth and dishes and everything else, and then the tablecloth spread itself out on the table as clean as ever you could wish.

"That's not a bad tablecloth," says the old woman; "but, of course, they owed me something for stealing all those turnips."

The old man said nothing. He was very tired, and he just laid down and went to sleep.

As soon as he was asleep the old woman took the tablecloth and hid it away in an iron chest, and put a tablecloth of her own in its place. "They were my turnips," says she, "and I don't see why he should have a share in the tablecloth. He's had a meal from it once at my expense, and once is enough." Then she lay down and went to sleep, grumbling to herself even in her dreams.

Early in the morning the old woman woke the old man and told him to go up to the dovecot and see how those turnips were getting on.

He got up and rubbed his eyes. When he saw the tablecloth on the table, the wish came to him to have a bite of food to begin the day with. So he stopped in the middle of putting on his shirt, and called to the tablecloth, "Tablecloth, turn inside out!"

Nothing happened. Why should anything happen? It was not the same tablecloth.

The old man told the old woman. "You should have made a good feast yesterday," says he, "for the tablecloth is no good any more. That is, it's no good that way; it's like any ordinary tablecloth."

"Most tablecloths are," says the old woman. "But what are you dawdling about? Up you go and have a look at those turnips."

The old man went climbing up the narrow twisting stairs. He held on with both hands for fear of falling, because they were so steep. He climbed to the top of the house, to the top of the tower, to the top of the dovecot, and looked at the turnips. He looked at the turnips, and he counted the turnips, and then he came slowly down the stairs again wondering what the old woman would say to him.

"Well," says the old woman in her sharp voice, "are they doing nicely? Because if not, I know whose fault it is."

"They are doing finely," said the old man; "but some of them have gone. Indeed, quite a lot of them have been stolen away."

"Stolen away!" screamed the old woman. "How dare you stand there and tell me that? Didn't you find the thieves yesterday? Go and find those children again, and take a stick with you, and don't show yourself here till you can tell me that they won't steal again in a hurry."

"Let me have a bite to eat," begs the old man. "It's a long way to go on an empty stomach."

"Not a mouthful!" yells the old woman. "Off with you. Letting my turnips be stolen every night, and then talking to me about bites of food!"

So the old man went off again without his dinner, and hobbled away into the forest as quickly as he could to get out of earshot of the old woman's scolding tongue.

As soon as he was out of sight the old woman stopped screaming after him, and went into the house and opened the iron chest and took out the tablecloth the children had given the old man, and laid it on the table instead of her own. She told it to turn inside out, and up it flew and whirled about and flopped down flat again, all covered with good things. She ate as much as she could hold. Then she told the tablecloth to turn outside in, and folded it up and hid it away again in the iron chest.

Meanwhile the old man tightened his belt, because he was so hungry. He hobbled along through the green forest till he came to the little hut standing under the pine trees. There was no smoke coming from the chimney, but there was such a chattering you would have thought that all the Vanyas and Maroosias in Holy Russia were talking to each other inside.

He had no sooner come in sight of the hut than the dozens and dozens of little queer children came pouring out of the door to meet him. And every single one of them had a turnip, and showed it to the old man, and laughed and laughed as if it were the best joke in the world.

"I knew it was you," said the old man.

"Of course it was us," cried the children. *"We* stole the turnips."

"But how did you get to the top of the dovecot when the door into the house was bolted and fast?"

The children laughed and laughed and did not answer a word.

"Laugh you may," says the old man; "but it is I who get the scolding when the turnips fly away in the night."

"Never mind! never mind!" cried the children. "We'll pay for the turnips."

"All very well," says the old man; "but that tablecloth of yours —it was fine yesterday, but this morning it would not give me even a glass of tea and a hunk of black bread."

At that the faces of the little queer children were troubled and grave. For a moment or two they all chattered together, and took no notice of the old man. Then one of them said,

79

"Well, this time we'll give you something better. We'll give you a goat."

"A goat?" says the old man.

"A goat with a cold in its head," said the children; and they crowded round him and took him behind the hut where there was a gray goat with a long beard cropping the short grass.

"It's a good enough goat," says the old man; "I don't see anything wrong with him."

"It's better than that," cried the children. "You tell it to sneeze."

The old man thought the children might be laughing at him, but he did not care, and he remembered the tablecloth. So he took off his hat and bowed to the goat. "Sneeze, goat," says he.

And instantly the goat started sneezing as if it would shake itself to pieces. And as it sneezed, good gold pieces flew from it in all directions, till the ground was thick with them.

"That's enough," said the children hurriedly; "tell him to stop, for all this gold is no use to us, and it's such a bother having to sweep it away."

"Stop sneezing, goat," says the old man; and the goat stopped sneezing, and stood there panting and out of breath in the middle of the sea of gold pieces.

The children began kicking the gold pieces about, spreading them by walking through them as if they were dead leaves. My old father used to say that those gold pieces are lying about still for anybody to pick up; but I doubt if he knew just where to look for them, or he would have had better clothes on his back and a little more food on the table. But who knows? Some day we may come upon that little hut somewhere in the forest, and then we shall know what to look for.

The children laughed and chattered and kicked the gold pieces this way and that into the green bushes. Then they brought the old man into the hut and gave him a bowl of kasha to eat, because he had had no dinner. There was no magic about the kasha; but it was good enough kasha for all that, and hunger made it better. When the old man had finished the kasha and drunk a glass of tea and smoked a little pipe, he got up and made a low bow and thanked the children.

And the children tied a rope to the goat and sent the old man home with it. He hobbled away through the forest, and as he went he looked back, and there were the little queer children all dancing together, and he heard them chattering and shouting: "Who stole the turnips? *We* stole the turnips. Who paid for the turnips? *We* paid for the turnips. Who stole the tablecloth? Who will pay for the tablecloth? Who will steal turnips again? *We* will steal turnips again."

But the old man was too pleased with the goat to give much heed to what they said; and he hobbled home through the green forest as fast as he could, with the goat trotting and walking behind him, pulling leaves off the bushes to chew as they hurried along.

The old woman was waiting in the doorway of the house. She was still as angry as ever.

"Have you beaten the children?" she screamed. "Have you beaten the children for stealing my good turnips?"

"No," said the old man; "they paid for the turnips."

"What did they pay?"

"They gave me this goat."

"That skinny old goat! I have three already, and the worst of them is better than that."

"It has a cold in the head," says the old man.

"Worse than ever!" screams the old woman.

"Wait a minute," says the old man as quickly as he could, to stop her scolding: "Sneeze, goat."

And the goat began to shake itself almost to bits, sneezing and sneezing and sneezing. The good gold pieces flew all ways at once. And the old woman threw herself after the gold pieces, picking them up like an old hen picking up corn. As fast as she picked them up more gold pieces came showering down on her like heavy gold hail, beating her on her head and her hands as she grubbed after those that had fallen already.

"Stop sneezing, goat," says the old man; and the goat stood there tired and panting, trying to get its breath. But the old woman did not look up till she had gathered every one of the gold pieces. When she did look up, she said,

"There's no supper for you. I've had supper already."

81

The old man said nothing. He tied up the goat to the doorpost of the house, where it could eat the green grass. Then he went into the house and lay down, and fell asleep at once, because he was an old man and had done a lot of walking.

As soon as he was asleep the old woman untied the goat and took it away and hid it in the bushes, and tied up one of her own goats instead. "They were my turnips," says she to herself, "and I don't see why he should have a share in the gold." Then she went in, and lay down grumbling to herself.

Early in the morning she woke the old man.

"Get up, you lazy fellow," says she; "you would lie all day and let all the thieves in the world come in and steal my turnips. Up with you to the dovecot and see how my turnips are getting on."

The old man got up and rubbed his eyes, and climbed up the rickety stairs, creak, creak, creak, holding on with both hands, till he came to the top of the house, to the top of the tower, to the top of the dovecot, and looked at the turnips.

He was afraid to come down, for there were hardly any turnips left at all.

And when he did come down, the scolding the old woman gave him was worse than the other two scoldings rolled into one. She was so angry that she shook like a rag in the high wind, and the old man put both hands to his ears and hobbled away into the forest.

He hobbled along as fast as he could hobble, until he came to the hut under the pine trees. This time the little queer children were not hiding under the blankets or in the stove, or chattering in the hut. They were all over the roof of the hut, dancing and crawling about. Some of them were even sitting on the chimney. And every one of the little queer children was playing with a turnip. As soon as they saw the old man they all came tumbling off the roof, one after another, head over heels, like a lot of peas rolling off a shovel.

"*We* stole the turnips!" they shouted, before the old man could say anything at all.

"I know you did," says the old man; "but that does not make it any better for me. And it is I who get the scolding when the turnips fly away in the night."

"Never again!" shouted the children.

"I'm glad to hear that," says the old man.

"And we'll pay for the turnips."

"Thank you kindly," says the old man. He hadn't the heart to be angry with those little queer children.

Three or four of them ran into the hut and came out again with a wooden whistle, a regular whistle-pipe, such as shepherds use. They gave it to the old man.

"I can never play that," says the old man. "I don't know one tune from another; and if I did, my old fingers are as stiff as oak twigs."

"Blow in it," cried the children; and all the others came crowding round, laughing and chattering and whispering to each other. "Is he going to blow in it?" they asked. "He *is* going to blow in it." How they laughed!

The old man took the whistle, and gathered his breath and puffed out his cheeks, and blew in the whistle-pipe as hard as he could. And before he could take the whistle from his lips, three lively whips had slipped out of it, and were beating him as hard as they could go, although there was nobody to hold them. Phew! phew! phew! The three whips came down on him one after the other.

"Blow again!" the children shouted, laughing as if they were mad. "Blow again—quick, quick, quick!—and tell the whips to get into the whistle."

The old man did not wait to be told twice. He blew for all he was worth, and instantly the three whips stopped beating him. "Into the whistle!" he cried; and the three lively whips shot up into the whistle, like three snakes going into a hole. He could hardly have believed they had been out at all if it had not been for the soreness of his back.

"You take that home," cried the children. "That'll pay for the turnips, and put everything right."

"Who knows?" said the old man; and he thanked the children, and set off home through the green forest.

"Good-by," cried the little queer children. But as soon as he had started they forgot all about him. When he looked round to wave his hand to them, not one of them was thinking of him. They were up again on the roof of the hut, jumping over each other and dancing and crawling about, and rolling each other down the roof and climbing up again, as if they had been doing nothing else all day, and were going to do nothing else till the end of the world.

The old man hobbled home through the green forest with the whistle stuck safely away into his shirt. As soon as he came to the door of the hut, the old woman, who was sitting inside counting the gold pieces, jumped up and started her scolding.

"What have the children tricked you with this time?" she screamed at him.

"They gave me a whistle-pipe," says the old man, "and they are not going to steal the turnips any more."

"A whistle-pipe!" she screamed. "What's the good of that? It's worse than the tablecloth and the skinny old goat."

The old man said nothing.

"Give it to me!" screamed the old woman. "They were my turnips, so it is my whistle-pipe."

"Well, whatever you do, don't blow in it," says the old man, and he hands over the whistle-pipe.

She wouldn't listen to him.

"What?" says she; "I must not blow my own whistle-pipe?"

And with that she put the whistle-pipe to her lips and blew.

Out jumped the three lively whips, flew up in the air, and began to beat her—phew! phew! phew!—one after another. If they made the old man sore, it was nothing to what they did to the cross old woman.

"Stop them! Stop them!" she screamed, running this way and that in the hut, with the whips flying after her beating her all the time. "I'll never scold again. I am to blame. I stole the magic tablecloth, and put an old one instead of it. I hid it in the iron chest." She ran to the iron chest and opened it, and pulled out the tablecloth. "Stop them! Stop them!" she screamed, while the whips laid it on hard and fast, one after the other. "I am to blame. The goat that sneezes gold pieces is hidden in the bushes. The goat by the door is one of the old ones. I wanted all the gold for myself."

All this time the old man was trying to get hold of the whistle-pipe. But the old woman was running about the hut so fast, with the whips flying after her and beating her, that he could not get it out of her hands. At last he grabbed it. "Into the whistle," says he, and put it to his lips and blew.

In a moment the three lively whips had hidden themselves in the whistle. And there was the cross old woman, kissing his hand and promising never to scold any more.

"That's all right," says the old man; and he fetched the sneezing goat out of the bushes and made it sneeze a little gold, just to be sure that it was that goat and no other. Then he laid the tablecloth on the table and told it to turn inside out. Up it flew, and came down again with the best dinner that ever was cooked, only waiting to be eaten. And the old man and the old woman sat down and ate till they could eat no more. The old woman rubbed herself now and again. And the old man rubbed himself too. But there was never a cross word between them, and they went to bed singing like nightingales.

"Is that the end?" Maroosia always asked.

"Is that all?" asked Vanya, though he knew it was not.

"Not quite," said old Peter; "but the tale won't go any quicker than my old tongue."

In the morning the old woman had forgotten about her promise. And just from habit, she set about scolding the old man as if the whips had never jumped out of the whistle. She scolded him for sleeping too long, sent him upstairs, with a lot of cross words after him, to go to the top of the dovecot to see how those turnips were getting on.

After a little the old man came down.

"The turnips are coming on grandly," says he, "and not a single one has gone in the night. I told you the children said they would not steal any more."

"I don't believe you," said the old woman. "I'll see for myself. And if any are gone, you shall pay for it, and pay for it well."

Up she jumped, and tried to climb the stairs. But the stairs were narrow and steep and twisting. She tried and tried, and could not get up at all. So she gets angrier than ever, and starts scolding the old man again.

"You must carry me up," says she.

"I have to hold on with both hands, or I couldn't get up myself," says the old man.

"I'll get in the flour sack, and you must carry me up with your teeth," says she; "they're strong enough."

And the old woman got into the flour sack.

"Don't ask me any questions," says the old man; and he took the sack in his teeth and began slowly climbing up the stairs, holding on with both hands.

He climbed and climbed, but he did not climb fast enough for the old woman.

"Are we at the top?" says she.

The old man said nothing, but went on, climbing up and up, nearly dead with the weight of the old woman in the sack which he was holding in his teeth.

He climbed a little further, and the old woman screamed out,

"Are we at the top now? We must be at the top. Let me out . . ."

The old man said nothing; he climbed on and on.

The old woman raged in the flour sack. She jumped about in the sack, and screamed at the old man,

"Are we near the top now? Answer me, can't you! Answer me at once, or you'll pay for it later. Are we near the top?"

"Very near," said the old man.

And as he opened his mouth to say that, the sack slipped from between his teeth, and bump, bump, bumpety bump, the old woman in the sack fell all the way to the very bottom, bumping on every step. That was the end of her.

After that the old man lived alone in the hut. When he wanted tobacco or clothes or a new ax, he made the goat sneeze some gold pieces, and off he went to the town with plenty of money in his pocket. When he wanted his dinner he had only to lay the tablecloth. He never had any washing up to do, because the tablecloth did it for him. When he wanted to get rid of troublesome guests, he gave them the whistle to blow. And when he was lonely and wanted company, he went to the little hut under the pine trees and played with the little queer children.

The Broad Man, the Tall Man, and the Man with Eyes of Flame

IT WAS in those days when cats wore shoes, when frogs croaked in grandmothers' chairs, when donkeys clanked their spurs on the pavements like brave knights, and when hares chased dogs. So you see it must have been a very, very long time ago.

In those days the king of a certain country had a daughter, who was not only exceedingly beautiful but also remarkably clever. Many kings and princes traveled from far distant lands, each one with the hope of making her his wife. But she would have nothing to do with any one of them. Finally, it was proclaimed that she would marry that man who for three successive nights should keep such strict watch upon her that she could not escape unnoticed. Those who failed were to have their heads cut off.

The news of this offer was noised about in all parts of the world. A great many kings and princes hastened to make the trial, taking their turn and keeping watch. But each one lost his life in the attempt, for they could not prevent, indeed they were not even able to see, the princess take her flight.

Now it happened that Matthias, prince of a royal city, heard of what was going on and resolved to watch through the three nights. He was young, handsome as a deer, and brave as a falcon. His father did all he could to turn him from his purpose: he used entreaties, prayers, threats, in fact he forbade him to go, but in vain,

87

nothing could prevent him. What could the poor father do? Worn-out with contention, he was at last obliged to consent. Matthias filled his purse with gold, girded a well-tried sword to his side, and quite alone started off to seek the fortune of the brave.

Walking along next day, he met a man who seemed hardly able to drag one leg after the other.

"Whither are you going?" asked Matthias.

"I am traveling all over the world in search of happiness."

"What is your profession?"

"I have no profession, but I can do what no one else can. I am called *Broad*, because I have the power of swelling myself out to such a size that there is room for a whole regiment of soldiers inside me."

So saying he puffed himself out till he formed a barricade from one side of the road to the other.

"Bravo!" cried Matthias, delighted at this proof of his capacities. "By the way, would you mind coming with me? I, too, am traveling across the world in search of happiness."

"If there is nothing bad in it I am quite willing," answered Broad. And they continued their journey together.

A little further on they met a very slender man, frightfully thin, and tall and straight as a portico.

"Whither are you going, good man?" asked Matthias, filled with curiosity at his strange appearance.

"I am traveling about the world."

"To what profession do you belong?"

"To no profession, but I know something every one else is ignorant of. I am called Tall, and with good reason. For without leaving the earth I can stretch out and reach up to the clouds. When I walk I clear a mile at each step."

Without more ado he lengthened himself out until his head was lost in the clouds, while he really cleared a mile at each step.

"I like that, my fine fellow," said Matthias. "Come, would you not like to travel with us?"

"Why not?" replied he. "I'll come."

So they proceeded on their way together. While passing through a forest they saw a man placing trunks of trees one upon another.

"What are you trying to do there?" asked Matthias, addressing him.

"I have Eyes of Flame," said he, "and I am building a pile here." So saying he fixed his flaming eyes upon the wood, and the whole was instantly set alight.

"You are a very clever and powerful man," said Matthias, "would you like to join our party?"

"All right, I am willing."

So the four traveled along together. Matthias was overjoyed to have met with such gifted companions, and paid their expenses generously, without complaining of the enormous sum of money he had to spend on the amount of food Broad consumed.

After some days they reached the princess's palace. Matthias had told them the object of his journey, and had promised each a large reward if he was successful. They gave him their word to work with a will at the task which every one up till then had failed to accomplish. The prince bought them each a handsome suit of clothes, and when they were all presentable sent them to tell the king, the princess's father, that he had come with his attendants to watch three nights in the lady's boudoir. But he took very good care not to say who he was, nor whence he had come.

The king received them kindly, and after hearing their request said: "Reflect well before engaging yourselves in this, for if the princess should escape, you will have to die."

"We very much doubt her escaping from us," they replied, "but come what will, we intend to make the attempt and to begin at once."

"My duty was to warn you," replied the monarch, smiling, "but if you still persist in your resolution I myself will take you to the lady's apartments."

Matthias was dazzled at the loveliness of the royal maiden, while she, on her side, received the brilliant and handsome young man most graciously, not trying to hide how much she liked his good looks and gentle manner. Hardly had the king retired when Broad lay down across the threshold; Tall and the Man with Eyes of Flame

89

placed themselves near the window; while Matthias talked with the princess, and watched her every movement attentively.

Suddenly she ceased to speak, then after a few moments said, "I feel as if a shower of poppies were falling on my eyelids."

And she lay down on the couch, pretending to sleep.

Matthias did not breathe a word. Seeing her asleep he sat down at a table near the sofa, leaned his elbows upon it, and rested his chin in the hollow of his hands. Gradually he felt drowsy and his eyes closed, as did those of his companions.

Now this was the moment the princess was waiting for. Quickly changing herself into a dove, she flew towards the window. If it had not happened that one of her wings touched Tall's hair he would not have awakened, and he would certainly never have succeeded in catching her if it had not been for the Man with Eyes of Flame, for he, as soon as he knew which direction she had taken, sent such a glance after her, that is, a flame of fire, that in the twinkling of an eye her wings were burnt, and having been thus stopped, she was obliged to perch on the top of a tree. From thence Tall reached her easily, and placed her in Matthias's hands, where she became a princess again. Matthias had hardly awakened out of his sleep.

Next morning and the morning after, the king was greatly astonished to find his daughter sitting by the prince's side, but he was obliged to keep silent and accept facts as they were, at the same time entertaining his guests royally. At the approach of the third night he spoke with his daughter, and begged her to practice all the magic of which she was capable, and to act in such a way as to free him from the presence of intruders of whom he knew neither the rank nor the fortune.

As for Matthias, he used every means in his power to bring about a happy ending to such a hitherto successful undertaking. Before entering the princess's apartments he took his comrades aside and said, "There is but one more stroke of luck, dear friends, and then we have succeeded. If we fail, do not forget that our four heads will roll on the scaffold."

"Come along," replied the three; "never fear, we shall be able to keep good watch."

When they came into the princess's room they hastened to take up their positions, and Matthias sat down facing the lady. He would have much preferred to remain with her without being obliged to keep watch all the time for fear of losing her forever. Resolving not to sleep this time, he said to himself, "Now I will keep watch upon you, but when you are my wife I will rest."

At midnight, when sleep was beginning to overpower her watchers, the princess kept silence, and, stretching herself on the couch, shut her beautiful eyes as if she were really asleep.

Matthias, his elbows on the table, his chin in the palms of his hands, his eyes fixed upon her, admired her silently. But as sleep closes even the eyes of the eagle, so it shut those of the prince and his companions.

The princess, who all this time had been watching them narrowly and only waiting for this moment, got up from her seat, and changing herself into a little fly, flew out of the window. Once free, she again changed herself into a fish, and falling into the palace well, plunged and hid herself in the depths of the water.

She would certainly have made her escape if, as a fly, she had not just touched the tip of the nose of the Man with Eyes of Flame. He sneezed, and opened his eyes in time to notice the direction in which she had disappeared. Without losing an instant he gave the alarm, and all four ran into the courtyard. The well was very deep, but that did not matter. Tall soon stretched himself to the required depth, and searched in all the corners: but he was unable to find the little fish, and it seemed impossible that it could ever have been there.

"Now then, get out of that, I will take your place," said Broad.

And getting in at the top by the rim, he filled up all the inside of the well, stopping it so completely with his huge body that the water sprang out: but nothing was seen of the little fish.

"Now it is my turn," said the Man with Eyes of Flame, "I warrant I'll dislodge this clever magician."

When Broad had cleared the well of his enormous person, the water returned to its place, but it soon began to boil from the heat of the eyes of flame. It boiled and boiled, till it boiled over the rim; then, as it went on boiling and rising ever higher and higher, a little fish was seen to throw itself out on the grass half cooked. As it touched the ground it again took the form of the princess.

Matthias went to her and kissed her tenderly.

"You have conquered, my master and husband," she said, "you have succeeded in preventing my escape. Henceforth I am yours, both by right of conquest and of my own free will."

The young man's courtesy, strength, and gentleness, as well as his beauty, were very pleasing to the princess; but her father, the king, was not so ready to approve of her choice, and he resolved not to let her go with them. But this did not trouble Matthias, who determined to carry her off, aided by his three comrades. They soon all left the palace.

The king was furious, and ordered his guards to follow them and bring them back under pain of death. Meanwhile Matthias, the princess, and the three comrades had already traveled a distance of some miles. When she heard the steps of the pursuers, she begged the Man with Eyes of Flame to see who they were. Having turned to look, he told her that a large army of men on horseback were advancing at a gallop.

"They are my father's guards," said she, "we shall have some difficulty in escaping them."

Then, seeing the horsemen draw nearer, she took the veil from her face, and throwing it behind her in the direction of the wind, said, "I command as many trees to spring up as there are threads in this veil."

Instantly, in the twinkling of an eye, a high thick forest rose up between them. Before the soldiers had time to clear for themselves a pathway through this dense mass, Matthias and his party had been able to get far ahead, and even to take a little rest.

"Look," said the princess, "and see if they are still coming after us."

The Man with Eyes of Flame looked back, and replied that the king's guards were out of the forest and coming towards them with all speed.

"They will not be able to reach us," cried she. And she let fall a tear from her eyes, saying as she did so, "Tear, become a river."

At the same moment a wide river flowed between them and their pursuers, and before the latter had found means of crossing it, Matthias and his party were far on in front.

"Man with Eyes of Flame," said the princess, "look behind and tell me how closely we are followed."

"They are quite near to us again," he replied, "they are almost upon our heels."

"Darkness, cover them," said she.

At these words Tall drew himself up. He stretched and stretched and stretched until he reached the clouds, and there, with his hat he half covered the face of the sun. The side towards the soldiers was black as night, while Matthias and his party, lit up by the shining half, went a good way without hindrance.

When they had traveled some distance, Tall uncovered the sun, and soon joined his companions by taking a mile at each step. They were already in sight of Matthias's home, when they noticed that the royal guards were again following them closely.

"Now it is my turn," said Broad; "go on your way in safety, I will remain here. I shall be ready for them."

He quietly awaited their arrival, standing motionless, with his large mouth open from ear to ear. The royal army, who were determined not to turn back without having taken the princess, advanced towards the town at a gallop. They had decided among themselves that if it resisted they would lay siege to it.

Mistaking Broad's open mouth for one of the city gates, they all dashed through and disappeared.

Broad closed his mouth, and having swallowed them, ran to rejoin his comrades in the palace of Matthias's father. He felt somewhat disturbed with a whole army inside him, and the earth groaned and trembled beneath him as he ran. He could hear the shouts of the people assembled round Matthias, as they rejoiced at his safe return.

"Ah, here you are at last, brother Broad," cried Matthias, directly he caught sight of him. "But what have you done with the army? Where have you left it?"

"The army is here, quite safe," answered he, patting his enormous person. "I shall be very pleased to return them as they are, for the morsel is not very easy to digest."

"Come then, let them out of their prison," said Matthias, enjoying the joke, and at the same time calling all the inhabitants to assist at the entertainment.

Broad, who looked upon it as a common occurrence, stood in the middle of the palace square, and putting his hands to his sides, began to cough. Then—it was really a sight worth seeing—at each cough horsemen and horses fell out of his mouth, one over the other, plunging, hopping, jumping, trying who could get out of the way the quickest. The last one had a little difficulty in getting free, for he somehow got into one of Broad's nostrils and was unable to move. It was only by giving a good sneeze that Broad could release him, the last of the royal cavaliers, and he lost no time in following his companions at the top of his speed.

A few days later a splendid feast was given at the wedding of Prince Matthias and the princess. The king, her father, was also present. Tall had been sent to invite him. Owing to his knowledge of the road and the length of his limbs, he accomplished the journey so quickly that he was there before the royal horsemen had time to get back. It was well for them that it was so, for, had he not pleaded that their lives might be saved, their heads would certainly have been cut off for returning empty-handed.

Everything was now arranged to everybody's satisfaction. The princess's father was delighted to know that his daughter was married to a rich and noble prince, and Matthias generously rewarded his brave traveling companions, who remained with him to the end of their days.

From "Slav Fairy Tales," by Chodska. n. d. The A. L. Burt Co.

The Squire's Bride

ONCE upon a time there was a squire who owned a large farm, and had plenty of silver at the bottom of his chest and money in the bank besides; but he felt there was something wanting, for he had no wife.

One day the daughter of a neighboring farmer was working for him in the hayfield. The squire saw her and liked her, and because he was a squire, he thought if he only hinted that he wanted her she would be ready to marry him at once.

So he told her that he had been thinking of getting married.

"Ay! one may think of many things," said the girl, laughing slyly, and looking at his bald head.

"Well, you see, I thought that you should be my wife!"

"No, thank you all the same," said she, "but that's not to my liking."

Now the squire was not accustomed to be gainsaid, and the more the maid refused him the more determined he was to get her. But as he made no progress in her favor, he sent for her father and told him that if he could arrange the matter with his daughter he would forgive him the money he had lent him and give him the piece of land which lay close to his meadow into the bargain.

"Yes, you may be sure I'll bring my daughter to her senses," said the father. "She is only a child, and she doesn't know what's best for her." But all his coaxing and talking did not help matters. She would not have the squire, she said, if he sat buried in gold up to his ears.

The squire waited day after day, but at last he became so angry and impatient that he told the father, if he expected him to stand by his promise, he would have to put his foot down and settle the matter now.

The man knew no other way out of it but to let the squire get everything ready for the wedding and send for the girl as if she were wanted for some work on the farm. When she arrived, the parson and the wedding guests would be there and she would have to be married right away, and would have no time to think it over.

The squire thought this was well and good, and his household be-

95

gan brewing and baking and getting ready for the wedding in grand style. When the day came and the guests had arrived, the squire called one of his farm lads and told him to run down to his neighbor and ask him to send him what he had promised.

"But if you are not back in a twinkling," he said, shaking his fist at him, "I'll—" and with that the lad ran off.

"My master has sent me to ask for that you promised him," said the lad, when he got to the neighbor, "and there is no time to be lost, for he is very angry."

"Yes, yes! Run down into the meadow and take her with you. There she goes!" answered the neighbor.

The lad ran off and when he came to the meadow he found the daughter there raking the hay.

"I am to fetch what your father has promised my master," said the lad.

"Ah, ha!" thought she. "Is that what they are up to?"

"Ah, indeed!" she said. "I suppose it's that little bay mare of ours. You had better go and take her. She stands there tethered on the other side of the field," said the girl.

The boy jumped on the back of the bay mare and rode home at full gallop.

"Have you brought her with you?" asked the squire.

"She is down at the door," said the lad.

"Take her up to the room my mother had," said the squire.

"But, master, how can that be managed?" said the lad.

"You must do as I tell you," said the squire. "If you cannot manage her alone you must get the men to help you," for he thought the girl might turn obstreperous.

When the lad saw his master's face he knew it would be no use to gainsay him. So he got all the farm tenants who were there, to help him. Some pulled at the head and the forelegs of the mare and others pushed from behind, and at last they got her up the stairs and into the room. There lay all the wedding finery ready.

"Now, that's done, master!" said the lad; "but it was a terrible job. It was the worst I have ever had here on the farm."

"Never mind, you shall not have done it for nothing," said his master. "Now send the women up to dress her."

"But I say, master—" said the lad.

"None of your talk!" said the squire. "Tell them they must dress her and not forget either wreath or crown."

The lad ran into the kitchen.

"Look here, lasses," he said; "you must go upstairs and dress up the bay mare as bride. I expect the master wants to give the guests a laugh."

The women dressed the bay mare in everything that was there, and then the lad told his master that now she was dressed, with wreath and crown and all.

"Very well, bring her down!" said the squire. "I will receive her myself at the door."

There was a terrible clatter on the stairs; for that bride, as you know, did not wear silken shoes.

When the door was opened and the squire's bride entered the parlor everyone laughed loudly.

And as for the squire you may be sure he had had enough of that bride, and they say he never went courting again.

From "Fairy Tales from the Far North," by P. C. Asbjornsen, tr. from the Norwegian by H. L. Braekstad. n. d. The A. L. Burt Co.

The Old Woman and the Tramp

THERE was once a tramp, who went plodding his way through a forest. The distance between the houses was so great that he had little hope of finding a shelter before the night set in. But all of a sudden he saw some lights between the trees. He then discovered a cottage, where there was a fire burning on the hearth. How nice it would be to roast oneself before that fire, and to get a bite of something, he thought; and so he dragged himself towards the cottage.

Just then an old woman came towards him.

"Good evening, and well met!" said the tramp.

"Good evening," said the woman. "Where do you come from?"

"South of the sun, and east of the moon," said the tramp; "and now I am on the way home again, for I have been all over the world with the exception of this parish," he said.

"You must be a great traveler, then," said the woman. "What may be your business here?"

"Oh, I want a shelter for the night," he said.

"I thought as much," said the woman; "but you may as well get away from here at once, for my husband is not at home, and my place is not an inn," she said.

"My good woman," said the tramp, "you must not be so cross and hard-hearted, for we are both human beings, and should help one another, it is written."

"Help one another?" said the woman, "help? Did you ever hear such a thing? Who'll help me, do you think? I haven't got a morsel in the house! No, you'll have to look for quarters elsewhere," she said.

But the tramp was like the rest of his kind; he did not consider himself beaten at the first rebuff. Although the old woman grumbled and complained as much as she could, he was just as persistent as ever, and went on begging and praying like a starved dog, until at last she gave in, and he got permission to lie on the floor for the night.

That was very kind, he thought, and he thanked her for it.

"Better on the floor without sleep, than suffer cold in the forest deep," he said; for he was a merry fellow, this tramp, and was always ready with a rhyme.

When he came into the room he could see that the woman was not so badly off as she had pretended; but she was a greedy and stingy woman of the worst sort, and was always complaining and grumbling.

He now made himself very agreeable, of course, and asked her in his most insinuating manner for something to eat.

"Where am I to get it from?" said the woman. "I haven't tasted a morsel myself the whole day."

But the tramp was a cunning fellow, he was.

"Poor old granny, you must be starving," he said. "Well, well, I suppose I shall have to ask you to have something with me, then."

"Have something with you!" said the woman. "You don't look as if you could ask anyone to have anything! What have you got to offer one, I should like to know?"

"He who far and wide does roam sees many things not known at home; and he who many things has seen has wits about him and senses keen," said the tramp. "Better dead than lose one's head! Lend me a pot, grannie!"

The old woman now became very inquisitive, as you may guess, and so she let him have a pot.

He filled it with water and put it on the fire, and then he blew with all his might till the fire was burning fiercely all round it. Then he took a four-inch nail from his pocket, turned it three times in his hand and put it into the pot.

The woman stared with all her might.

"What's this going to be?" she asked.

"Nail broth," said the tramp, and began to stir the water with the porridge stick.

"Nail broth?" asked the woman.

"Yes, nail broth," said the tramp.

The old woman had seen and heard a good deal in her time, but that anybody could have made broth with a nail, well, she had never heard the like before.

"That's something for poor people to know," she said, "and I should like to learn how to make it."

"That which is not worth having, will always go a-begging," said the tramp.

But if she wanted to learn how to make it she had only to watch him, he said, and went on stirring the broth.

The old woman squatted on the ground, her hands clasping her knees, and her eyes following his hand as he stirred the broth.

"This generally makes good broth," he said; "but this time it will very likely be rather thin, for I have been making broth the whole week with the same nail. If one only had a handful of sifted oatmeal to put in, that would make it all right," he said. "But what one has to go without, it's no use thinking more about," and so he stirred the broth again.

"Well, I think I have a scrap of flour somewhere," said the old woman, and went out to fetch some, and it was both good and fine.

The tramp began putting the flour into the broth, and went on stirring, while the woman sat staring now at him and then at the pot until her eyes nearly burst their sockets.

"This broth would be good enough for company," he said, putting in one handful of flour after another. "If I had only a bit of salted beef and a few potatoes to put in, it would be fit for gentlefolks, however particular they might be," he said. "But what one has to go without, it's no use thinking more about."

When the old woman really began to think it over, she thought she had some potatoes, and perhaps a bit of beef as well; and these she gave the tramp, who went on stirring, while she sat and stared as hard as ever.

"This will be grand enough for the best in the land," he said.

"Well, I never!" said the woman; "and just fancy—all with a nail!"

He was really a wonderful man, that tramp! He could do more than drink a sup and turn the tankard up, he could.

"If one had only a little barley and a drop of milk, we could ask the king himself to have some of it," he said; "for this is what he has every blessed evening—that I know, for I have been in service under the king's cook," he said.

"Dear me! Ask the king to have some! Well, I never!" exclaimed the woman, slapping her knees. She was quite awestruck at the tramp and his grand connections.

"But what one has to go without, it's no use thinking more about," said the tramp.

And then she remembered she had a little barley; and as for milk, well, she wasn't quite out of that, she said, for her best cow had just calved. And then she went to fetch both the one and the other.

The tramp went on stirring, and the woman sat staring, one moment at him and the next at the pot.

Then all at once the tramp took out the nail.

"Now it's ready, and now we'll have a real good feast," he said. "But to this kind of soup the king and the queen always take a dram or two, and one sandwich at least. And then they always have a cloth on the table when they eat," he said. "But what one has to go without, it's no use thinking more about."

But by this time the old woman herself had begun to feel quite grand and fine, I can tell you; and if that was all that was wanted to make it just as the king had it, she thought it would be nice to have it just the same way for once, and play at being king and queen with the tramp. She went straight to a cupboard and brought out the brandy bottle, dram glasses, butter and cheese, smoked beef and veal, until at last the table looked as if it were decked out for company.

Never in her life had the old woman had such a grand feast, and never had she tasted such broth, and just fancy, made only with a nail!

She was in such a good and merry humor at having learnt such an economical way of making broth that she did not know how to make enough of the tramp who had taught her such a useful thing.

So they ate and drank, and drank and ate, until they became both tired and sleepy.

The tramp was now going to lie down on the floor. But that would never do, thought the old woman; no, that was impossible. "Such a grand person must have a bed to lie in," she said.

He did not need much pressing. "It's just like the sweet Christmas time," he said, "and a nicer woman I never came across. Ah, well! Happy are they who meet with such good people," said he, and he lay down on the bed and went asleep.

And next morning when he woke the first thing he got was coffee and a dram.

When he was going the old woman gave him a bright dollar piece.

"And thanks, many thanks, for what you have taught me," she said. "Now I shall live in comfort, since I have learnt how to make broth with a nail."

"Well, it isn't very difficult, if one only has something good to add to it," said the tramp as he went his way.

101

The woman stood at the door staring after him.
"Such people don't grow on every bush," she said.

The Sleeping Beauty

IN TIMES past there lived a king and queen, who said to each other
every day of their lives, "Would that we had a child!" and yet they
had none. But it happened once that when the queen was bathing,
there came a frog out of the water, and he squatted on the ground,
and said to her,

"Thy wish shall be fulfilled; before a year has gone by, thou shalt
bring a daughter into the world."

And as the frog foretold, so it happened; and the queen bore a
daughter so beautiful that the king could not contain himself for joy,
and he ordained a great feast. Not only did he bid to it his relations,
friends, and acquaintances, but also the wise women, that they might
be kind and favorable to the child. There were thirteen of them in his
kingdom, but as he had only provided twelve golden plates for them
to eat from, one of them had to be left out. However, the feast was
celebrated with all splendor; and as it drew to an end, the wise wom-
en stood forward to present to the child their wonderful gifts: one
bestowed virtue, one beauty, a third riches, and so on, whatever there
is in the world to wish for. And when eleven of them had said their
say, in came the uninvited thirteenth, burning to revenge herself, and
without greeting or respect, she cried with a loud voice,

"In the fifteenth year of her age the princess shall prick herself
with a spindle and shall fall down dead."

And without speaking one more word she turned away and left the hall. Everyone was terrified at her saying, when the twelfth came forward, for she had not yet bestowed her gift, and though she could not do away with the evil prophecy, yet she could soften it, so she said,

"The princess shall not die, but fall into a deep sleep for a hundred years."

Now the king, being desirous of saving his child even from this misfortune, gave commandment that all the spindles in his kingdom should be burnt up.

The maiden grew up, adorned with all the gifts of the wise women; and she was so lovely, modest, sweet, and kind and clever, that no one who saw her could help loving her.

It happened one day, she being already fifteen years old, that the king and queen rode abroad, and the maiden was left behind alone in the castle. She wandered about into all the nooks and corners, and into all the chambers and parlors, as the fancy took her, till at last she came to an old tower. She climbed the narrow winding stair which led to a little door, with a rusty key sticking out of the lock; she turned the key, and the door opened, and there in the little room sat an old woman with a spindle, diligently spinning her flax.

"Good day, mother," said the princess, "what are you doing?"

"I am spinning," answered the old woman, nodding her head.

"What thing is that that twists round so briskly?" asked the maiden, and taking the spindle into her hand she began to spin; but no sooner had she touched it than the evil prophecy was fulfilled, and she pricked her finger with it. In that very moment she fell back upon the bed that stood there, and lay in a deep sleep. And this sleep fell upon the whole castle; the king and queen, who had returned and were in the great hall, fell fast asleep, and with them the whole court. The horses in their stalls, and dogs in the yard, the pigeons on the roof, the flies on the wall, the very fire that flickered on the hearth, became still, and slept like the rest; and the meat on the spit ceased roasting, and the cook, who was going to pull the scullion's hair for some mistake he had made, let him go, and went to sleep. And the wind ceased, and not a leaf fell from the trees about the castle.

Then round about that place there grew a hedge of thorns thicker

103

every year, until at last the whole castle was hidden from view, and nothing of it could be seen but the vane on the roof. And a rumor went abroad in all that country of the beautiful sleeping Rosamond, for so was the princess called; and from time to time many kings' sons came and tried to force their way through the hedge; but it was impossible for them to do so, for the thorns held fast together like strong hands, and the young men were caught by them, and not being able to get free, there died a lamentable death.

Many a long year afterwards there came a king's son into that country, and heard an old man tell how there should be a castle standing behind the hedge of thorns, and that there a beautiful enchanted princess named Rosamond had slept for a hundred years, and with her the king and queen, and the whole court. The old man had been told by his grandfather that many kings' sons had sought to pass the thorn-hedge, but had been caught and pierced by the thorns, and had died a miserable death. Then said the young man, "Nevertheless, I do not fear to try; I shall win through and see the lovely Rosamond." The good old man tried to dissuade him, but he would not listen to his words.

For now the hundred years were at an end, and the day had come when Rosamond should be awakened. When the prince drew near the hedge of thorns, it was changed into a hedge of beautiful large flowers, which parted and bent aside to let him pass, and then closed behind him in a thick hedge. When he reached the castle-yard, he saw the horses and brindled hunting-dogs lying asleep, and on the roof the pigeons were sitting with their heads under their wings. And when he came indoors, the flies on the wall were asleep, the cook in the kitchen had his hand uplifted to strike the scullion, and the kitchen-maid had the black fowl on her lap ready to pluck. Then he mounted higher, and saw in the hall the whole court lying asleep, and above them, on their thrones, slept the king and the queen. And still he went farther, and all was so quiet that he could hear his own breathing; and at last he came to the tower, and went up the winding stair, and opened the door of the little room where Rosamond lay. And when he saw her looking so lovely in her sleep, he could not turn away his eyes; and presently he stooped and kissed her, and she awaked, and opened her eyes, and looked very kindly on him. And she rose, and they went forth together, and the king and the queen and the whole court waked up, and gazed on each other with great eyes of wonderment. And the horses in the yard got up and shook themselves, the hounds sprang up and wagged their tails, the pigeons on the roof drew their heads from under their wings, looked round, and flew into the field, the flies on the wall crept on a little farther, the kitchen fire leapt up and blazed and cooked the meat, the joint on the spit began to roast, the cook gave the scullion such a box on the ear that he roared out, and the maid went on plucking the fowl.

Then the wedding of the Prince and Rosamond was held with all splendor, and they lived very happily together until their lives' end.

From "Fairy Tales," by Brothers Grimm.

East O' the Sun and West O' the Moon

ONCE on a time there was a poor woodcutter who had so many children that he had not much of either food or clothing to give them. Pretty children they all were, but the prettiest was the youngest daughter, who was so lovely there was no end to her loveliness.

It was on a Thursday evening late in the fall of the year. The weather was wild and rough outside, and it was cruelly dark. The rain fell and the wind blew till the walls of the cottage shook. There they all sat round the fire busy with this thing and that. Just then, all at once, something gave three taps at the window pane. Then the father went out to see what was the matter, and, when he got out of doors, what should he see but a great White Bear.

"Good evening to you!" said the White Bear.

"The same to you," said the man.

"Will you give me your youngest daughter? If you will, I'll make you as rich as you are now poor," said the Bear.

105

Well, the man would not be at all sorry to be so rich;—but give him his prettiest lassie, no, that he couldn't do, so he said "No" outright and closed the door both tight and well. But the Bear called out, "I'll give you time to think; next Thursday night I'll come for your answer."

Now, the lassie had heard every word that the Bear had said, and before the next Thursday evening came, she had washed and mended her rags, made herself as neat as she could, and was ready to start. I can't say her packing gave her much trouble.

Next Thursday evening came the White Bear to fetch her, and she got upon his back with her bundle, and off they went. So when they had gone a bit of the way, the White Bear said, "Are you afraid?"

"No, not at all," said the lassie.

"Well! mind and hold tight by my shaggy coat, and then there's nothing to fear," added the Bear.

So she rode a long, long way, till they came to a great steep hill. There on the face of it the White Bear gave a knock, and a door opened, and they came into a castle, where there were many rooms all lit up, gleaming with silver and gold, and there too was a table ready laid, and it was all as grand as grand could be. Then the White Bear gave her a silver bell. When she wanted anything she had only to ring it, and she would get what she wanted at once.

Well, when she had had supper and evening wore on, she became sleepy because of her journey. She thought she would like to go to bed, so she rang the bell. She had scarce taken hold of it before she came into a chamber where there were two beds as fair and white as any one would wish to sleep in. But when she had put out the light and gone to bed some one came into the room and lay down in the other bed. Now this happened every night, but she never saw who it was, for he always came after she had put out the light; and, before the day dawned, he was up and off again.

So things went on for a while, the lassie having everything she wanted. But you must know, that no human being did she see from morning till night, only the White Bear could she talk to, and she did not know what man or monster it might be who came to sleep in her room by night. At last she began to be silent and sorrowful and would neither eat nor drink.

One day the White Bear came to her and said: "Lassie, why are you so sorrowful? This castle and all that is in it are yours, the silver bell will give you anything that you wish. I only beg one thing of you —ask no questions, trust me and nothing shall harm you. So now be happy again." But still the lassie had no peace of mind, for one thing she wished to know: Who it was who came in the night and slept in her room? All day long and all night long she wondered and longed to know, and she fretted and pined away.

So one night, when she could not stand it any longer and she heard that he slept, she got up, lit a bit of a candle, and let the light shine on him. Then she saw that he was the loveliest Prince one ever set eyes on, and she bent over and kissed him. But, as she kissed him, she dropped three drops of hot tallow on his shirt, and he woke up.

"What have you done?" he cried. "Now you have made us both unlucky, for had you held out only this one year, I had been freed. For I am the White Bear by day and a man by night. It is a wicked witch who has bewitched me; and now I must set off from you to her. She lives in a castle which stands East O' the Sun and West O' the Moon, and there are many trolls and witches there and one of those is the wife I must now have."

She wept, but there was no help for it; go he must.

Then she asked if she mightn't go with him?

No, she mightn't.

"Tell me the way then," she said, "and I'll search you out; that, surely, I may get leave to do."

"Yes, you may do that," he said, "but there is no way to that place. It lies East O' the Sun and West O' the Moon and thither you can never find your way." And at that very moment both Prince and castle were gone, and she lay on a little green patch in the midst of the gloomy thick wood, and by her side lay the same bundle of rags she had brought with her from home.

Then she wept and wept till she was tired, and all the while she thought of the lovely Prince and how she should find him.

So at last she set out on her way and walked many, many days and

107

whomever she met she asked: "Can you tell me the way to the castle that lies East O' the Sun and West O' the Moon?" But no one could tell her.

And on she went a weary time. Both hungry and tired was she when she got to the East Wind's house one morning. There she asked the East Wind if he could tell her the way to the Prince who dwelt East O' the Sun and West O' the Moon. Yes, the East Wind had often heard tell of it, the Prince, the castle, but he couldn't tell the way, for he had never blown so far.

"But, if you will, I'll go with you to my brother the West Wind. Maybe he knows, for he's much stronger. So, if you will just get on my back, I'll carry you thither."

Yes, she got on his back, and I can tell you they went briskly along.

So when they got there, they went into the West Wind's house, and the East Wind said that the lassie he had brought was the one who ought to marry the Prince who lived in the castle East O' the Sun and West O' the Moon; and that she had set out to seek him, and would be glad to know if the West Wind knew how to get to the castle.

"Nay," said the West Wind, "so far I've never blown; but if you will, I'll go with you to our brother the South Wind, for he is much stronger than either of us, and he has flapped his wings far and wide. Maybe he'll tell you. You can get on my back and I'll carry you to him."

Yes, she got on his back, and so they traveled to the South Wind, and were not long on the way, either.

When they got there, the West Wind asked him if he could tell her the way to the castle that lay East O' the Sun and West O' the Moon, for it was she who ought to marry the Prince who lived there.

"You don't say so. That's she, is it?" said the South Wind.

"Well, I have blustered about in most places in my time, but that far I have never blown; however, if you will, I'll take you to my brother the North Wind; he is the oldest and strongest of all of us, and if he doesn't know where it is, you'll never find anyone in the world to tell you. You can get on my back and I'll carry you thither."

Yes, she got on his back, and away he went from his house at a fine rate. And this time, too, she was not long on the way. When they got near the North Wind's house he was so wild and cross that cold puffs came from him.

"Heigh, there, what do you want?" he bawled out to them ever so far off, so that it struck them with an icy shiver.

"Well," said the South Wind, "you needn't be so put out, for here I am your brother, the South Wind, and here is the lassie who ought to marry the Prince who dwells in the castle that lies East O' the Sun and West O' the Moon. She wants to ask you, if you ever were there, and can tell her the way, for she would be so glad to find him again."

"Yes, I know well enough where it is," said the North Wind. "Once in my life I blew an aspen leaf thither, but I was so tired I couldn't blow a puff for ever so many days after it. But if you really wish to go thither, and aren't afraid to come along with me, I'll take you on my back and see if I can blow you there."

"Yes! and thank you," she said, for she must and would get thither if it were possible in any way; and as for fear, however madly he went, she wouldn't be at all afraid.

"Very well then," said the North Wind, "but you must sleep here tonight, for we must have the whole day before us if we're to get thither at all."

Early next morning the North Wind woke her, and puffed himself up, and blew himself out, and made himself so stout and big, it was gruesome to look at him. And so off she went, high on the back of the North Wind up through the air, as if they would never stop till they got to the world's end.

Down here below there was a terrible storm; it threw down long tracts of woodland and many houses, and when it swept over the great sea ships foundered by hundreds.

So they tore on and on—no one can believe how far they went— and all the while they still went over the sea, and the North Wind got more and more weary, and so out of breath he could scarce bring out a puff, and his wings drooped and drooped, till at last he sunk so low that the crests of the waves lashed over her heels.

"Are you afraid?" said the North Wind.

She wasn't.

But they were not very far from land; and the North Wind had still so much strength left in him that he managed to throw her up on shore close by the castle which lay East O' the Sun and West O' the Moon; but then he was so weak and worn out that he had to stay there and rest many days before he could get home again.

And now the lassie began to look about her and to think of how she might free the Prince, but nowhere did she see a sign of life.

Then she sat herself down right under the castle windows, and as soon as the sun went down, out they came, trolls and witches, red-eyed, long-nosed, hunch-backed hags, tumbling over each other, scolding, hurrying and scurrying hither and thither.

At first they almost frightened the life out of her, but when she had watched them awhile and they had not noticed her, she took courage and walked up to one of them and said: "Pray tell me what goes on here tonight that you are all so busy, and could I perhaps get something to do for a night's lodging and a bit of food?"

"Ha, ha, ha!" laughed the horrid witch, "and where do you come from that you do not know that it is tonight that the Prince chooses his bride. When the moon stands high over the tree tops yonder we meet in the clearing by the old oak. There the caldrons are ready with boiling lye, for don't you know?—he's going to choose for his bride the one who can wash three spots of tallow from his shirt. Ha, ha, ha!"

And the wicked witch hurried off again, laughing such a horrible laugh that it made the lassie's blood run cold.

But now the trolls and witches came trooping out of the very earth, it seemed, and all turned their steps toward the clearing in the woods.

So the lassie went too, and found a place among the rest. Now the moon stood high above the tree tops, and there was the caldron in the middle and round about sat the trolls and witches—such gruesome company I'm sure you were never in. Then came the Prince; he looked about from one to the other, and he saw the lassie, and his face grew white, but he said nothing.

"Now, let's begin," said a witch with a nose three ells long. She was sure she was going to have the Prince, and she began to wash away as hard as she could, but the more she rubbed and scrubbed, the bigger the spots grew.

"Ah!" said an old hag, "you can't wash, let me try."

But she hadn't long taken the shirt in hand, before it was far worse than ever, and with all her rubbing and scrubbing and wringing, the spots grew bigger and blacker, and the darker and uglier was the shirt.

Then all the other trolls began to wash, but the longer it lasted, the blacker and uglier the shirt grew, till at last it was as black all over as if it had been up the chimney.

"Ah!" said the Prince, "you're none of you worth a straw, you can't wash. Why there sits a beggar lassie, I'll be bound she knows how to wash better than the whole lot of you. Come here, lassie," he shouted.

"Can you wash the shirt clean, lassie?" said he.

"I don't know," she said, "but I think I can."

And almost before she had taken it and dipped it in the water, it was as white as snow, and whiter still.

"Yes; you are the lassie for me," said the Prince.

At that moment the sun rose and the whole pack of trolls turned to stone.

There you may see them to this very day sitting around in a circle, big ones and little ones, all hard, cold stone.

But the Prince took the lassie by the hand and they flitted away as far as they could from the castle that lay East O' the Sun and West O' the Moon.

From "East O' the Sun and West O' the Moon," comp. and tr. by Gudrun Thorne-Thomsen. Copyright, 1912, by Row, Peterson & Co., and reprinted by permission of the publishers.

Cinderella

ONCE upon a time there was a nobleman, who took for a second wife the haughtiest and proudest woman that had ever been seen. She had two daughters who resembled her in everything. The husband, on his side, had a daughter of unexampled gentleness and goodness.

The wedding was hardly over before the step-mother's ill-humor broke out. She could not endure the young girl, whose good qualities made her own daughters appear still more detestable. She put her to do all the most menial work in the house. It was she who washed up the plates and dishes and cleaned the stairs; who scrubbed the step-mother's room and those of her daughters. She slept in a garret at the top of the house, on a wretched straw mattress, while her sisters occupied rooms with inlaid floors, and had the latest-fashioned beds, and mirrors in which they could see themselves from head to foot. The poor girl bore everything with patience, and did not dare complain to her father, who would only have scolded her, as he was entirely governed by his wife. When she had done her work, she was in the habit of going into the chimney-corner and sitting down amongst the cinders, which caused her to be nicknamed Cindertail by the household in general. The second daughter, however, who was not quite so rude as her sister, called her Cinderella. Nevertheless, Cinderella in her shabby clothes still looked a thousand times more beautiful than her sisters, magnificently dressed as they were.

It happened that the King's son gave a ball, to which he invited everyone of position. Our two fine ladies were among those who received an invitation, for they made a great show in the neighborhood. They were now in great delight, and very busy choosing the most becoming gowns and headdresses. A new mortification for poor Cinderella, for it was she who had to iron her sisters' fine linen and gauffer their ruffles. No one talked of anything but of the style in which they were to be dressed.

"I," said the eldest, "will wear my red velvet dress, and my English point-lace trimmings."

"I," said the youngest, "shall only wear my usual petticoat, but, to

112

make up for that, I shall put on my gold-flowered cloak, and my clasp of diamonds, which are none of the least valuable." They sent for a first-rate milliner, that their caps might be made to fashion, and they bought their patches from the best maker. They called Cinderella to give them her opinion, for her taste was excellent. Cinderella gave them the best advice in the world, and even offered to dress their hair for them, which they were very willing she should do.

Whilst she was busy with the hairdressing, they said to her, "Cinderella, should you be very glad to go to the ball?"

"Alas! you only make fun of me; such a thing would not be suitable for me at all."

"You are right; they would indeed laugh to see a Cindertail at the ball!"

Any other than Cinderella would have dressed their hair awry, but she had a good disposition, and arranged it for both of them to perfection. They could eat nothing for nearly two days, so transported were they with joy. More than a dozen laces were broken in making their waists as small as possible, and they were continually before their looking-glasses. At last the happy day arrived. They set off, and Cinderella followed them with her eyes as long as she could. When they were out of sight she began to cry. Her godmother, who saw her all in tears, asked her what was the matter. "I should so like—I should so like—" she sobbed so violently that she could not finish the sentence.

"You would so like to go to the ball, is not that it?"

"Alas! yes," said Cinderella, sighing.

"Well, if you will be a good girl, I will undertake that you shall go." She took her into her room, and said to her, "Go into the garden and bring me a pumpkin." Cinderella went at once, gathered the finest she could find, and brought it to her godmother, wondering the while how a pumpkin could enable her to go to the ball. Her godmother scooped it out, and, having left nothing but the rind, struck it with her wand, and the pumpkin was immediately changed into a beautiful coach, gilt all over. She then went and looked into the mouse-trap, where she found six mice, all alive. She told Cinderella to lift the door of the mouse-trap a little, and to each mouse, as it ran out, she gave a tap with her wand, and the mouse was immediately changed into a fine horse, so that at last there stood ready a handsome train of six horses of a beautiful dappled mouse-gray color. Cinderella then brought her the rat-trap, in which there were three large rats. The fairy chose one from the three on account of its ample beard, and having touched it, it was changed into a fat coachman, with the finest whiskers that ever were seen. She then said, "Go into the garden, and there, behind the watering-pot, you will find six lizards, bring them to me." Cinderella had no sooner brought them than the godmother changed them into six footmen, with their liveries all covered with lace, who immediately jumped up behind the coach, and hung on to it as if they had done nothing else all their lives. The fairy then said to Cinderella, "Well, there is something in which to go to the ball; are you not well pleased?"

"Yes, but am I to go in these dirty old clothes?" Her godmother touched her lightly with her wand, and in the same instant her dress was changed into one of gold and silver covered with precious stones. She then gave her a pair of glass slippers, the prettiest in the world. When she was thus attired, she got into the coach; but her godmother told her, above all things not to stay past midnight, warning her that if she remained at the ball a minute longer, her coach would again become a pumpkin; her horses, mice; her coachman a rat; her footmen, lizards; and her clothes turn again into her old ones. She promised her godmother that she would not fail to leave the ball before midnight, and drove off, almost out of her mind with joy.

The King's son, who was informed that a grand Princess had arrived whom nobody knew, ran to receive her. He handed her out of the coach and led her into the hall, where the guests were assembled. There was immediately a dead silence; the dancing stopped, and the fiddlers ceased to play, so engaged did everyone become in gazing upon the wonderful beauty of the unknown lady. Nothing was heard but a general murmur of "Oh! how lovely she is!" The King himself, old as he was, could not take his eyes from her, and observed to the Queen, that it was a long time since he had seen so lovely and amiable a person. All the ladies were intently occupied in examining her headdress and her clothes, that they might order some like them the very next day, provided that they might be able to find materials as costly and work-people sufficiently clever to make them up.

The King's son conducted her to the most honorable seat, and then led her out to dance. She danced so gracefully that everybody's admiration of her was increased. A very grand supper was served, of which the Prince ate not a morsel, so absorbed was he in the contemplation of her beauty. She seated herself beside her sisters, and showed them a thousand civilities. She shared with them the oranges and citrons which the Prince had given her, at which they were greatly surprised, for she appeared a perfect stranger to them. While they were thus talking together, Cinderella heard the clock strike the three quarters past eleven. She at once made a profound curtsey to the company, and left as quickly as she could. As soon as she had reached home, she went to find her godmother, and after having thanked her, said she much wished to go to the ball again next day, because the King's son had invited her. She was telling her godmother all that had passed at the ball, when the two sisters knocked at the door. Cinderella went and opened it. "How late you are!" said she to them, yawning, rubbing her eyes, and then stretching herself as if she had but just awoke, although she had had no inclination to sleep since she parted from them.

"If you had been at the ball," said one of her sisters to her, "you would not have been weary of it. There came to it the most beautiful Princess—the most beautiful that ever was seen; she paid us many attentions, and gave us oranges and citrons." Cinderella was beside herself with delight. She asked them the name of the Princess, but they replied that nobody knew her, that the King's son was much puzzled about it, and that he would give everything in the world to know who she was.

Cinderella smiled and said, "She was very lovely, then. How fortunate you are! Could not I get a sight of her? Alas! Miss Javotte, lend me the yellow gown you wear every day."

"Truly," said Miss Javotte, "I like that! Lend one's gown to a dirty Cindertail like you! I should be mad indeed!" Cinderella fully expected this refusal, and was rejoiced at it, for she would not have known what to do if her sister had lent her the gown.

115

The next day the sisters went again to the ball, and Cinderella also, but still more splendidly dressed than before. The King's son never left her side, or ceased saying tender things to her. Cinderella found the evening pass very pleasantly, and forgot her godmother's warning, so that she heard the clock begin to strike twelve while still thinking that it was not yet eleven. She rose and fled as lightly as a fawn. The Prince followed her, but could not overtake her. She dropped one of her glass slippers, which the Prince carefully picked up. Cinderella reached home almost breathless, without coach or footmen, and in her shabby clothes, with nothing remaining of her finery but one of her little slippers, the mate of that which she had dropped.

The guards at the palace gate were asked if they had not seen a Princess pass out. They answered that they had seen no one pass but a poorly dressed girl, who had more the appearance of a peasant than of a lady.

When the two sisters returned from the ball, Cinderella asked them if they had been as much entertained as before, and if the beautiful lady had been present. They said yes, but that she had fled as soon as it had struck twelve.

A few days afterwards the King's son caused it to be proclaimed by sound of trumpet that he would marry her whose foot would exactly fit the slipper. They began by trying it on the princesses, then on the duchesses, and so on throughout the Court; but in vain. It was taken to the two sisters, who did their utmost to force one of their feet into the slipper, but they could not manage to do so. Cinderella, who was looking on, and who recognized the slipper, said laughingly, "Let me see if it will not fit me." Her sisters began to laugh and ridicule her. The gentleman of the Court who had been entrusted to try the slipper, having looked attentively at Cinderella, and seeing that she was very beautiful, said that it was only fair that her request should be granted, as he had received orders to try the slipper on all maidens, without exception. He made Cinderella sit down, and putting the slipper to her little foot, he saw it slip on easily and fit like wax. Great was the astonishment of the two sisters, but it was still greater when Cinderella took the other little slipper out of her pocket and put it on her other foot. At that moment the godmother appeared,

116

and gave a tap with her wand to Cinderella's clothes, which became still more magnificent than those she had worn before.

The two sisters then recognized in her the beautiful person they had seen at the ball. They threw themselves at her feet to beg for forgiveness for all the ill-treatment she had suffered from them. Cinderella raised and embraced them, said that she forgave them with all her heart, and begged them to love her dearly for the future. She was conducted, dressed as she was, to the young Prince. He found her more charming than ever, and a few days afterwards he married her. Cinderella, who was as kind as she was beautiful, gave her sisters apartments in the palace, and married them the very same day to two great lords of the Court.

From "Fairy Tales," by Chas. Perrault. n. d. Reprinted by permission of E. P. Dutton & Co., Inc., publishers.

What the Good Man Does Is Always Right

I WILL tell you a story which was told to me when I was a little boy. Every time I thought of the story, it seemed to me to become more and more charming; for it is with stories as with many people—they become better as they grow older.

I take it for granted that you have been in the country, and seen a very old farmhouse with a thatched roof, and mosses and small plants growing wild upon the thatch. There is a stork's nest on the summit of the gable; for we can't do without the stork. The walls of the house are sloping, and the windows are low, and only one of the latter is made so that it will open. The baking-oven sticks out of the wall like a little fat body. The elder-tree hangs over the paling, and beneath its branches, at the foot of the paling, is a pool of water in which a few ducks are disporting themselves. There is a yard-dog, too, who barks at all comers.

Just such a farmhouse stood out in the country; and in this house dwelt an old couple—a man and his wife. Small as was their property, there was one article among it that they could do without—a horse, which made a living out of the grass it found by the side of the high-road. The old farmer rode into the town on this horse; and often his neighbors borrowed it from him, and rendered the couple some service in return for the loan of it. But they thought it would be best if they sold the horse, or exchanged it for something that might be more useful to them. But what might this something be?

"You'll know that best, good man," said his wife. "It is fair-day today, so ride into town, and get rid of the horse for money, or make a good exchange: whichever you do will be right to me. Ride to the fair."

And she fastened his neckerchief for him, for she could do that better than he could; and she tied it in a double bow, for she could do that very prettily. Then she brushed his hat round and round with the palm of her hand, and gave him a kiss. So he rode away upon the horse that was to be sold or to be bartered for something else. Yes, the good man knew what he was about.

The sun shone hotly down, not a cloud was to be seen in the sky. The road was very dusty, for many people who were all bound for the fair were driving, or riding, or walking upon it. There was no shelter anywhere from the sunbeams.

Among the rest, was a man trudging along, and driving a cow to the fair. The cow was as beautiful a creature as any cow can be.

"She gives good milk, I'm sure," said the farmer. "That would be a very good exchange—the cow for the horse."

"Hallo, you there with the cow!" he said; "I'll tell you what— I fancy a horse costs more than a cow, but I don't care for that; a cow would be more useful to me. If you like, we'll exchange."

"To be sure I will," said the man; and they exchanged accordingly.

So that was settled, and the farmer might have turned back, for he had done the business he came to do; but as he had once made up his mind to go to the fair, he determined to proceed, merely to have a look at it; so he went on to the town with his cow.

Leading the animal, he strode sturdily on; and after a time he

118

overtook a man who was driving a sheep. It was a good fat sheep, with a fine fleece on its back.

"I should like to have that fellow," said our farmer to himself. "He would find plenty of grass by our palings, and in the winter we could keep him in the room with us. Perhaps it would be more practical to have a sheep instead of a cow. Shall we exchange?"

The man with the sheep was quite ready, and the bargain was struck. So the farmer went on in the high-road with his sheep.

Soon he overtook another man, who came into the road from a field, carrying a great goose under his arm.

"That's a heavy thing you have there. It has plenty of feathers and plenty of fat, and would look well tied to a string, and paddling in the water at our place. That would be something for my wife; she could make all kinds of profit out of it. How often she has said, 'If we only had a goose!' Now, perhaps, she can have one; and, if possible, it shall be hers. Shall we exchange? I'll give you my sheep for your goose, and thank you into the bargain."

The other man had not the least objection; and accordingly they exchanged, and our farmer became proprietor of the goose.

By this time he was very near the town. The crowd on the high-road became greater and greater; there was quite a crush of men and cattle. They walked in the road, and close by the palings; and at the barrier they even walked into the toll-man's potato-field, where his one fowl was strutting about, with a string to its leg, lest it should take fright at the crowd, and stray away, and so be lost. This fowl had short tail-feathers, and winked with both its eyes, and looked very cunning. "Cluck, cluck!" said the fowl. What it thought when it said this I cannot tell you; but directly our good man saw it, he thought, "That's the finest fowl I've ever seen in my life! Why, it's finer than our parson's brood hen. On my word, I should like to have that fowl. A fowl can always find a grain or two, and can almost keep itself. I think it would be a good exchange if I could get that for my goose."

"Shall we exchange?" he asked the toll-taker.

"Exchange!" repeated the man. "Well, that would not be a bad thing."

And so they exchanged; the toll-taker at the barrier kept the goose, and the farmer carried away the fowl.

Now, he had done a good deal of business on his way to the fair, and he was hot and tired. He wanted something to eat, and something to drink; and soon he was in front of the inn. He was just about to step in when the hostler came out, so they met at the door. The hostler was carrying a sack.

"What have you in that sack?" asked the farmer.

"Rotten apples," answered the hostler, "a whole sackful of them —enough to feed the pigs."

"Why, that's terrible waste! I should like to take them to my wife at home. Last year the old tree by the turf-hole only bore a single apple, and we kept it on the cupboard till it was quite rotten and spoilt. 'It was always property,' my wife said; but here she could see a quantity of property—a whole sackful. Yes, I shall be glad to show them to her."

"What will you give me for the sackful?" asked the hostler.

"What will I give? I will give my fowl in exchange."

And he gave the fowl accordingly, and received the apples, which he carried into the guest room. He leaned the sack carefully by the stove, and then went to the table. But the stove was hot: he had not thought of that. Many guests were present—horse-dealers, ox-herds, and two Englishmen.

Hiss-s-s! hiss-s-s! What was that by the stove? The apples were beginning to roast!

"What is that?"

"Why, do you know—" said our farmer.

And he told the whole story of the horse that he had changed for a cow, and all the rest of it, down to the apples.

"Well, your wife will give it you well when you get home!" said one of the two Englishmen. "There will be a disturbance."

"What?—give me what?" said the farmer. "She will kiss me, and say, 'What the good man does is always right.'"

"Shall we wager?" said the Englishman. "We'll wager coined gold by the ton—a hundred pounds to the hundred-weight!"

"A bushel will be enough," replied the peasant. "I can only set the bushel of apples against it; and I'll throw myself and my wife into the bargain—and I fancy that's piling up the measure."

"Done—taken!"

And the bet was made. The host's carriage came up, and the Englishmen got in, and the peasant got in; away they went, and soon they stopped before the farmer's hut.

"Good evening, wife."

"Good evening, good man."

"I've made the exchange."

"Yes, you understand what you're about," said the woman.

And she embraced him, and paid no attention to the stranger guests, nor did she notice the sack.

"I got a cow in exchange for the horse," said he.

"Heaven be thanked!" said she. "What glorious milk we shall have, and butter and cheese on the table! That was a capital exchange!"

"Yes, but I changed the cow for a sheep."

"Ah, that's better still!" cried the wife. "You always think of everything: we have just pasture enough for a sheep. Ewe's milk and cheese, and woolen jackets and stockings! The cow cannot give those, and her hairs will only come off. How you think of everything!"

"But I changed away the sheep for a goose."

"Then this year we shall really have roast goose to eat, my dear man. You are always thinking of something to give me pleasure. How charming that is! We can let the goose walk about with a string to her leg, and she'll grow fatter still before we roast her."

"But I gave away the goose for a fowl," said the man.

"A fowl? That was a good exchange!" replied the woman. "The fowl will lay eggs and hatch them, and we shall have chickens: we shall have a whole poultry yard! Oh, that's just what I was wishing for."

"Yes, but I exchanged the fowl for a sack of shriveled apples."

"What!—I must positively kiss you for that," exclaimed the wife. "My dear, good husband! Now, I'll tell you something. Do you know, you had hardly left me this morning, before I began thinking how I could give you something very nice this evening. I thought it should

121

be pancakes with savory herbs. I had eggs, and bacon too; but I wanted herbs. So I went to the schoolmaster's and begged his wife to lend me a handful of herbs. 'Lend!' she answered me; 'nothing at all grows in our garden, not even a shriveled apple. I could not even lend you a shriveled apple, my dear woman.' But now I can lend her ten, or a whole sackful. That I'm very glad of; that makes me laugh!" And with that she gave him a sounding kiss.

"I like that!" exclaimed both the Englishmen together. "Always going down-hill, and always merry; that's worth the money." So they paid a hundred-weight of gold to the farmer who was not scolded, but kissed.

Yes, it always pays, when the wife sees and always asserts that her husband knows best, and that whatever he does is right.

You see, that is my story. I heard it when I was a child; and now you have heard it too, and know that "What the good man does is always right."

From "Fairy Tales," by Hans Christian Andersen.

Put Your Shoulder to the Wheel

A WAGONER was once driving a heavy load along a muddy road. At last he came to a place where the wheels sank into the mire and he could go no farther.

The more the horses pulled the deeper sank the wheels. The wagoner was in despair. He threw down his whip, knelt in the road and prayed to Hercules, the Strong. "O, Hercules! help me!" said he.

But Hercules appeared in person and said: "Tut, tut, man, don't sprawl there. Get up and put your shoulder to the wheel."

And so "The gods help them that help themselves."

From "Fables," by Æsop.

The Hare and the Tortoise

A HARE met a tortoise one day and made fun of him for the slow and clumsy way in which he walked.

The tortoise laughed and said, "I will run a race with you any time that you choose."

"Very well," replied the hare, "we will start at once."

The tortoise immediately set off in his slow and steady way without waiting a moment or looking back. The hare, on the other hand, treated the matter as a joke and decided to take a little nap before starting, for she thought that it would be an easy matter to overtake her rival.

The tortoise plodded on, and meanwhile the hare overslept herself, with the result that she arrived at the winning-post only to see that the tortoise had got in before her.

Slow and steady wins the race.

From "Fables," by Æsop.

The Contest

ONCE upon a time a Hare and a Pig held a contest to see which could leap across a ditch.

The Hare tried first but fell short by an inch. Then the Pig tried but his short legs carried him only half the way.

After that they both began to argue as to which was the better animal and the Fox was called in to settle the dispute.

The Fox said:

"Both in the ditch,
Can't say which."

From "Fables," by Æsop.

123

The Talkative Tortoise

In India, the land of Buddha, there dwelt a tortoise by a pond of water where two wild ducks were wont to come. One day when they had become friends, the ducks said: "Tortoise, our home in the distant mountains is very beautiful. Why remain in this dull place? Will you not come with us?" "But how can I travel so far?" answered the tortoise. "We can take you if you can only hold your tongue, and will say nothing to anybody," said the ducks. "That I can do," said the tortoise.

The ducks took the two ends of a stick in their bills and bade the tortoise bite it firmly in the middle. Then they flew high into the air. When the villagers saw this strange sight they began to babble. "See the tortoise being carried by ducks," they called. "What is that to you?" thought the tortoise but he held on as tightly as ever.

On they flew and more and more curious villagers kept calling: "See the tortoise being carried by ducks." Finally the tortoise could bear it no longer. They had reached a king's palace in the hills when he let go of the stick he was biting to answer them, and falling in the open courtyard, split in two.

> "You see how, by his talking overmuch,
> The tortoise fell into this wretched plight."

And so it often happens that he who talks beyond measure meets with mishap.

From "Fables," of Bidpai.

Phoebus and Boreas

OLD Boreas and the Sun, one day,
Espied a traveler on his way,
Whose dress did happily provide
Against whatever might betide.
The time was autumn, when, indeed,
All prudent travelers take heed.
The rains that then the sunshine dash,
And Iris with her splendid sash,
Warn one who does not like to soak
To wear abroad a good thick coat.
Our man was therefore well bedight
With double mantle, strong and tight.
"This fellow," said the Wind, "has meant
To guard from every ill event;
But little does he wot that I
 Can blow him such a blast
 That, not a button fast,
His cloak shall cleave the sky.
Come, here's a pleasant game, Sir Sun!
 Wilt play?" Said Phoebus, "Done!
 We'll bet between us here
 Which first will take the gear
 From off this cavalier.
 Begin, and shut away
 The brightness of my ray."
"Enough." Our blower, on the bet,
 Swelled out his pursy form
 With all the stuff for storm—
The thunder, hail, and drenching wet,
And all the fury he could muster;
Then, with a very demon's bluster,
He whistled, whirled, and splashed,
And down the torrents dashed,

125

Full many a roof uptearing
  He never did before,
Full many a vessel bearing
  To wreck upon the shore—
And all to doff a single cloak.
But vain the furious stroke;
  The traveler was stout,
  And kept the tempest out,
  Defied the hurricane,
  Defied the pelting rain;
And as the fiercer roared the blast,
His cloak the tighter held he fast.
The Sun broke out, to win the bet;
  He caused the clouds to disappear,
  Refreshed and warmed the cavalier,
And through his mantle made him sweat,
  Till off it came, of course,
In less than half an hour;
And yet the Sun saved half his power—
  So much does mildness more than force.

From "Fables," by Jean de La Fontaine, tr. by Wright.

Hundred-Wit, Thousand-Wit, and Single-Wit

IN A CERTAIN pond lived two fishes whose names were Hundred-Wit and Thousand-Wit. And a frog named Single-Wit made friends with them. Thus all three would for some time enjoy at the water's edge the pleasure of conversation spiced with witticisms, then would dive into the water again.

One day at sunset they were engaged in conversation, when fishermen with nets came there, who said to one another on seeing the pond:

126

"Look! This pond appears to contain plenty of fish, and the water seems shallow. We will return at dawn." With this they went home.

The three friends felt this speech to be dreadful as the fall of a thunderbolt, and they took counsel together. The frog spoke first: "Hundred-Wit and Thousand-Wit, my dear friends, what should we do now: flee or stick it out?"

At this Thousand-Wit laughed and said: "My good friend, do not be frightened merely because you have heard words. An actual invasion is not to be anticipated. Yet should it take place, I will save you and myself by virtue of my wit. For I know plenty of tricks in the water." And Hundred-Wit added: "Yes, Thousand-Wit is quite right. For

> Where wind is checked, and light of day,
> The wise man's wit soon finds a way.

One cannot, because he has heard a few mere words, abandon his birthplace, the home of his ancestors. You must not go away. I will save you by virtue of my wit."

"Well," said the frog, "I have only a single wit, and that tells me to flee. My wife and I are going to some other body of water this very night."

So spoke the frog and under cover of night he went to another body of water. At dawn the next day came the fish-catchers, who seemed the servants of Death, and inclosed the pond with nets. And all the fishes, turtles, frogs, crabs, and other water-creatures were caught in the nets and captured. Even Hundred-Wit and Thousand-Wit fell into a net and were killed, though they struggled to save their lives by fancy turns.

On the following day the fishermen gleefully started home. One of them carried Hundred-Wit, who was heavy, on his head. Another carried Thousand-Wit tied to a cord. Then the frog, safe in the throat of a cistern, said to his wife: "Look, darling, look!

> While Hundred-Wit is on a head,
> While Thousand-Wit hangs limp and dead,

Your humble Single-Wit, my dear,
Is paddling in the water clear."

From "The Panchatantra," by G. W. Ryder. Copyright, 1925, University of Chicago Press, and reprinted by permission of the publishers.

The Farmer and the Money-Lender

THERE was once a farmer who suffered much at the hands of a money-lender. Good harvests, or bad, the farmer was always poor, the money-lender rich. At last, when he hadn't a farthing left, the farmer went to the money-lender's house, and said, "You can't squeeze water from a stone, and as you have nothing to get by me now, you might tell me the secret of becoming rich."

"My friend," returned the money-lender piously, "riches come from Ram—ask him."

"Thank you, I will!" replied the simple farmer; so he prepared three griddle-cakes to last him on the journey, and set out to find Ram.

First he met a Brahman, and to him he gave a cake, asking him to point out the road to Ram; but the Brahman only took the cake and went on his way without a word. Next the farmer met a Jogi or devotee, and to him he gave a cake, without receiving any help in return. At last he came upon a poor man sitting under a tree, and finding out he was hungry, the kindly farmer gave him his last cake, and sitting down to rest beside him, entered into conversation.

"And where are you going?" asked the poor man, at length.

"Oh, I have a long journey before me, for I am going to find Ram!" replied the farmer. "I don't suppose you could tell me which way to go?"

"Perhaps I can," said the poor man, smiling, "for I am Ram! What do you want of me?"

128

Then the farmer told the whole story, and Ram, taking pity on him, gave him a conch shell, and showed him how to blow it in a particular way, saying, "Remember! whatever you wish for, you have only to blow the conch that way, and your wish will be fulfilled. Only have a care of that money-lender, for even magic is not proof against their wiles!"

The farmer went back to his village rejoicing. In fact the money-lender noticed his high spirits at once, and said to himself, "Some good fortune must have befallen the stupid fellow, to make him hold his head so jauntily." Therefore he went over to the simple farmer's house, and congratulated him on his good fortune in such cunning words, pretending to have heard all about it, that before long the farmer found himself telling the whole story—all except the secret of blowing the conch, for, with all his simplicity, the farmer was not quite such a fool as to tell that.

Nevertheless, the money-lender determined to have the conch by hook or by crook, and as he was villain enough not to stick at trifles, he waited for a favorable opportunity and stole the conch.

But, after nearly bursting himself with blowing the conch in every conceivable way, he was obliged to give up the secret as a bad job. However, being determined to succeed, he went back to the farmer and said coolly, "Look here; I've got your conch, but I can't use it; you haven't got it, so it's clear you can't use it either. Business is at a standstill unless we make a bargain. Now, I promise to give you back your conch, and never to interfere with your using it, on one condition, which is this, whatever you get from it, I am to get double."

"Never!" cried the farmer; "that would be the old business all over again!"

"Not at all!" replied the wily money-lender, "you will have your share! Now, don't be a dog in the manger, for if you get all you want, what can it matter to you if I am rich or poor?"

At last, though it went sorely against the grain to be of any benefit to a money-lender, the farmer was forced to yield, and from that time, no matter what he gained by the power of the conch, the money-lender gained double. And the knowledge that this was so preyed upon the farmer's mind day and night, so that he had no satisfaction out of anything.

At last, there came a very dry season—so dry that the farmer's crops withered for want of rain. Then he blew his conch, and wished for a well to water them, and lo! there was the well, but the money-lender had two!—two beautiful new wells! This was too much for any farmer to stand; and our friend brooded over it, and brooded over it, till at last a bright idea came into his head. He seized the conch, blew it loudly, and cried out, "Oh, Ram! I wish to be blind of one eye!" And so he was, in a twinkling, but the money-lender of course was blind of both, and in trying to steer his way between the two new wells, he fell into one, and was drowned.

Now this true story shows that a farmer once got the better of a money-lender—but only by losing one of his eyes.

From "Indian Fairy Tales," ed. by Joseph Jacobs. n. d., G. P. Putnam's Sons, and reprinted by permission of the publishers.

Collections of Folk Tales and Fables

Æsop Fables; told anew and their history, traced by Joseph Jacobs. The Macmillan Company.

Æsop. *A Hundred Fables;* tr. by Sir Roger L'Estrange. Dodd, Mead and Company.

Asbjörnsen, Peter C. *Tales from the Fjeld.* G. P. Putnam's Sons. Familiar Norwegian folk tales; "The Pancake," "Taper Tom," "The Sheep and the Pig Who Set Up House," and many others.

Bidpai. *Tortoise and the Geese and Other Tales of Bidpai,* ed. by Maud Dutton. Houghton Mifflin Co. Fables from India.

Borski and Miller. *Jolly Tailor.* Longmans, Green & Co. Polish folk tales, delightfully humorous, with some gruesome elements.

Brooke, L. L. *Golden Goose Book.* Frederick Warne & Co., Ltd.

Dasent, Sir George W. *East O' the Sun and West O' the Moon.* McKay. The Macmillan Company. Norse folk tales.

FOLK TALES AND FABLES

Djurklou, N. G. *Fairy Tales from the Swedish*, tr. by Braekstad. Frederick A. Stokes Co.

Eells, E. S. *Tales of Enchantment from Spain*. Harcourt, Brace & Company.

Fillmore, P. H. *Czecho-Slovak Fairy Tales*. Harcourt, Brace & Company.

Fleming, R. M. *Round the World in Folk Tales*. Harcourt, Brace & Company.

Gibson, Katherine. *Golden Bird and Other Stories*. The Macmillan Company.

Grimm, J. and W. *Household Stories*. The Macmillan Company.

Grimm, J. and W. *Household Tales*. E. P. Dutton & Co., Inc.

Harris, J. C. *Uncle Remus, His Songs and His Sayings*. D. Appleton-Century Co., Inc.

Houghton, Mrs. L. S. *Russian Grandmother's Tales*. Chas. Scribner's Sons.

Jacobs, Joseph. *Celtic Fairy Tales*. G. P. Putnam's Sons.

Jacobs, Joseph. *More Celtic Fairy Tales*. G. P. Putnam's Sons. Contains "The Children of Lir."

Jacobs, Joseph. *English Fairy Tales*. G. P. Putnam's Sons. *More English Fairy Tales*. G. P. Putnam's Sons.

Jacobs, Joseph. *Indian Fairy Tales*. G. P. Putnam's Sons. Hindu fables and stories.

Kennedy, H. A. *New World Fairy Book*. Doubleday, Doran & Co. Modernized American Indian stories.

Lang, Andrew, ed. *Blue Fairy Book*. Longmans, Green & Co. *Green Fairy Book*. Longmans, Green & Co. Collections of old favorites from many sources.

MacManus, Seumas. *Donegal Fairy Stories*. Doubleday, Doran & Co. Irish folk and hero tales. Humorous.

Nemcova, B. *The Shepherd and the Dragon and Other Stories*. Robert M. McBride & Co.

Nyblom, Helena. *Jolly Calle and Other Swedish Fairy Tales*. E. P. Dutton & Co., Inc.

Olcott, F. J. ed. *Book of Elves and Fairies*. Houghton Mifflin Co.

Olcott, F. J. *Wonder Garden*. Houghton Mifflin Co.

Ozaki, Yei T. *Japanese Fairy Book*. E. P. Dutton & Co., Inc.

Ransome, Arthur. *Old Peter's Russian Tales*. Thomas Nelson & Sons.

Rhys, Ernest. *Fairy-Gold*. E. P. Dutton & Co., Inc. Old English fairy tales.

Ryder, G. W. translator. *The Panchatantra*. University of Chicago Press. Fables from the Sanskrit.

Scudder, H. E. *Children's Book*. Houghton Mifflin Co. A family book.

Shedlock, M. L. *Eastern Stories and Legends*. E. P. Dutton & Co., Inc. Jataka tales.

Stephens, James. *Irish Fairy Tales*. The Macmillan Company.

Thomsen, Mrs. Gudrun Thorne. *East O' the Sun and West O' the Moon.* Row Peterson & Co. Norse stories from Asbjörnsen in form for telling.

Topelius, Zakarias. *Canute Whistlewinks and Other Stories,* ed. by Olcott. Longmans, Green & Co. Finnish tales.

Tyler, A. C. comp. *Twenty-four Unusual Stories.* Harcourt, Brace & Company.

Wiggin and Smith. *Fairy Ring.* Doubleday, Doran & Co.

Wiggin and Smith. *Talking Beasts.* Doubleday, Doran & Co. Fables from Aesop, Bidpai, La Fontaine and other sources.

Williston, T. P. *Japanese Fairy Tales,* 2 vols. Rand McNally & Co.

Zitkala-Sa. *Old Indian Legends.* Ginn & Company. North American Indian tales.

GREEK MYTHS AND EPICS

GREEK MYTHS AND EPICS

GREEK MYTHS

IT WAS Ovid, a Roman poet who lived about the time of Christ, who preserved for all time the majority of our Greek myths and legends. His *Metamorphoses*, which, as the name implies, includes those myths in which miraculous changes occur, is the main source for children's favorites.

Ovid's metrical versions have been put into modern literary English in both verse and prose forms. These translations are not to any extent suitable for reading or telling to children, but knowledge of them is necessary for the evaluation of adaptations. Familiarity with source material is an aid also in making choices of stories and in creating atmosphere for the story told.

For the beginning story-teller who wants, first of all, concise plots in keeping with original literary versions, there is no better book than Thomas Bulfinch's *Age of Fable*. Bulfinch drew his stories from Ovid and Virgil.

They are not literally translated, for, in the author's opinion, poetry translated into literal prose is very unattractive reading.

Neither are they in verse, as well for other reasons as from a conviction that to translate faithfully under all the embarrassments of rhyme and measure is impossible. The attempt has been made to tell the stories in prose, preserving so much of the poetry as resides in the thoughts and is separable from the language itself, and omitting those amplifications which are not suited to the altered form. *Preface.*

There are a number of collections of adaptations of Greek myths and hero tales, intended for children's own reading, which the storyteller will wish to use in her preparation to supplement Bulfinch's brief versions. These are listed, with annotations, at the close of this chapter.

Among the Greek stories enjoyed by children are found the following:

Clytie
Ceres and Proserpine
Arachne's Contest with Minerva
Latona and the Frogs
Baucis and Philemon Entertain the Gods
The Golden Touch of Midas
Cupid and Psyche
Story of Perseus
Jason's Quest for the Golden Fleece
Story of Theseus

For the most part all adaptations of the Greek myths and legends for children follow one of two forms: the warm, Gothic treatment found in Hawthorne's *Wonder Book* and *Tanglewood Tales* or the more classic presentation in Charles Kingsley's *The Heroes,* and Alfred Church's *Stories of the Old World.*

At first glance Hawthorne's versions appear much simpler than those of Kingsley, but what his treatment gains in story appeal is offset by the dramatic quality of Kingsley's style. In using the

Kingsley versions with young children it may be desirable to omit some of his moralizations and to cut descriptive passages and those filled with many proper names; e.g., the opening paragraphs in his "Perseus," a part of which is included later in this text; but ordinarily children like high sounding, magical words when they flow easily from the story-teller's lips.

It will be seen that in re-telling the Greek stories some editors follow the Greek forms of proper names, but more use the Latin. There are more Latin sources available, a few popular stories are not found elsewhere, and the Latin language is generally more familiar. It makes very little difference which form is used if the story-teller is consistent when telling a series of connected stories.

Roman mythology is substantially the Greek mythology. The Romans used Roman names for their deities, but they gave them Greek attributes.

This selection of Greek myths includes two nature myths and a short hero tale.

Clytie

CLYTIE was not always a sunflower, turning on her stem to watch the journeying sun. Long ago she was a water nymph and lived in a cave at the bottom of the sea. The walls of the cave were covered with pearls and lovely pink sea shells. The floor was made of snow-white sand, and the chairs were of amber, with soft mossy cushions.

On each side of the cave opening was a forest of coral and sea fans. Behind the cave were Clytie's gardens. Here she spent long hours taking care of her sea anemones, her star lilies, or in planting rare kinds of seaweed. Clytie kept her favorite horses in the garden grotto. These were the swift-darting gold fish and the slow-moving turtles.

For a long time she was very happy and contented. The sea nymphs loved Clytie, and wove for her dresses of the softest of green sea lace. They told her all their best stories.

One day they took her to the mermaid's rock to hear the mermaid sing. Clytie liked one song best of all. It told of a glorious light which shone on the top of the water. After Clytie heard this song, she could think of nothing else, but longed day and night to see the wonderful light. But no ocean nymph dared take her to it, and she grew unhappy. Soon she neglected her garden and all her sea treasures.

In vain the nymphs begged her to forget the enchanting light. They told her that no sea nymph had ever seen it, or ever could hope to see it. But Clytie would not listen, and to escape them she spent more and more of her time in her shell carriage, riding far away from her cave. In this way she could dream, undisturbed, of the glorious light which the mermaid had called the "sun."

Now it happened that late one summer night, when the sea was warm and the turtles were going very slowly, Clytie fell asleep. Unguided, the turtles went on and on and up and up, through the green waters, until they came out at last close to a wooded island.

As the waves dashed the carriage against the shore, Clytie awoke. Trembling and filled with wonder she climbed out of the shell and sat down upon a rock.

It was early dawn, and the waking world was very beautiful. Clytie had never seen the trees and the flowers. She had never heard the birds chirping, or the forest wind rustling the leaves. She had never smelled the fragrance of the meadows, or seen the morning dew upon the grass.

She was dazed by all these wonders, and thought that she must be dreaming, but soon she forgot all about them, for the eastern sky blazed suddenly with light. Great purple curtains were lifted, and slowly a great ball of dazzling fire appeared, blinding her eyes with its beauty. She held her breath and stretched out her arms toward it, for she knew at once that this was the glorious light she had dreamed about and longed for. This was the sun.

In the midst of the light was a golden chariot, drawn by four fiery steeds, and in the chariot sat a wonderful, smiling king, with seven rays of light playing around his crown.

As the steeds mounted higher and higher in their path, the birds began to sing, the plants opened their buds, and even the old sea looked happy.

Clytie sat all day upon the rock, her eyes fixed upon the sun with a great love and longing in her heart.

She wept when the chariot disappeared in the west and darkness came over the earth. The next day from sunrise to sunset she gazed upon the sun, and at night she refused to go home. For nine days and nights she sat with her golden hair unbound, tasting neither food nor drink, only longing more and more for the smile of the glorious king. She called to him and stretched out her arms, yet she had no hope that he would ever notice her or know of the great love that filled her heart.

On the tenth morning, when she leaned over the water, she was amazed, for instead of her own face, a beautiful flower looked up at her from the sea. She gazed long, and at length in wonder she knew the truth. Her yellow hair had become golden petals, her green lace dress had turned into leaves and stems, and her little feet had become roots which fastened her to the ground. Clytie had become the small and humble image of the sun.

The next morning, when she lifted her face to the beautiful light, it was so radiant with happiness that the great king himself seemed to smile back kindly at the happy little flower.

And so Clytie began her life upon the earth, and she became the mother of a large family of flowers with bright faces like her own. Her children are called sunflowers and you may find them scattered all over the country, even in the dry and dusty places where other flowers will not grow.

And if you care to, you may find out for yourselves whether or not it is true that all the sunflowers in the world turn upon their stalks, from sunrise until sunset, so that they may always keep their faces toward the sun.

From "Nature Myths," by Flora Cooke. Copyright 1895, 1922, by the A. Flanagan Co., and reprinted by permission of the publishers.

The following version of the story of Ceres and Proserpine is from Bulfinch's *Age of Fable:*

Ceres and Proserpine

IN THE vale of Enna there is a lake embowered in woods, which screen it from the fervid rays of the sun, while the moist ground is covered with flowers, and Spring reigns perpetual. Here Proserpine was playing with her companions, gathering lilies and violets, and filling her basket and her apron with them, when Pluto saw her, loved her, and carried her off. She screamed for help to her mother and companions; and when in her fright she dropped the corners of her apron and let the flowers fall, childlike she felt the loss of them as an addition to her grief. The ravisher urged on his steeds, calling them each by name, and throwing loose over their heads and necks his iron-colored reins. When he reached the River Cyane, and it opposed his passage, he struck the river-bank with his trident, and the earth opened and gave him a passage to Tartarus.

Ceres sought her daughter all the world over. Bright-haired Aurora, when she came forth in the morning, and Hesperus when he led out the stars in the evening, found her still busy in the search. But it was all unavailing. At length, weary and sad, she sat down upon a stone, and continued sitting nine days and nights, in the open air, under the sunlight and moonlight and falling showers. It was where now stands the city of Eleusis, then the home of an old man named

Celeus. He was out on the field, gathering acorns and blackberries, and sticks for his fire. His little girl was driving home their two goats, and as she passed the goddess, who appeared in the guise of an old woman, she said to her, "Mother,"—and the name was sweet to the ears of Ceres—"why do you sit here alone upon the rocks?" The old man also stopped, though his load was heavy, and begged her to come into his cottage, such as it was. She declined, and he urged her. "Go in peace," she replied, "and be happy in your daughter; I have lost mine." As she spoke, tears—or something like tears, for the gods never weep—fell down her cheeks upon her bosom. The compassionate old man and his child wept with her. Then said he, "Come with us, and despise not our humble roof; so may your daughter be restored to you in safety." "Lead on," said she, "I cannot resist that appeal!" So she rose from the stone and went with them. As they walked he told her that his only son, a little boy, lay very sick, feverish, and sleepless. She stopped and gathered some poppies. As they entered the cottage, they found all in great distress, for the boy seemed past hope of recovery. Metanira, his mother, received her kindly, and the goddess stopped and kissed the lips of the sick child. Instantly the paleness left his face, and healthy vigor returned to his body. The whole family were delighted—that is, the father, mother, and little girl, for they were all; they had no servants. They spread the table, and put upon it curds and cream, apples, and honey in the comb. While they ate, Ceres mingled poppy juice in the milk of the boy. When night came and all was still, she arose, and taking the sleeping boy, molded his limbs with her hands, and uttered over him three times a solemn charm, then went and laid him in the ashes. His mother, who had been watching what her guest was doing, sprang forward with a cry and snatched the child from the fire. Then Ceres assumed her own form, and a divine splendor shone all around. While they were overcome with astonishment, she said, "Mother, you have been cruel in your fondness to your son. I would have made him immortal, but you have frustrated my attempt. Nevertheless, he shall be great and useful. He shall teach men the use of the plow, and the rewards which labor can win from the cultivated soil." So saying, she wrapped a cloud about her, and mounting her chariot rode away.

Ceres continued her search for her daughter, passing from land to land, and across seas and rivers, till at length she returned to Sicily, whence she at first set out, and stood by the banks of the River Cyane, where Pluto made himself a passage with his prize to his own dominions. The river nymph would have told the goddess all she had witnessed, but dared not, for fear of Pluto; so she only ventured to take up the girdle which Proserpine had dropped in her flight, and waft it to the feet of the mother. Ceres, seeing this, was no longer in doubt of her loss, but she did not yet know the cause, and laid the blame on the innocent land. "Ungrateful soil," said she, "which I have endowed with fertility and clothed with herbage and nourishing grain, no more shall you enjoy my favors." Then the cattle died, the plow broke in the furrow, the seed failed to come up; there was too much sun, there was too much rain; the birds stole the seeds—thistles and brambles were the only growth. Seeing this, the fountain Arethusa interceded for the land. "Goddess," said she, "blame not the land; it opened unwillingly to yield a passage to your daughter. I can tell you of her fate, for I have seen her. This is not my native country; I came hither from Elis. I was a woodland nymph, and delighted in the chase. They praised my beauty, but I cared nothing for it, and rather boasted of my hunting exploits. One day I was returning from the wood, heated with exercise, when I came to a stream silently flowing, so clear that you might count the pebbles on the bottom. The willows shaded it, and the grassy bank sloped down to the water's edge. I approached, I touched the water with my foot. I stepped in knee-deep, and not content with that, I laid my garments on the willows and went in. While I sported in the water, I heard an indistinct murmur coming up as out of the depths of the stream; and made haste to escape to the nearest bank. The voice said, 'Why do you fly, Arethusa? I am Alpheus, the god of this stream.' I ran, he pursued; he was not more swift than I, but he was stronger, and gained upon me, as my strength failed. At last, exhausted, I cried for help to Diana. 'Help me, goddess! help your votary!' The goddess heard, and wrapped me suddenly in a thick cloud. The river god looked now this way and now that, and twice came close to me, but could not find me. 'Arethusa! Arethusa!' he cried. Oh, how I trembled—like a lamb that hears the wolf growling outside the fold. A cold sweat came over me, my hair flowed down in streams; where my foot stood there was a pool. In short, in less time than it takes to tell it I became a fountain. But in this form Alpheus knew me and attempted to mingle his stream with mine. Diana cleft the ground, and I, endeavoring to escape him, plunged into the cavern, and through the bowels of the earth came out here in Sicily. While I passed through the lower parts of the earth, I saw your Proserpine. She was sad, but no longer showing alarm in her countenance. Her look was such as became a queen— the queen of Erebus; the powerful bride of the monarch of the realms of the dead."

When Ceres heard this, she stood for a while like one stupefied; then turned her chariot towards heaven, and hastened to present herself before the throne of Jove. She told the story of her bereavement, and implored Jupiter to interfere to procure the restitution of her daughter. Jupiter consented on one condition, namely, that Proserpine should not during her stay in the lower world have taken any food; otherwise, the Fates forbade her release. Accordingly, Mercury was sent, accompanied by Spring, to demand Proserpine of Pluto. The wily monarch consented; but, alas! the maiden had taken a pomegranate which Pluto offered her, and had sucked the sweet pulp from a few of the seeds. This was enough to prevent her complete release; but a compromise was made, by which she was to pass half the time with her mother, and the rest with her husband Pluto.

Ceres allowed herself to be pacified with this arrangement, and restored the earth to her favor.

To illustrate Ovid's treatment of the same story the following excerpt from a metrical translation by Arthur Maynwaring is given:

> Near Enna's walls a spacious lake is spread,
> Famed for the sweetly singing swans it bred;
> Pergusa is its name: and never more
> Were heard, or sweeter on Cayster's shore.

Woods crown the lake; and Phoebus ne'er invades
The tufted fences, or offends the shades:
Fresh fragrant breezes fan the verdant bowers,
And the moist ground smiles with enamel'd flowers:
The cheerful birds their airy carols sing,
And the whole year is one eternal spring.

　　Here while young Proserpine, among the maids,
Diverts herself in these delicious shades;
While, like a child, with busy speed and care,
She gathers lilies here, and violets there;
While first to fill her little lap she strives,
Hell's grisly monarch at the shade arrives;
Sees her thus sporting on the flowery green,
And loves the blooming maid as soon as seen.
His urgent flame impatient of delay,
Swift as his thought he seized the beauteous prey,
And bore her in his sooty car away.
But frighted goddess to her mother cries;
But all in vain, for now far off she flies;
Far she behind her leaves her virgin train;
To them too cries, and cries to them in vain;
And while with passion she repeats her call,
The violets from her lap and lilies fall:
She misses them, poor heart! and makes new moan;
Her lilies, ah! are lost, her violets gone.

　　O'er hills the ravisher and valleys speeds,
By name encouraging his foamy steeds;
He rattles o'er their necks the rusty reins,
And ruffles with the stroke their shaggy manes.
O'er lakes he whirls his flying wheels, and comes
To the Palici, breathing sulph'rous fumes;
And thence to where the Bacchiads of renown,
Between unequal havens, built their town;
Where Arethusa, round the imprison'd sea,
Extends her crooked coast to Cyane;
The nymph who gave the neighb'ring lake a name,

Of all Sicilian nymphs the first in fame:
She from the waves advanced her beauteous head;
The goddess knew, and thus to Pluto said:
"Farther thou shalt not with the virgin run;
Ceres unwilling, canst thou be her son?
The maid should be by sweet persuasion won:
Force suits not with the softness of the fair;
For, if great things with small I may compare,
Me Anapis once loved; a milder course
He took, and won me by his words, not force."

Then, stretching out her arms, she stopp'd his way:
But he, impatient of the shortest stay,
Throws to his dreadful steeds the slacken'd rein,
And strikes his iron sceptre through the main;
The depths profound through yielding waves he cleaves,
And to hell's center a free passage leaves;
Down sinks his chariot, and his realms of night
The god soon reaches with a rapid flight.

Ovid

From "Age of Fable," by Bulfinch.

How Perseus Slew the Gorgon

So PERSEUS started on his journey, going dry-shod over land and sea;
and his heart was high and joyful, for the winged sandals bore him
each day a seven days' journey.

And he went by Cythnus, and by Ceos, and the pleasant Cyclades
to Attica; and past Athens and Thebes, and the Copaic lake, and up
the vale of Cephissus, and past the peaks of Oeta and Pindus, and
over the rich Thessalian plains, till the sunny hills of Greece were
behind him, and before him were the wilds of the north. Then he

145

passed the Thracian mountains, and many a barbarous tribe, Paeons and Dardans and Triballi, till he came to the Ister stream, and the dreary Scythian plains. And he walked across the Ister dry-shod, and away through the moors and fens, day and night toward the bleak northwest, turning neither to the right hand nor the left, till he came to the Unshapen Land, and the place which has no name.

And seven days he walked through it, on a path which few can tell; for those who have trodden it like least to speak of it, and those who go there again in dreams are glad enough when they awake; till he came to the edge of the everlasting night, where the air was full of feathers, and the soil was hard with ice; and there at last he found the three Grey Sisters, by the shore of the freezing sea, nodding upon a white log of drift-wood, beneath the cold white winter moon; and they chaunted a low song together, "Why the old times were better than the new."

There was no living thing around them, not a fly, not a moss upon the rocks. Neither seal nor sea-gull dare come near, lest the ice should clutch them in its claws. The surge broke up in foam, but it fell again in flakes of snow; and it frosted the hair of the three Grey Sisters, and the bones in the ice-cliff above their heads. They passed the eye from one to the other, but for all that they could not see; and they passed the tooth from one to the other, but for all that they could not eat; and they sat in the full glare of the moon, but they were none the warmer for her beams. And Perseus pitied the three Grey Sisters; but they did not pity themselves.

So he said, "Oh, venerable mothers, wisdom is the daughter of old age. You therefore should know many things. Tell me, if you can, the path to the Gorgon."

Then one cried, "Who is this who reproaches us with old age?" And another, "This is the voice of one of the children of men."

And he, "I do not reproach, but honor your old age, and I am one of the sons of men and of the heroes. The rulers of Olympus have sent me to you to ask the way to the Gorgon."

Then one, "There are new rulers in Olympus, and all new things are bad." And another, "We hate your rulers, and the heroes, and all the children of men. We are the kindred of the Titans, and the Giants,

146

and the Gorgons, and the ancient monsters of the deep." And another, "Who is this rash and insolent man who pushes unbidden into our world?" And the first, "There never was such a world as ours, nor will be; if we let him see it, he will spoil it all."

Then one cried, "Give me the eye, that I may see him"; and another, "Give me the tooth, that I may bite him." But Perseus, when he saw that they were foolish and proud, and did not love the children of men, left off pitying them, and said to himself, "Hungry men must needs be hasty; if I stay making many words here, I shall be starved."

Then he stepped close to them, and watched till they passed the eye from hand to hand. And as they groped about between themselves, he held out his own hand gently, till one of them put the eye into it, fancying that it was the hand of her sister. Then he sprang back, and laughed, and cried: "Cruel and proud old women, I have your eye; and I will throw it into the sea, unless you tell me the path to the Gorgon, and swear to me that you tell me right."

Then they wept, and chatted, and scolded; but in vain. They were forced to tell the truth, though, when they told it, Perseus could hardly make out the road.

"You must go," they said, "foolish boy, to the southward, into the ugly glare of the sun, till you come to Atlas the Giant, who holds the heaven and the earth apart. And you must ask his daughters, the Hesperides, who are young and foolish like yourself. And now give us back our eye, for we have forgotten all the rest."

So Perseus gave them back their eye; but instead of using it, they nodded and fell fast asleep, and were turned into blocks of ice, till the tide came up and washed them all away. And now they float up and down like icebergs for ever, weeping whenever they meet the sunshine, and the fruitful summer, and the warm south wind, which fill young hearts with joy.

But Perseus leaped away to the southward, leaving the snow and the ice behind: past the isle of the Hyperboreans, and the tin isles, and the long Iberian shore, while the sun rose higher day by day upon a bright blue summer sea. And the terns and the sea gulls swept laughing round his head, and called to him to stop and play, and the dolphins gamboled up as he passed, and offered to carry him on

147

their backs. And all night long the sea-nymphs sang sweetly, and the Tritons blew upon their conchs, as they played round Galatea their queen, in her car of pearled shells. Day by day the sun rose higher, and leaped more swiftly into the sea at night, and more swiftly out of the sea at dawn; while Perseus skimmed over the billows like a sea gull, and his feet were never wetted; and leapt on from wave to wave, and his limbs were never weary, till he saw far away a mighty mountain, all rose-red in the setting sun. Its feet were wrapped in forests, and its head in wreaths of cloud; and Perseus knew that it was Atlas, who holds the heavens and the earth apart.

He came to the mountain, and leapt on shore, and wandered upward, among pleasant valleys and waterfalls, and tall trees and strange ferns and flowers; but there was no smoke rising from any glen, nor house, nor sign of man.

At last he heard sweet voices singing; and he guessed that he was come to the garden of the Nymphs, the daughters of the Evening Star.

They sang like nightingales among the thickets, and Perseus stopped to hear their song; but the words which they spoke he could not understand; no, nor no man after him for many a hundred years. So he stepped forward and saw them dancing, hand in hand around the charmed tree, which bent under its golden fruit; and round the tree-foot was coiled the dragon, old Ladon the sleepless snake, who lies there for ever, listening to the song of the maidens, blinking and watching with dry bright eyes.

Then Perseus stopped, not because he feared the dragon, but because he was bashful before those fair maids; but when they saw him, they too stopped, and called to him with trembling voices: "Who are you? Are you Heracles the mighty, who will come to rob our garden, and carry off our golden fruit?"

And he answered: "I am not Heracles the mighty, and I want none of your golden fruit. Tell me, fair Nymphs, the way which leads to the Gorgon, that I may go on my way and slay her."

"Not yet, not yet, fair boy; come dance with us around the tree in the garden which knows no winter, the home of the south wind and the sun. Come hither and play with us awhile; we have danced along

148

here for a thousand years, and our hearts are weary with longing for a playfellow. So come, come, come!"

"I cannot dance with you, fair maidens; for I must do the errand of the Immortals. So tell me the way to the Gorgon, lest I wander and perish in the waves."

Then they sighed and wept; and answered: "The Gorgon! she will freeze you into stone."

"It is better to die like a hero than to live like an ox in a stall. The Immortals have lent me weapons, and they will give me wit to use them."

Then they sighed again and answered, "Fair boy, if you are bent on your own ruin, be it so. We know not the way to the Gorgon; but we will ask the giant Atlas, above upon the mountain peak, the brother of our father, the silver Evening Star. He sits aloft and sees across the ocean, and far away into the Unshapen Land."

So they went up the mountain to Atlas their uncle, and Perseus went up with them. And they found the giant kneeling, as he held the heavens and the earth apart.

They asked him, and he answered mildly, pointing to the sea-board with his mighty hand, "I can see the Gorgons lying on an island far away, but this youth can never come near them, unless he has the hat of darkness, which whosoever wears cannot be seen."

Then cried Perseus, "Where is that hat, that I may find it?"

But the giant smiled. "No living mortal can find that hat, for it lies in the depths of Hades, in the regions of the dead. But my nieces are immortal, and they shall fetch it for you, if you will promise me one thing and keep your faith."

Then Perseus promised; and the giant said, "When you come back with the head of Medusa, you shall show me the beautiful horror, that I may lose my feeling and my breathing, and become a stone for ever; for it is weary labor for me to hold the heavens and the earth apart."

Then Perseus promised, and the eldest of the Nymphs went down, and into a dark cavern among the cliffs, out of which came smoke and thunder, for it was one of the mouths of Hell.

And Perseus and the Nymphs sat down seven days, and waited

149

trembling, till the Nymph came up again; and her face was pale, and her eyes dazzled with the light, for she had been long in the dreary darkness; but in her hand was the magic hat.

Then all the Nymphs kissed Perseus, and wept over him a long while; but he was only impatient to be gone. And at last they put the hat upon his head, and he vanished out of their sight.

But Perseus went on boldly, past many an ugly sight, far away into the heart of the Unshapen Land, beyond the streams of Ocean, to the isles where no ship cruises, where is neither night nor day, where nothing is in its right place, and nothing has a name; till he heard the rustle of the Gorgons' wings and saw the glitter of their brazen talons; and then he knew that it was time to halt, lest Medusa should freeze him into stone.

He thought awhile with himself, and remembered Athene's words. He rose aloft into the air, and held the mirror of the shield above his head, and looked up into it that he might see all that was below him.

And he saw the three Gorgons sleeping, as huge as elephants. He knew that they could not see him, because the hat of darkness hid him; and yet he trembled as he sank down near them, so terrible were those brazen claws.

Two of the Gorgons were foul as swine, and lay sleeping heavily, as swine sleep, with their mighty wings outspread; but Medusa tossed to and fro restlessly, and as she tossed Perseus pitied her, she looked so fair and sad. Her plumage was like the rainbow, and her face was like the face of a nymph, only her eyebrows were knit, and her lips clenched, with everlasting care and pain; and her long neck gleamed so white in the mirror that Perseus had not the heart to strike, and said, "Ah, that it had been either of her sisters!"

But as he looked, from among her tresses the vipers' heads awoke, and peeped up with their bright dry eyes, and showed their fangs, and hissed; and Medusa, as she tossed, threw back her wings and showed her brazen claws; and Perseus saw that, for all her beauty, she was as foul and venomous as the rest.

Then he came down and stepped to her boldly, and looked steadfastly on his mirror, and struck with Harpe stoutly once; and he did not need to strike again.

Then he wrapped the head in the goat-skin, turning away his eyes, and sprang into the air aloft, faster than he ever sprang before.

For Medusa's wings and talons rattled as she sank dead upon the rocks; and her two foul sisters woke, and saw her lying dead.

Into the air they sprang yelling, and looked for him who had done the deed. Thrice they swung round and round, like hawks who beat for a partridge; and thrice they snuffed round and round, like hounds who draw upon a deer. At last they struck upon the scent of the blood, and they checked for a moment to make sure; and then on they rushed with a fearful howl, while the wind rattled hoarse in their wings.

On they rushed, sweeping and flapping, like eagles after a hare; and Perseus' blood ran cold, for all his courage, as he saw them come howling on his track; and he cried, "Bear me well now, brave sandals, for the hounds of Death are at my heels!"

And well the brave sandals bore him, aloft through cloud and sunshine, across the shoreless sea; and fast followed the hounds of Death, as the roar of their wings came down the wind. But the roar came down fainter and fainter, and the howl of their voices died away; for the sandals were too swift, even for Gorgons, and by nightfall they were far behind, two black specks in the southern sky, till the sun sank and he saw them no more.

Then he came again to Atlas, and the garden of the Nymphs; and when the giant heard him coming, he groaned, and said, "Fulfill thy promise to me." Then Perseus held up to him the Gorgon's head, and he had rest from all his toil; for he became a crag of stone, which sleeps for ever far above the clouds.

Then he thanked the Nymphs, and asked them, "By what road shall I go homeward again, for I wandered far round in coming hither?"

And they wept and cried, "Go home no more, but stay and play with us, the lonely maidens, who dwell for ever far away from Gods and men."

But he refused, and they told him his road, and said, "Take with you this magic fruit, which, if you eat once, you will not hunger for seven days. For you must go eastward and eastward ever, over the doleful Libyan shore, which Poseidon gave to Father Zeus, when he

151

burst open the Bosporus and the Hellespont, and drowned the fair Lectonian land. And Zeus took that land in exchange, a fair bargain, much bad ground for a little good, and to this day it lies waste and desert, with shingle, and rock, and sand."

Then they kissed Perseus, and wept over him, and he leapt down the mountain, and went on, lessening and lessening like a sea-gull, away and out to sea.

From "Heroes; or Greek Fairy Tales for my Children," by Charles Kingsley.

The Iliad and *The Odyssey*

THESE two epics attributed to the blind bard, Homer, are universal in appeal. The *Odyssey* being a one-hero type of narrative is simpler than the *Iliad*, and can be used with boys and girls as young as nine years. The *Iliad*, which relates the experiences of many heroes engaged in war, is more complicated in plot and motivation and is therefore better suited to those older. For these reasons, although the *Iliad* as a literary classic exhibits finer qualities than the *Odyssey* and precedes it in theme, stories from the *Odyssey* are usually told earliest.

James Baldwin's *Story of the Golden Age* is a useful introduction to both epics. It presents in a continuous narrative the legends of the causes of the Trojan War along with some of the most beautiful of the Greek myths all woven about the youthful Odysseus as hero. It ends where the *Iliad* begins. The story of the *Iliad* can be told to boys and girls in a series of six episodes as follows:

GREEK MYTHS AND EPICS

Stories from *The Iliad*

The story chosen for illustration is "The Slaying of Hector."
When used alone it will require an introduction. The one given has
been adapted from the account of the Trojan War in Bulfinch's *Age
of Fable*. There is a simpler introduction in Church's *Iliad for Boys
and Girls* from which the main text of the story is taken.

INTRODUCTION

Minerva was the goddess of wisdom, but on one occasion she did
a very foolish thing; she entered into competition with Juno and
Venus for the prize of beauty. It happened thus: At the wedding
feast of Peleus and Thetis all the gods were invited with the exception of Eris. Enraged at her exclusion, the goddess threw a golden
apple among the guests, with the inscription, "For the fairest." There-
upon Juno, Venus, and Minerva each claimed the apple. Jupiter, not
willing to decide in so delicate a matter, sent the goddesses to Mount
Ida, where the beautiful shepherd Paris was tending his flocks, and
to him was committed the decision. The goddesses accordingly appeared before him. Juno promised him power and riches, Minerva
glory and renown in war, and Venus the fairest of women for his
wife, each attempting to bias his decision in her own favor. Paris
decided in favor of Venus and gave her the golden apple, thus
making the two other goddesses his enemies. Under the protection
of Venus, Paris sailed to Greece, and was hospitably received by

153

Menelaus, king of Sparta. Now Helen, the wife of Menelaus, was the very woman whom Venus had destined for Paris, the fairest of her sex. She had been sought as a bride by numerous suitors, and before her decision was made known, they all, at the suggestion of Ulysses, one of their number, took an oath that they would defend her from all injury and avenge her cause if necessary. She chose Menelaus, and was living with him happily when Paris became their guest. Paris, aided by Venus, persuaded her to elope with him, and carried her to Troy, whence arose the famous Trojan War, the story of which is told in the *Iliad* by Homer.

Priam, the king of Troy, was an old man, and while Paris, the shepherd, who stole the beautiful Helen was his son, the real support of his throne was another son, Hector, who proved himself a great hero in the war that followed. According to Homer's account, when Patroclus, one of the Greek heroes, was killed presumably by the hand of Hector, Achilles, one of the noblest warriors among the Greeks and Patroclus' dearest friend, went forth to avenge his death. Our story opens here.

The Slaying of Hector

KING PRIAM stood on a tower of the wall and saw how Achilles was driving the men of Troy before him, and his heart was much troubled within him, thinking how he could help his people. So he went down and spoke to those who kept the gates: "Keep now the wicket-gates open, holding them in your hand, that the people may enter by them, for they are flying before Achilles." So the keepers held the wicket-gates in their hands, and the people made haste to come in; they were wearied with toil and consumed with thirst, and Achilles followed close after them. And the Greeks would have taken the city of Troy that hour but that Apollo saved it, for the gates being open they could enter with the Trojans, whereas the gates being shut, the people were left to perish. And the way in which he saved the city was this. He put courage into the heart of Agēnor, son to Antenor, standing also by him that he should not be slain. Agēnor, therefore, stood thinking to himself: "Shall I flee with these others? Not so: for Achilles will overtake me, so swift of foot is he, and shall slay me, and I shall die the death of a coward. Or shall I flee across the plain to Mount Ida, and hide myself in the thicket, and come back to the city when it is dark? But if he see me, he will pursue me and overtake me. Shall I not rather stand here and meet him before the gates? For he too is a mortal man, and may be slain by the spear."

Therefore he stood by the gates waiting for Achilles, for Apollo had given him courage. And when Achilles came near Agēnor cast his spear, and struck his leg beneath the knee, but the greave turned the spear, so strong was it, having been made by a god. But when Achilles rushed at him to slay him, Apollo lifted him up from the ground and set him safe within the walls. And that the men of Troy might have time to enter, the god took Agēnor's shape and fled before Achilles, and Achilles pursued him. Meanwhile the Trojans flocked into the city through the wicket-gates, nor did they stay to ask who was safe and who was dead, so great was their fear and such their haste. Only Hector remained outside the city, in front of the great gates which were called the Scaean Gates. All the while Achilles was fiercely pursuing the false Agēnor, till at last Apollo turned and spoke to him: "Why do you pursue me, swift-footed Achilles? Have you not yet found out that I am a god, and that all your fury is in vain? And now all the Trojans are safe in the city, and you are here, far out of the way, seeking to kill one who cannot die."

Achilles answered him in great anger: "You have done me a great wrong in this. Surely of all the gods you are the one who loves mischief most. If it had not been for this many Trojans more would have fallen; but you have saved your favorites and robbed me of great glory. Oh that I could take vengeance on you! truly you would have paid dearly for your cheat."

Then he turned and ran towards the city, swift as a racehorse when it whirls a chariot across the plains. And his armor shone upon him as bright as Orion, which men call also the Dog, shines in the autumn, when the vintage is gathered, an evil light, bringing fevers to men. Old Priam saw him and groaned aloud, and stretched out his hands crying to Hector his son, where he stood before the gates waiting to fight with this terrible warrior:

"O my son, wait not for this man, lest he kill you, for indeed he is stronger than you. I would that the gods had such love for him as I have. Soon would he be food for dogs and vultures. Of many sons has he bereaved me, but if he should bereave me of you, then would not I only and the mother who bore you mourn, but every man and woman in Troy. Come within the walls, my dear son, come, for you are the hope of the city. Come, lest an evil fate come upon me in my old age, that I should see my sons slain with the sword and my daughters carried into captivity, and the babes dashed upon the ground."

So spoke old Priam, but he could not move the heart of his son. Then from the other side of the wall his mother, Queen Hecuba, cried to him. She wept aloud, and hoping that she might so persuade him, she laid bare her bosom, saying: "O Hector, my son, have pity on me. Think of the breast which in old days I gave you, when you were hungry, and stilled your crying. Come, I beseech you, inside the walls, and do not wait for him, or stand up in battle against him. For if he conquers you, then not only will you die, but dogs and vultures will eat your flesh far from here, by the ships of the Greeks."

But all her prayers were in vain, for he was still minded to await the coming of Achilles, and stand up to him in battle. And as he waited many thoughts passed through his mind: "Woe is me, if I go within the walls! Will not they reproach me who gave me good advice which I would not hear, saying that I should bring the people within the walls, when the great Achilles roused himself to the battle? Would that I had done this thing! it had been by far better for us; but now I have destroyed the people. I fear the sons and daughters of Troy, lest they should say: 'Hector trusted in his strength, and he has brought the people whom he should have saved to harm.' It would be far better for me to stay here and meet the great Achilles, and either slay him, or, if it must be so, be slain by him. Or shall I lay down my shield and take off my helmet and lean my spear against the wall, and go to meet him and say: 'We will give back the Fair

Helen and all the riches which Paris carried off with her; also we will give all the precious things that there are in the city that the Greeks may divide them among themselves, taking an oath that we are keeping nothing back, if only you will leave us in peace'? But this is idle talk. He will have neither shame nor pity, and will slay me as I stand without defense before him. No: it is better far to meet in arms and see whether Zeus will give the victory to him or to me."

These were the things which Hector thought in his heart. And Achilles came near, shaking over his right shoulder the great Pelian spear, and the flashing of his arms was like to fire or to the sun when it rises. But Hector trembled when he saw him, and his heart failed him so that he turned his back and fled. Fast he fled from the place where he stood by the great Scaean Gate, and fast did Achilles pursue him, just as a hawk, which is more swift than all other birds, pursues a dove among the hills. The two ran past the watch-tower, and past the wild fig tree, along the wagon-road which ran round the walls, till they came to the springs from which the river rises. Two springs there were, one hot as though it had been heated with fire, and the other cold, cold as ice or snow, even in the summer. There were two basins of stone in which the daughters of Troy had been used to wash their garments; but that was in the old days, when there was peace, before the Greeks came to the land. Past the springs they ran; it was no race which men run for some prize, a sheep, maybe, or an ox-hide shield. Rather the prize was the life of Hector. So they ran round the city, and the Trojans on the wall and the Greeks upon the plain looked on. And the gods looked on as they sat in their palace on the top of Olympus. And Zeus said:

"Now this is a piteous thing which I see. My heart is grieved for Hector—Hector, who has never failed to honor me and the other gods with sacrifice. See how the great Achilles is pursuing him! Come, let us take counsel together. Shall we save him from death, or shall we let him fall by the spear of Achilles?"

Athené said: "What is this that you purpose? Will you save a man whom the fates appoint to die? Do this, if you will, but the other gods do not approve."

Then said Zeus: "This is a thing that I hate; but be it as you will."

All this time Hector still fled, and Achilles still pursued. Hector sought for shelter in the walls, and Achilles ever drove him towards the plain. Just as in a dream, when one seems to fly and another seems to pursue, and the first cannot escape, neither can the second overtake, so these two ran. Yet Apollo helped Hector, giving strength to his knees, else he had not held out against Achilles, than whom there was no faster runner among the sons of men. Three times did they run round the city, but when they came for the fourth time to the springs Athené lighted from the air close to Achilles and said: "This is your day of glory, for you shall slay Hector, though he be a mighty warrior. It is his doom to die, and Apollo's self shall not save him. Stand here and take breath, and I will make him meet you."

So Achilles stood leaning on his spear. And Athené took the shape of Deïphobus, and came near to Hector and said to him: "My brother, Achilles presses you hard; but come, we two will stand up against him." Hector answered, "O Deïphobus, I have always loved you above all my brothers, and now I love you still more, for you only have come to my help, while they remain within the walls." Then said Deïphobus: "Much did my father and my mother and my comrades entreat me to stay within the walls, but I would not, for I could not bear to leave you alone. Come, therefore, let us fight this man together, and see whether he will carry our spoils to the ships or we shall slay him here."

Then Hector said to Achilles: "Three times have you pursued me round the walls, and I dared not stand against you, but now I fear you no more. Only let us make this covenant. If Zeus gives me the victory today, I will give back your body to the Greeks, only I will keep your arms: do you, therefore, promise to do the same with me?"

Achilles frowned at him and said: "Hector, talk not of covenants to me. Men and lions make no oaths to each other, neither is there any agreement between wolves and sheep. Make no delay; let us fight together, that I may have vengeance for the blood of all my comrades whom thou hast slain, and especially of Patroclus, the man whom I loved beyond all others."

Then he threw the great spear, but Hector saw it coming and avoided it, crouching down so that the spear flew over his head and fixed itself in the ground. But Athené snatched it up and gave it back to Achilles; but this Hector did not see. Then said Hector to Achilles: "You have missed your aim, Achilles. Now see whether I have not a truer aim." Then he cast his spear, and the aim, indeed, was true, for it struck full upon the shield; it struck, but it bounded far away. Then he cried to Deïphobus: "Give me another spear"; but lo! Deïphobus was gone. Then he knew that his end was come, and he said to himself: "The gods have brought my doom upon me. I thought that Deïphobus was with me; but he is behind the walls, and this was but a cheat with which Athené cheated me. Nevertheless, if I must die, let me at least die in the doing of such a deed as men shall remember in the years to come."

So he spoke, and drew his great sword, and rushed upon Achilles as an eagle rushes down from the clouds upon its prey. But never a blow did he deal; for Achilles ran to meet him, holding his shield before him, and the plumes of his helmet streamed behind him as he ran, and the point of his spear was as bright as the evening star. For a moment he doubted where he should drive it home, for the armor of Patroclus which Hector wore guarded him well. But a spot there was, where the stroke of spear or sword is deadliest, by the collarbone where the neck joins the shoulder. There he drove in the spear, and the point stood out behind the neck, and Hector fell in the dust. Then Achilles cried aloud: "Hector, you thought not of me when you slew Patroclus and spoiled him of his arms. But now you have fallen, and the dogs and vultures shall eat your flesh, but to him the Greeks will give honorable burial."

But Hector said, his voice now growing faint: "O Achilles, I entreat you, by all that you hold dear, to give my body to my father and mother that they may duly bury it. Large ransoms will they pay of gold and silver and bronze."

"Speak not to me of ransom," said Achilles. "Priam shall not buy thee back, no, not for your weight in gold."

Then Hector said: "I know you well, what manner of man you are, and that the heart in your breast is of iron. Only beware lest the anger of the gods come upon you for such deeds in the days when Paris and Apollo shall slay you hard by these very gates."

So speaking, he died. And Achilles said: "Die, dog that you are; but my doom I will meet when it shall please the gods to send it."

From "The Iliad for Boys and Girls," by Alfred J. Church. Copyright, 1924, by the Macmillan Co. and reprinted by permission of the publishers.

Stories from *The Odyssey*

THE gods call a council concerning Odysseus (Ulysses) and send a summons to Telemachus.
Telemachus goes in search of his father.
Odysseus starts for home but has an adventure with the Cyclops that excites the wrath of Poseidon.
Odysseus visits the Home of the Winds and the Island of Circe.
He escapes the Sirens, and Scylla and Charybdis.
He is held captive by Calypso who finally sends him on his way.
He is shipwrecked on the coast of Phaeacia and is found by the Princess Nausicaa and her maidens.
He is entertained at the court of Alcinous.
He reaches Ithaca and meets with Eumaeus, the swineherd.
Telemachus returns and finds his father.
Odysseus triumphs over the suitors and is given a welcome by Penelope.

Some changes from the sequence of events in the original have been made in the above outline of stories suggested for telling to children. The first two follow Homer in picturing Odysseus' home and family. These give the motive behind his persistent efforts to reach Ithaca. To avoid the complications of several stories told within a story, his adventures on his way home are given in the order in which they occur. Also, since all of Odysseus' disasters are a consequence of his blinding of the Cyclops, it simplifies presentation to tell this story early in the series. This story is strongly symbolic and should not be softened to a point of weakness. It is necessary to remember that in all the Greek tales, the gods rule.

The selections which follow have been taken from three sources for the purpose of illustrating differences in style in adaptations as well as content. The first three are from *The Adventures of Odysseus* by Marvin, Mayor and Stawell. These editors have followed the sequence of events in the original Homeric text and have used in most cases Greek proper names. Their version for children is one of the best.

✵

How Athena Pleaded for Odysseus in the Council of the Gods and of the Troubles at His House in Ithaca

SING us the song of the hero, steadfast, skillful, and strong,
Taker of Troy's high towers who wandered for ten years long
Over the perilous waters, through unknown cities of men,
Leading his comrades onward, seeking his home again.
Sing us the song of the Wanderer, sing us the wonderful song!

It was ten years since the Greeks had taken Troy, and all the heroes who had escaped from the war and the perils of the sea were safe at home again in Greece. Odysseus alone had never returned, and was left to waste his soul in Calypso's island, far away from Ithaca, his native land. But Father Zeus had determined that he should reach his home at last, though he was not to be free of trouble even there; and all the Gods pitied him, except Poseidon, the lord of the sea, who wished him ill and raged against him continually, for he had his own cause of spite.

Now one day Poseidon had gone to visit the Ethiopians who dwell

161

at the ends of the earth, and the other Gods were sitting together on Olympus, in the hall of Zeus, and speaking of the fate of mortal men.

"They blame us," said Father Zeus, "and say that we send them their evil lot. But it is not so. It is their own blindness and wickedness that work their ruin."

Then Athena spoke, the wise Goddess with the clear gray eyes: "Father and king, some men, it is true, deserve their fate. But what of Odysseus? My heart is torn when I think of him, pining away in that lonely island where Calypso dwells, the daughter of Atlas, the wizard who knows all the secrets of the sea and guards the pillars that keep heaven and earth apart. She holds him there and woos him with soft and winning words. But his one desire is to reach his native land again, were it only to see the smoke curling up from the roof of his house. Will the lord of Olympus let him die? How can he be wroth with Odysseus, after all the sacrifices he offered on the spreading plains of Troy?"

And Zeus replied, "No, my child, I could never forget Odysseus, the wisest man on earth. But Poseidon is wroth with him, ever since he blinded his son, the giant Cyclops. And so he keeps him away from Ithaca and will not let him reach his home. But if we are all agreed, Odysseus shall return in spite of this, for one God cannot strive alone against the rest, and Poseidon must give up his wrath."

Then she answered, "If such is the will of the Gods, let Hermes, the messenger, go to Calypso and tell her our decree. But I will go to Ithaca and arouse Telemachus, Odysseus' son, and bid him call an assembly and speak out against the princes, who are devouring his father's substance and wooing his father's wife. Then I will send him to Pylos and Sparta to seek tidings of Odysseus there."

So saying, she bound on her beautiful sandals that bear her like the wind over sea and land, and shot down from the heights of Olympus to the house of Odysseus in Ithaca. There she took the shape of a prince called Mentes, a friend of his, and went up to the palace and stood in the gateway, with her bronze spear in her hand.

The courtyard was strewn with the hides of the oxen that had been slaughtered for the feast, and the princes were lying upon them and playing at draughts, while the banquet was being prepared. Their henchmen were busy in the hall, washing the tables and mixing the wine and carving the joints of meat.

Telemachus was in the courtyard too, sitting among the princes, dreaming of his father and wondering if he would ever return and scatter them all and come into his own again. He was the first to notice the Goddess, and he rose at once and went out to meet her, for he could not bear to think that a stranger should be kept standing at the gates. So he took her by the hand and greeted her warmly and led her into the hall. He put her spear against a pillar in a polished stand where the spears of Odysseus stood, and gave her a beautiful carved chair in a quiet corner of the hall, and sat down beside her himself. Then a maid-servant brought a silver basin and poured water over their hands from a golden ewer, and another loaded a table with all kinds of bread and meat. The princes came in after them to their feast, and when it was over they made Phemius the minstrel take his lyre and sing to them.

But Telemachus and Athena were sitting close together, and talking low, so that the others could not hear. "Stranger," said Telemachus, "those men are light of heart and love the lyre and song, for they are devouring another man's substance and paying nothing for all they take. And his bones, maybe, are rotting on some distant shore or floating in the waves. Ah! if they saw him home again they would pray for swift feet sooner than all the gold and raiment in the world. But he will never come now. I would not believe it, even if some one told me that he was on the way. But tell me now who you are yourself and how you came here. Is it your first visit, or are you an old friend of my father's, for he had many guests?"

Then the Goddess replied, "My name is Mentes and I am an old friend of your house. I am on a voyage to Cyprus, to buy copper in exchange for iron. If you would know more of me, ask old Laertes, your father's sire. His life is sad now, I hear, and he stays alone on the farmland with one old servant and never comes to the city. I thought to find your father here when I came and, though he is so long delayed, I believe with all my heart that he will soon come back. He must be kept somewhere against his will, perhaps on an island in the far-off seas. But he would know how to find a way out, even if he were bound in iron chains. I am no seer, but I am sure of that. And so you are his son! I can see for myself how like you are. You have his head and his beautiful eyes that I remember so well in the old days, when we used to talk together before he set sail for Troy. We have never met since then. But come now, tell me, what is this rout I see? Can these be guests of yours? How wantonly they revel in your house!"

"Sir," said Telemachus, "it is the ruin of our house that you see. My father is gone for ever, and these men are the princes from Ithaca and the islands round, who have come to demand my mother in marriage. They destroy our wealth, but she will not give them an answer; and so it goes on from day to day, and I shall soon perish too."

Then the Goddess said, "Alas, poor son, how sorely you need the mighty hand of your father to right your wrongs. If he were only standing in the doorway now with helmet and shield and spear as I knew him in his prime! But listen and I will tell you what to do. Tomorrow summon all the lords of Ithaca together, and there before the assembly bid these men leave your house; and if your mother desires to marry, let her return to her father's house and be married thence. But for yourself, fit out a ship, the best you have, and go to Pylos and to Sparta to seek for news of your father. If he is still alive, wait and endure this ruin for another year; but if you hear that he is really dead, come home to build him a funeral mound and pay him every honor, and give your mother in marriage to one of the lords. And now farewell, for I must be going, and remember what I say. You are a child no longer and must talk and act like a man."

Then Telemachus begged his guest to stay or at least to take some worthy gift in memory of him. But Athena would not wait. She rose and turned herself into an eagle and flew away over the sea. Then Telemachus knew that he had seen a Goddess, and took her words to heart and went back among the suitors, stronger and braver than before.

Now the minstrel was singing to them the sad story of the return of the Greeks from Troy and they were listening in silence, when Penelope the queen appeared, standing in the doorway, with her bright veil before her face. She had heard the song from her upper chamber and had come down weeping, to beg the minstrel for some other lay.

"Phemius," she said, "you know many other songs that charm the minds of men. But this one will break my heart, for it tells me of my dear lord, whom I think of day and night."

Then Telemachus said, "Mother, let the minstrel sing as he pleases. He is not to blame, but Father Zeus, who gives men joy and sorrow as he will and to us this grief. Be brave and listen, for all men love to hear the newest song."

Penelope was astonished as she heard him and went back to her room, and Telemachus turned to the princes and said, "Go on with your feast, proud lords, and be merry, if you will: I too delight to hear a minstrel who can sing us such songs as these. But in the morning I bid you all assemble in the public square, for I have a word to say. There I shall demand that you leave these halls and find your feasts elsewhere. And, if you refuse, I shall call on the Gods to repay you for all your crimes."

And the princes, too, were astonished when they heard him speak so boldly, and bit their lips; and Antinous, who was ever the foremost, said, "My lord Telemachus, you speak like a man inspired. It would be an ill day for us all, if Zeus made you king in sea-girt Ithaca, as your fathers were before you."

And Telemachus answered, "I will take the kingship gladly, if Zeus will give it me. But it may pass to some other lord, now that Odysseus is dead and gone. Only I claim for myself, and will maintain, the rule in my father's house."

Then another of the suitors, called Eurymachus, joined in, "Who shall be king in Ithaca, only the Gods can tell. But we are all content that you should keep your own possessions, Telemachus, and be master in your own house. But tell us, who was the stranger that came here just now? Did he bring any news of your father? He was gone so quickly that no one could see who he was. But he had a noble mien."

"I expect no more news of my father," said Telemachus, "and I have no faith in signs. That man was a prince called Mentes, a friend of our house."

But he knew in his heart that it was the heavenly Goddess, and when the song and the dance were over, he went to his own chamber to think over all she had said. And Eurycleia, the old nurse, went with him and lighted him to his room. She had nursed him as a baby and no one in the household loved him more. She waited there and took his doublet and folded it up and hung it on a peg. Then she went away and closed the door carefully behind her. And he lay awake all night, wrapt in his soft sheep-skin, and thinking of the journey that Athena would have him make.

From "Adventures of Odysseus," by F. S. Marvin, R. J. C. Mayor and F. M. Stawell. Published by J. M. Dent & Sons, London, and E. P. Dutton & Co., Inc., New York, and reprinted by permission of the publishers.

How Odysseus Met the Princess Nausicaa

So THERE the stout-hearted Odysseus lay and slept, worn out with all his toil. But meanwhile Athena went to the Sea-kings' city, up to the palace of their ruler, the wise Alcinous, and into the beautiful chamber where his daughter lay asleep, the young princess Nausicaa, fair as the Immortals. On either side of the threshold two maidens were sleeping, as lovely as the Graces, and the glittering doors were shut. But the Goddess floated through them like a breath of wind up to the head of the couch, and spoke to Nausicaa in a dream. She seemed to her one of her dear companions, the daughter of Dymas, the sailor.

"How heedless you are, Nausicaa!" so the vision said. "You let all your fine clothing lie uncared for, and your marriage day is close at hand, when you ought to have beautiful robes for yourself and for your maidens, if you wish your friends to praise you and your father and mother to be glad. Let us take the clothes down to the river and wash them early tomorrow morning. I will help you in the work, for we must get ready as quickly as we can; the best men among your people are suitors for you already. And ask the king your father to give you a pair of mules and a car, for the river is a long way off."

Then Athena went back to Olympus, the peaceful home of the Gods. No winds blow there, so men say, and no rain falls, and the snow never comes near it, but the whole sky is calm and cloudless and all the air is full of light.

So the night passed away, and the young dawn appeared on her glorious throne in the sky and awakened the princess. She was full of wonder at the dream and went through the house to tell her parents and found them in the hall. Her mother was sitting by the hearth among her maidens spinning her sea-blue yarn, and she met her father at the door on his way to the council of his lords. Nausicaa ran up to him and said:

"Father dear, we have so much fine linen lying soiled in the house —could you not lend me a pair of mules and a car, and I will take it all down to the river and wash it? You must have clean robes to wear yourself when you sit at the council among the chiefs, and you have five sons at home, three of them young and bachelors, and they always want fresh linen for the dances, and I must think of it all."

She was too shy to speak about her marriage to her father; but he understood, and answered, "You may have the mules, my child, and anything you wish."

So the princess brought out the bright garments and put them on the car; and her mother packed a store of dainties in a basket and gave her a goatskin full of wine and olive-oil in a golden flask. Then Nausicaa mounted the car and her maidens went with her, and she took the whip and the glistening reins and started the mules, and they clattered off at once and carried her willingly all the way.

At last they came to the flowing river, and there they stopped and unyoked the mules, and sent them to feed on the sweet clover that grew along the banks; and they lifted out the clothes and laid them in the trenches and trod them in the dark water, vying with one another in the work. And when they had finished they spread them out

167

on the beach to dry in the sun, just where the sea had washed the pebbles clean. Then they bathed and anointed themselves and took their meal at the riverside, and afterwards they threw aside their veils and played at ball, and white-armed Nausicaa led the song. And she looked like Artemis the huntress on the hillside among the mountain nymphs, taller by the head and fairer and statelier than them all.

At last it was time to go home, and they harnessed the mules and folded up the clothes. But now Athena planned that Odysseus should awake and see the maiden. Just then the princess had the ball and threw it to one of the girls, but it missed her and dropped into the eddying river and they cried out as they saw it fall. The cry woke Odysseus and he sprang up in wonder.

"Where am I?" he asked himself, "what country can this be? I hear the sound of women's voices. Are they mortals or nymphs of the meadows and the stream? I will go and see."

Then he broke off a leafy bough to cover his loins and went out from his shelter in the wood to meet the fair-haired maidens, all rough and naked as he was,—his need was so great—like a mountain-lion stalking through wind and rain after the forest deer. But they were terrified when they saw him, covered with the salt sea-brine, and they ran away from him to the end of the curving beach. Only the daughter of Alcinous stood where she was and waited for him face-to-face without trembling, for Athena gave her courage. Then Odysseus spoke to her gently and he knew what was best to say.

"Maiden," he said, "whoever you are, I need your help. Surely you must be Artemis the huntress, if you are one of the Immortals. Or are you a mortal maiden? Then how happy must your father be and your mother and your brothers when they watch you moving in the dance. Only once have I seen a thing so fair, long ago in Delos, a young sapling palm tree, straight and tall and wonderful, that grew by Apollo's temple. Princess, I have suffered much. I have been wandering over the dark sea for twenty days and nights, tossed to and fro by wave and storm, and at last I have landed here. But I am a stranger, and do not know the people of the land. You are the first I have met and I ask you to help me. In kindness show me the way to the city and give me clothing, some wrapper you have used for the linen. So may the Gods grant you your heart's desire, a worthy husband and love and unity in your home. For no power in the world is stronger than the husband and wife who are one at heart; their enemies cannot hurt them and their friends rejoice, but they know their own joy best themselves."

And Nausicaa said to him, "Stranger, it is Zeus who gives us everything, sorrow and happiness alike. You must bear what he has sent you, and you seem to me brave and wise. And now that you have come to us and asked me for help you shall have everything you need. This is the land of the Sea-kings, and I am the daughter of their ruler, the great-hearted Alcinous."

Then she called to her maidens, "Come back to me, girls; why do you run away? This man is no enemy, but a shipwrecked wanderer, and we must treat him kindly. All strangers and suppliants are sent to us by Zeus. Give him food and drink and let him bathe in the river, somewhere out of the wind."

So they took Odysseus to a sheltered place, and gave him a vest and a cloak and soft olive-oil in a golden flask, and showed him where to bathe. And he washed away the salt sea-brine from his limbs and the scurf of salt from his hair, and anointed himself and put on the garments, and his long curls fell clustering round his shoulders and Athena gave him grace and stateliness. Then he came back to the maiden and sat down on the beach, and the princess looked at him and said to her women:

"The Gods themselves have sent this stranger here. At first I thought him ill-favored, but now he looks like one of the Immortals, the lords of heaven and earth. Oh that such a hero would stay with us and be my husband! Go now, give him food and drink."

But when Odysseus had eaten and drunk his fill, another thought came into Nausicaa's mind. She folded away the linen and mounted the car, and then called Odysseus to her side and said:

"Come, stranger, let us go to the city and I will send you to my father's house. But you must do as I tell you, and you will understand, I think, why it is best. So long as we go through the meadows, follow close behind me with my maidens, and I will lead the way. But when we come near the city—you will see a high wall round it and a noble harbor on either side with a narrow neck of land between, and the ships drawn up along the road, each one in its own station. Close by is the public square and Poseidon's sacred place and the shipyards where they make the ropes and sails and shave the oars. Now there are insolent men among our folk, and some of them might say, 'Who is the tall kingly stranger with Nausicaa? Some wanderer from a distant land, or a God perhaps, come down from heaven at her prayer! It is well that she had found a foreign husband for herself, since she scorns the noble Sea-kings who make their suit to her!' Thus they will reproach me, and I should blame it myself in another maid. So listen to my plan. You will find a grove of Athena on the way, tall poplars and a running spring and a meadow close beside them. Sit there and wait until we are home again. And when you think it time follow us to the city and ask for my father's house: it is easy to find, for none of the rest are like it. Go straight up through the hall to my mother: she will be sitting by the hearth in the firelight, her chair against a pillar, spinning her wonderful sea-blue yarn, and her maidens sit behind her. My father's throne is next to hers: there he sits and drinks his wine like one of the Immortals. But go past him and put your hands on my mother's knees, for you will soon see your home again if you can win her favor."

Then Nausicaa lifted the whip and the mules started for home. And as the sun set they came to the sacred grove of Athena. There Odysseus sat down and waited, and he prayed to the Goddess that the Sea-kings might pity him and give him help, and she heard his prayer.

From "Adventures of Odysseus," by F. S. Marvin, R. J. C. Mayor and F. M. Stawell. Published by J. M. Dent & Sons, London, and E. P. Dutton & Co., Inc., New York, and reprinted by permission of the publishers.

How the Swineherd Welcomed Odysseus

So ODYSSEUS went up along the rough mountain path, through the forest and over the hills, till he came to the house where his faithful steward lived. It stood in an open space, and there was a large court-yard in front with a wall of heavy stones and hawthorn boughs and a stout oak palisade. Inside the yard there were twelve sties for the pigs, and the swineherd kept four watch-dogs to guard the place, great beasts and fierce as wolves, that he had reared himself. Odysseus found him at home, sitting in the porch alone and cutting himself a pair of sandals from a brown oxhide.

The dogs caught sight of the king as soon as he came up and flew at him, barking, but he had the wit to let go his staff and sit down at once on the ground. Still it might have gone hard with him there in front of his own servant's house had not Eumaeus rushed out of the porch, dropping the leather in his haste, and scolded the dogs, driving them off with a volley of stones.

Then he said to Odysseus, "A little more, old man, and the dogs would have torn you in pieces and disgraced me for ever! And I have my full share of trouble as it is, for I have lost the best master in all the world and must sit here to mourn for him and fatten his swine for other men, while he is wandering somewhere in foreign lands, hungry and thirsty perhaps, if he is still alive at all. But now come in yourself, and let me give you food and drink and tell me your own tale."

So he took Odysseus into the house and made a seat for him with a pile of brushwood boughs and a great thick shaggy goatskin which he used for his own bed, and all with so kind a welcome that it warmed the king's heart and made him pray the Gods to bless him for his goodness. But Eumaeus only said, "How could I neglect a stranger though he were a worse man than you? All strangers and beggars are sent to us by Zeus. Take my gift and welcome; though it is little enough I have to give, a servant such as I, with new masters to lord it over him. For we have lost the king who would have loved me and given me house and lands and all that a faithful servant ought

171

to have whose work is blest by the Gods and prospers, as mine does here. Alas! he is dead and gone! He went away with Agamemnon to fight at Troy and never came home again."

So saying, the good swineherd rose and fetched what meat and wine he had, and set it before Odysseus, grieving that he had nothing better for him because the shameless suitors plundered everything.

But Odysseus ate and drank eagerly, and when his strength had come again he asked Eumaeus, "My friend, who is this master of yours you tell me of? Did you not say he was lost for Agamemnon's sake? Perhaps I may have seen him, for I have traveled far."

But the swineherd answered, "Old man, his wife and son will believe no traveler's tale. They have heard too many such. Every wandering beggar who comes to Ithaca goes to my mistress with some empty story to get a meal for himself, and she welcomes him and treats him kindly and asks him about it all, with the tears running down her cheeks in a woman's way. Yes, even you, old man, might learn to weave such tales if you thought they would get you a cloak or a vest. No, he is dead, and dogs and birds have eaten him, or else he has fed the fishes and his bones lie somewhere on the seashore; buried in the sand. And he has left us all to grieve for him, but no one more than me, who can never have so kind a master again, not though I had my heart's desire and went back to my native land and saw my father and mother and the dear home where I was born. It is Odysseus above all whom I long to see once more. There, stranger, I have called him by his name, and that I should not do; for he is still my dear master though he is far away."

Then Odysseus said, "My friend, your hope has gone and you will never believe me. But I tell you this and seal it with an oath: Odysseus will return! Poor as I am, I will take no reward for my news till he comes to his own again, but you shall give me a new vest and cloak that day, and I will wear them."

But the swineherd answered, "Ah, my friend, I shall never need to pay you that reward. He will never come back again. But now drink your wine in peace, and let us talk of something else; and do not call to mind the sorrow that almost breaks my heart. Tell me of

172

yourself and your own troubles and who you are, and what ship brought you here, for you will not say you came afoot."

Then Odysseus pretended he was a Cretan and had fought at Troy, and told Eumaeus a long tale of adventures and how he had been wrecked at last on the coast of Epirus. The king of the country, he said, had rescued him, and he had learned that Odysseus had been there a little while before, and was already on his way to Ithaca.

The swineherd listened eagerly to it all, but when Odysseus had finished he said, "Poor friend, my heart aches to hear of all your sufferings. But there is one thing you should not have said, one thing I can never believe, and that is that Odysseus will return. And why need you lie to please me? I can see for myself that you are old and unhappy, a wanderer whom the Gods have sent to me. It is not for such a tale I will show you the kindness that you need, but because I pity you myself and reverence the law of Zeus."

"If I lie," Odysseus answered, "you may have me thrown from the cliff as a warning to other cheats. I swear it, and call the Gods to witness."

But the true-hearted swineherd only said, "I should get a good name by that, my friend, if I took you into my house and had you for my guest, and then murdered you brutally! Do you think I could pray to Zeus after that without a fear? But now it is supper-time, and my men will be coming home."

While they spoke, the herdsmen came up with the swine, and the sows were driven into the pens, grunting and squealing noisily as they settled in for the night. Then Eumaeus called out, "Bring in the fattest boar, and let us make a sacrifice in honor of our guest, and get some reward ourselves for all the trouble we have spent upon the drove, trouble lost, since strangers take the fruit of it all."

So they brought in a big fat white-tusked boar, while Eumaeus split the wood for the fire. And he did not forget the Immortals, for he had a pious heart: he made the due offerings first and prayed for his master's return, and then he stood up at the board to carve, and gave each man his share and a special slice for his guest from the whole length of the chine. Odysseus took it and thanked him with all his heart:

"May Father Zeus be your friend, Eumaeus, and give you what I would give you for your kindness to a poor old man like me."

But the swineherd said, "Take it, my good friend, take it and enjoy it. Zeus will give or withhold as it may please him, for he can do all things."

So they sat down to the feast, and after they had had their fill the swineherd's servant cleared everything away, and then they made ready for sleep. The evening closed in black and stormy, and a west wind sprang up bringing the rain with it, and blew hard all the night: so Eumaeus made up a bed of fleeces for Odysseus by the fire and gave him a great thick cloak as well, that he kept for the roughest weather. But he could not bring himself to stay there too, away from his herd of pigs, and he wrapped himself up warmly and went out to sleep beside them in the open. Odysseus saw, and smiled to see, what care he took of everything, while he thought his master was far away.

From "Adventures of Odysseus," by F. S. Marvin, R. J. C. Mayor and F. M. Stawell. Published by J. M. Dent & Sons, London, and E. P. Dutton & Co., Inc., New York, and reprinted by permission of the publishers.

A second notable adaptation of the *Odyssey* is that made for children by Alfred J. Church. Mr. Church has used Latin forms of proper names but his versions are none the less Greek in spirit. His stories are told with a directness that children like.

The Cyclops

WHEN Troy had been taken, Ulysses and his men set sail for his home, the Island of Ithaca. He had twelve ships with him, and fifty men or thereabouts in each ship. The first place they came to was a city called Ismărus. This they took and plundered. Ulysses said to his men: "Let us sail away with what we have got." They would not listen to him, but sat on the sea-shore, and feasted, for they had found plenty of wine in the city, and many sheep and oxen in the fields round it. Meanwhile the people who had escaped out of the city fetched their countrymen who dwelt in the mountains, and brought an army to fight with the Greeks. The battle began early in the morning of the next day, and lasted nearly till sunset. At first the Greeks had the better of it, but in the afternoon the people of the country prevailed, and drove them to their ships. Very glad were they to get away; but when they came to count, they found that they had lost six men out of each ship.

After this a great storm fell upon the ships, and carried them far to the south, past the very island to which they were bound. It was very hard on Ulysses. He was close to his home, if he could only have stopped; but he could not, and though he saw it again soon after, it was ten years before he reached it, having gone through many adventures in the meantime.

The first of these was in the country of the Cyclopes or Round-eyed people. Late on a certain day Ulysses came with his ships to an island, and found in it a beautiful harbor, with a stream falling into it, and a flat beach on which to draw up the ships. That night he and his men slept by the ships, and the next day they made a great feast. The island was full of wild goats. These the men hunted and killed, using their spears and bows. They had been on shipboard for many days, and had had but little food. Now they had plenty, eight goats to every ship, and nine for the ship of Ulysses, because he was the chief. So they ate till they were satisfied, and drank wine which they had carried away from Ismărus.

Now there was another island about a mile away, and they could see that it was larger, and it seemed as if there might be people living in it. The island where they were was not inhabited. So on the second morning Ulysses said to his men: "Stay here, my dear friends; I with my own ship and my own company will go to yonder island, and find out who dwells there, whether they are good people or no." So he and his men took their ship, and rowed over to the other island.

Then Ulysses took twelve men, the bravest that there were in the ship, and went to search out the country. He took with him a goatskin of wine, very strong and sweet, which the priest of Apollo at Ismărus had given him for saving him and his house and family, when the city was taken. There never was a more precious wine; one measure of it could be mixed with twenty measures of water, and the smell of it was wondrously sweet. Also he took with him some parched corn, for he felt in his heart that he might need some food.

After a while they came to a cave which seemed to be the dwelling of some rich and skillful shepherd. Inside there were pens for the young sheep and the young goats, and baskets full of cheeses, and milk-pans ranged against the walls. Then Ulysses' men said to him: "Let us go away before the master comes back. We can take some of the cheeses, and some of the kids and lambs." But Ulysses would not listen to them. He wanted to see what kind of man this shepherd might be, and he hoped to get something from him.

In the evening the Cyclops, the Round-eye, came home. He was a great giant, with one big eye in the middle of his forehead, and an eyebrow above it. He bore on his shoulder a huge bundle of pine logs for his fire. This he threw down outside the cave with a great crash, and drove the flock inside, and then closed up the mouth with a big rock so big that twenty wagons could not carry it. After this he milked the ewes and the she-goats. Half the milk he curdled for cheese, and half he set aside for his own supper. This done, he threw some logs on the fire, which burnt up with a great flame, showing the Greeks, who had fled into the depths of the cave, when they saw the giant come in.

"Who are you?" said the giant, "traders or pirates?"

"We are no pirates, mighty sir," said Ulysses, "but Greeks sailing home from Troy, where we have been fighting for Agamemnon, the great king, whose fame is spread abroad from one end of heaven to the other. And we beg you to show hospitality to us, for the gods love them who are hospitable."

"Nay," said the giant, "talk not to me about the gods. We care not for them, for we are better and stronger than they. But tell me, where have you left your ship?"

176

But Ulysses saw what he was thinking of when he asked about the ship, namely, that he meant to break it up so as to leave them no hope of getting away. So he said, "Oh, sir, we have no ship; that which we had was driven by the wind upon a rock and broken, and we whom you see here are all that escaped from the wreck."

The giant said nothing, but without more ado caught up two of the men, as a man might catch up two puppies, and dashed them on the ground, and tore them limb from limb, and devoured them, with huge draughts of milk between, leaving not a morsel, not even the bones. And when he had filled himself with this horrible food and with the milk of the flocks, he lay down among his sheep, and slept.

Then Ulysses thought: "Shall I slay this monster as he sleeps, for I do not doubt that with my good sword I can pierce him to the heart. But no; if I do this, then shall I and my comrades here perish miserably, for who shall be able to roll away the great rock that is laid against the mouth of the cave?"

So he waited till the morning, very sad at heart. And when the giant awoke, he milked his flocks, and afterwards seized two of the men, and devoured them as before. This done, he went forth to the pastures, his flocks following him, but first he put the rock on the mouth of the cave, just as a man shuts down the lid of his quiver.

All day Ulysses thought how he might save himself and his companions, and the end of his thinking was this. There was a great pole in the cave, the trunk of an olive tree, green wood which the giant was going to use as a staff for walking when it should have been dried by the smoke. Ulysses cut off this a piece some six feet long, and his companions hardened it in the fire, and hid it away. In the evening the giant came back and did as before, seizing two of the prisoners and devouring them. When he had finished his meal, Ulysses came to him with the skin of wine in his hand and said, "Drink, Cyclops, now that you have supped. Drink this wine, and see what good things we had in our ship. But no one will bring the like to you in your island here if you are so cruel to strangers."

The Cyclops took the skin and drank, and was mightily pleased with the wine.

"Give me more," he said, "and tell me your name, and I will give you a gift such as a host should. Truly this is a fine drink, like, I take it, to that which the gods have in heaven."

Then Ulysses said: "My name is No Man. And now give me your gift."

And the giant said: "My gift is this: you shall be eaten last." And as he said this, he fell back in a drunken sleep.

Then Ulysses said to his companions, "Be brave, my friends, for the time is come for us to be delivered from this prison."

So they put the stake into the fire, and kept it there till it was ready, green as it was, to burst into flame. Then they thrust it into his eye, for, as has been told, he had but one, and Ulysses leant with all his force upon the stake, and turned it about, just as a man turns a drill about when he would make a hole in a ship timber. And the wood hissed in the eye as the red-hot iron hisses in the water when a smith would temper it to make a sword.

Then the giant leapt up, and tore away the stake, and cried out so loudly that the Round-eyed people in the island came to see what had happened.

"What ails you," they asked, "that you make so great an uproar, waking us all out of our sleep? Is any one stealing your sheep, or seeking to hurt you?"

And the giant bellowed, "No Man is hurting me."

"Well," said the Round-eyed people, "if no man is hurting you, then it must be the gods that do it, and we cannot help you against them."

But Ulysses laughed when he thought how he had beguiled them by his name. But he was still in doubt how he and his companions should escape, for the giant sat in the mouth of the cave, and felt to see whether the men were trying to get out among the sheep. And Ulysses, after long thinking, made a plan by which he and his companions might escape. By great good luck the giant had driven the rams into the cave, for he commonly left them outside. These rams were very big and strong, and Ulysses took six of the biggest, and tied the six men that were left out of the twelve underneath their bellies with osier twigs. And on each side of the six rams to which a man was tied, he put another ram. So he himself was left, for there was no one who could do the same for him. Yet this also he managed. There was a very big ram, much bigger than all the others, and to this he clung, grasping the fleece with both his hands. So, when the morning came, the flocks went out of the cave as they were wont, and the giant felt them as they passed by him, and did not perceive the men. And when he felt the biggest ram, he said,

"How is this? You are not used to lag behind; you are always the first to run to the pasture in the morning and to come back to the fold at night. Perhaps you are troubled about thy master's eye which this villain No Man has destroyed. First he overcame me with wine, and then he put out my eye. Oh! that you could speak and tell me where he is. I would dash out his brains upon the ground." And then he let the big ram go.

When they were out of the giant's reach, Ulysses let go his hold of the ram, and loosed his companions, and they all made as much haste as they could to get to the place where they had left their ship, looking back to see whether the giant was following them. The crew at the ship were very glad to see them, but wondered that there should be only six. Ulysses made signs to them to say nothing, for he was afraid that the giant might know where they were if he heard their voices. So they all got on board and rowed with all their might. But when they were a hundred yards from the shore, Ulysses stood up in the ship and shouted: "You are an evil beast, Cyclops, to devour strangers in your cave, and are rightly served in losing your eye. May the gods make you suffer worse things than this!"

The Cyclops, when he heard Ulysses speak, broke off the top of a rock and threw it to the place from which the voice seemed to come. The rock fell just in front of the ship, and the wave which it made washed it back to the shore. But Ulysses caught up a long pole and pushed the ship off, and he nodded with his head, being afraid to speak, to his companions to row with all their might. So they rowed; and when they were twice as far off as before, Ulysses stood up again in the ship, as if he were going to speak again. And his comrades begged him to be silent.

"Do not make the giant angry," they said; "we were almost lost

179

just now when the wave washed us back to the shore. The monster throws a mighty bolt, and throws it far."

But Ulysses would not listen, but cried out: "Hear, Cyclops, if any man ask you who put out your eye, say that it was Ulysses of Ithaca."

Then the giant took up another great rock and threw it. This time it almost touched the end of the rudder, but missed it by a hand's breadth. This time, therefore, the wave helped them on. So big was it that it carried the ship to the other shore.

Now Ulysses had not forgotten to carry off sheep from the island for his companions. These he divided among the crews of all the ships. The great ram he had for his own share. So that day the whole company feasted, and they lay down on the sea-shore and slept.

From "The Odyssey for Boys and Girls," by Alfred J. Church. Copyright, 1906, by The Macmillan Co. and reprinted by permission of the publishers.

Charles Lamb (1775–1824) was among the first to adapt the literary classics for children's own reading. The selection which follows is from his *Adventures of Ulysses* based on the translation of Homer made by Chapman in the reign of James I. This excerpt represents a formal poetic treatment which is enjoyed by children having a degree of cultivated taste.

The Song of the Sirens

THE time for departure being come, Ulysses and his men set their sails, and took a final leave of great Circe; who by her art calmed the heavens, and gave them smooth seas, and a right forewind (the seaman's friend) to bear them on their way to Ithaca.

They had not sailed past a hundred leagues before the breeze which Circe had lent them suddenly stopped. It was stricken dead. All the sea lay in prostrate slumber. Not a gasp of air could be felt. The ship stood still. Ulysses guessed that the island of the Sirens was not far off, and that they had charmed the air so with their devilish singing. Therefore he made him cakes of wax, as Circe had instructed him, and stopped the ears of his men with them; then causing himself to be bound hand and foot, he commanded the rowers to ply their oars and row as fast as speed could carry them past that fatal shore. They soon came within sight of the Sirens, who sang in Ulysses' hearing:

> Come here, thou, worthy of a world of praise,
> That dost so high the Grecian glory raise;
> Ulysses! stay thy ship; and that song hear
> That none pass'd ever, but it bent his ear,
> But left him ravish'd, and instructed more
> By us than any ever heard before.
> For we know all things, whatsoever were
> In wide Troy labor'd; whatsoever there
> The Grecians and the Trojans both sustain'd,
> By those high issues that the gods ordain'd;
> And whatsoever all the earth can show
> To inform a knowledge of desert, we know.

These were the words, but the celestial harmony of the voices which sang them no tongue can describe: it took the ear of Ulysses with ravishment. He would have broken his bonds to rush after them; and threatened, wept, sued, entreated, commanded, crying out with tears and passionate imprecations, conjuring his men by all the ties of perils past which they had endured in common, by fellowship and love, and the authority which he retained among them, to let him loose; but at no rate would they obey him. And still the Sirens sang. Ulysses made signs, motions, gestures, promising mountains of gold if they would set him free; but their oars only moved faster. And still the Sirens sang. And still the more he adjured them to set him free, the faster with cords and ropes they bound him; till they were quite out of hearing of the Sirens' notes, whose effect great Circe had so truly predicted.

From "The Adventures of Ulysses," by Charles Lamb.

Sources for the Story-teller

Baldwin, James. *Old Greek Stories*. American Book Co. Simple versions.

Baldwin, James. *Story of the Golden Age*. Chas. Scribner's Sons. Introduction to *Iliad*.

Buckley, E. F. *Children of the Dawn, Old Tales of Greece*. The Macmillan Company.

Bulfinch, Thomas. *Age of Fable*. McKay. E. P. Dutton & Co., Inc.

Bulfinch, Thomas. *Golden Age of Myth and Legend*. Frederick A. Stokes Co. Includes Greek and Norse mythology.

Church, Alfred J. *The Aeneid for Boys and Girls*. The Macmillan Company.

Church, Alfred J. *Iliad for Boys and Girls*. The Macmillan Company.

Church, Alfred J. *Odyssey for Boys and Girls*. The Macmillan Company.

Church, Alfred J. *Stories of the Old World*. Ginn & Company.

Colum, Padraic. *Adventures of Odysseus*. The Macmillan Company.

Colum, Padraic. *Golden Fleece and the Heroes Who Lived before Achilles*. The Macmillan Company. Story of Jason.

Cox, C. W. *Tales of Ancient Greece*. E. P. Dutton & Co., Inc.

Cruse, Amy. *Young Folks' Book of Epic Heroes*. Little, Brown & Company.

Francillon, R. E. *Gods and Heroes*. Ginn & Company. Follows Ovid.

Hawthorne, Nathaniel. *Wonder Book* and *Tanglewood Tales*. Houghton. Macrae Smith.

Homer. *The Iliad*. Prose translation by Lang, Leaf and Myers. The Macmillan Company.

Homer. *The Odyssey*. Prose translation by Butcher and Lang. The Macmillan Company.

Homer. *The Odyssey*. Poetical version by William Cullen Bryant. Houghton Mifflin Co.

Homer. *The Odyssey*. Prose translation by George Herbert Palmer. Houghton Mifflin Co. Excellent for reading aloud.

Hutchinson, W. M. L. *Golden Porch*. Longmans, Green & Co. Greek fairy tales taken from the Odes of Pindar.

GREEK MYTHS AND EPICS

Kingsley, Charles. *The Heroes; or Greek Fairy Tales.* The Macmillan Company. Perseus, Jason and Theseus.

Lamb, Charles. *The Adventures of Ulysses.* Frederick A. Stokes Co.

Lang, Andrew. *Tales of Greece and Troy.* Longmans, Green & Co.

Marvin, and others. *Adventures of Odysseus.* E. P. Dutton & Co., Inc.

Peabody, J. P. *Old Greek Folk Stories Told Anew.* Houghton Mifflin Co.

Pyle, Katherine. *Stories from Greek Mythology.* J. B. Lippincott & Co.

Storr, Francis. *Half a Hundred Hero Tales of Odysseus and the Men of Old.* Henry Holt & Co.

NORTHERN MYTHS, SAGAS AND EPIC
OF BEOWULF

NORTHERN MYTHS, SAGAS AND EPIC
OF BEOWULF

THE Norse myths and legends which form the basis of Northern
Literature come to us chiefly from three Icelandic sources: the
Poetic or Elder *Edda,* the Prose or Younger *Edda,* the *Volsunga
Saga.*

The Poetic *Edda* consists of fragmentary poems which relate the
doings of Scandinavian gods and heroes. According to authorities
these poems were written about the year 1000. Snorri Sturluson,
who wrote the Prose *Edda* in the Eleventh or Twelfth Century, repeated some of the stories in the Poetic *Edda* and added others from
sources now lost.

The *Volsunga Saga* is myth, legend and history evidently derived
from the Poetic *Edda* and lost sources. It tells the story of the
descendants of Odin, chief among whom were King Volsung, Sigmund and Sigurd, later called Siegfried in German literature.

NORSE MYTHS

Norse mythology reflects man's spiritual struggle through tales of

187

conflict between gods who are forces of Nature personified. These dramatic stories move in large patterns, and in a cycle, and cannot be adapted to any extent without loss of vigor and unity. There are many simplified versions which offer little more than some familiarity with proper names.

Because this Norse drama of the gods is made up of a series of interdependent stories, selection is more or less determined for the story-teller. The arrangement followed by the majority of editors is given.

The Beginning of All Things.
How Odin Lost His Eye and How He Brought the Mead from
    Asgard.
Sif's Hair.
The Apples of Youth.
How Thor's Hammer Was Lost and Found.
Balder and the Mistletoe.
Binding of the Fenris Wolf.
Punishment of Loki.
Twilight of the Gods and a New Earth.

Good sources for the above stories are Wilmot-Buxton's *Stories of Norse Heroes: Told by the Northmen* and Brown's *In the Days of Giants*. Other versions are listed with annotations at the end of this chapter.

The Apples of Youth

*This is the tale which the Northmen tell of how the Apples of
Youth were once very nearly lost to Asgard*

SWEETEST of all the Asa folk was Idun, the fair young goddess of
Springtime and Youth, and dearly loved was she by the other Asas,
both for herself and for her magic apples.

Fast locked in a golden casket were her apples, ripe and sweet
and rosy. And each day, at dawn, Idun came to the table where the
gods sat and feasted together, and gave those who wished a taste of
the fruit.

And it came to pass that everyone who ate the magic fruit grew
fresh and young again, however old and weary he had been before.
For even the gods of Asgard grew old and weary sometimes; and
then nothing would make them young again but the Apples of
Youth.

So Idun treasured the fruit with the greatest care, and never let
it out of her charge for a moment. And however many she took out
of her casket wherewith to feed the gods, there always remained just
the same number as before.

> Bright Iduna, maid immortal!
> Standing at Valhalla's portal,
> In her casket has rich store
> Of rare apples, gilded o'er;
> Those rare apples, not of earth,
> To ageing Asas gave new birth.

It was only to be expected, of course, that the fame of this magic
fruit should spread, and as nobody liked to grow old, many of the
giants, as well as the little dwarf people, used to come to the gates
of Asgard and beg that Idun would give them a taste of her apples.
But this, though they offered her the richest gifts they could think
of, she never would do.

189

Now one day it so fell out that Odin grew weary of watching his heroes feast and fight in Valhalla, and determined to go forth and seek an adventure elsewhere.

So he called for his brother Hoenir, the clear-eyed Asa who first gave hope to the heart of man, and Loki, the mischievous fellow who yet by reason of his fun and gayety was no bad traveling companion, and bade them accompany him on a journey.

Speeding over the Rainbow Bridge they came down to the world below, and presently found themselves in a desolate region of mountain and moorland, through which they wandered for a long, long time, without coming across any kind of human habitation.

At length, grown weary and very hungry, they began to look about for food, and presently saw, to their great joy, a herd of oxen feeding upon the mountain side. It took no long time to kill a fine bull and to kindle an immense fire; after which the Asas hung up the animal to roast and sat down to wait till it was done.

But though the fire flamed bravely over the logs, it made no difference whatever to the meat, which remained raw and cold.

Heaping on fresh fuel, the three Asas put the carcass still nearer the flame and waited hungrily. All in vain, the meat remained uneatable.

Looking at each other in dismay, the Asas exclaimed:

"There is some magic spell at work here."

And at that very moment they heard the loud croak of a bird in the tree above them.

Hastily searching the branches, the Asas soon found an immense eagle perched there and looking down upon them with an evil expression.

"Ho!" cried Odin, "is it you who has bewitched our food?"

The eagle nodded and croaked maliciously again.

"Then come at once and remove the spell," cried the famished Hoenir.

"If I do so, will you give me as much as I want to eat?" asked the eagle.

At this Odin hesitated, for he feared a trick, but Loki's mouth was watering, and he called out:

"Yes, yes, anything you like if you will only let the meat be cooked."

Then the great bird swooped down and began to fan the flame with his huge wings, and behold! in a very few minutes the gravy began to run, a delicious smell of roast beef filled the air, and there was the meat done to a turn.

Just as the three Asas were putting out hungry hands to seize their portions, however, the eagle, which had been hovering overhead, swooped down and seized more than three-quarters of the animal, leaving barely enough for one of the famished gods.

This was too much for Loki. With a roar of rage like that of an angry lion, he seized a great stake that stood near and struck with all his might at the greedy bird.

The eagle shook himself after the blow, but instead of dropping his booty he rose slowly into the air. And then, to Loki's dismay, he found that one end of the pole had stuck fast to the body of the bird, the other to his own hands.

Try as he would he could not let go, and so found himself being dragged along over stones and bushes and briers, while his arms were almost torn out of their sockets.

In vain he begged and implored the eagle to let him go; it took no notice of him whatever, but flew on and on, just a little way above the earth, until at length Loki, feeling that he could endure no longer, promised to give him anything he asked if he would only release him.

Then at last the eagle spoke, telling him that he would set him free on one condition only, and that was that he should manage, by some trick, to tempt Idun out of Asgard, in order that he could obtain possession of her and of the magic fruit. He told Loki, moreover, that he was the Storm Giant Thiassi in disguise, and bade him beware of the consequences if he broke his solemn promise to one of giant race.

By this time Loki was ready to promise anything to save his life, and so at length he found himself free.

Bruised and torn he made his way back to Odin and Hoenir, by whom he was closely questioned concerning his adventures.

But Loki never hesitated to depart from the truth, and, knowing that it would not do to tell what he had promised, he answered glibly that the eagle had captured him in mistake for someone else, and that when he found out it was Red Loki himself, he had set him free, with many expressions of sorrow for his error.

So the three Asas returned to Asgard, and from that moment Loki did not cease to plot and plan the means by which he could entice Idun outside the gates.

And indeed this was no easy matter, for the Apples of Youth were so precious to the gods that Idun was well guarded by night and day. Sometimes, however, even the Asas were off their guard, and that was the opportunity for Loki.

Strolling one day through the groves of Asgard, Loki found the beautiful maiden all alone in a sunny corner playing at ball with her golden fruit.

"Aha!" cried he, approaching gently so as not to startle her, "what a fair game thou playest here, maiden!"

But Idun only smiled at him happily and went on tossing her apples.

Then Loki pulled a long face, and came nearer, and said:

"Till this day, fair Idun, I had said that nowhere in the wide world grew apples like thine. But now have I found a tree whereon the fruit is of finer gold, and of greater size than these, and a taste of it needs not to be renewed again, but makes one young for ever-more."

Then Idun stopped playing and her blue eyes grew dark and stormy, for she could not bear to think that her apples would no longer be the joy and delight of the Asas.

But then she remembered Loki's deceitful ways, and said: "I believe thee not. This is one of thy tricks, Red Loki."

"Ho, you think so, do you?" said the crafty one. "Then come and see them for yourself, and bring your own to compare with them."

"Are they near by?" said Idun, rising doubtfully to her feet, and still holding fast to the casket of fruit.

"Only just a little way off," replied Loki, and taking hold of her hand he drew her outside the thicket.

192

On and on they went, and when she asked where they were going he always replied that the grove where the apples grew was just a little farther than he had thought.

At length, without noticing that she had passed the boundaries, Idun stood outside the walls of Asgard on a dreary region of barren heath, and then she at last began to suspect mischief.

"Where am I?" she cried, "and where, O Loki, are the golden apples?"

But she only heard the jeering ha! ha! ha! of the Asa as he returned to Asgard, and that was soon lost in the *whirr-r-r* of wings as a mighty eagle, swooping down upon her, fixed his talons in her girdle and rose with her into the air.

And this, of course, was Thiassi, the Storm Giant, who had been on the watch for her all the time, and who now carried her off, casket and all, to the bleak and desolate abode over which he ruled. Well had it been said that Loki was at the bottom of all the misfortunes that ever befell in Asgard. And never until the End of All Things would he work so dire a mischief again.

Poor Idun grew pale and thin and sad in her captivity, but she would not purchase freedom with a taste of the Apples of Youth, although the Storm Giant coaxed and begged and threatened by turns.

For a time the Asas took little notice of her absence, for they thought she was amusing herself somewhere in the sunny groves of Asgard and had forgotten her daily visit. Then they began to feel old and weary, and at first scarcely knew what was wrong.

Glancing at each other they saw, with startled eyes, wrinkles and lines and gray hairs where these things were not wont to be. Their youth and beauty were disappearing, and then they suddenly awoke to the need of a thorough search for the missing Idun.

And, when she could nowhere be found, All-Father Odin, mindful of former tricks, sent for Red Loki and began very closely to question him. Others had seen Idun in his company on that eventful day when she had been carried away, and so, finding it impossible to keep the matter hidden, Loki confessed, with a mocking laugh, that he had betrayed her into the power of the Storm Giant.

Then all of the Asas arose in hot wrath and threatened Loki with death or torture if he did not at once restore the beautiful Goddess of Youth with her magic fruit. And at length, being fairly frightened, he undertook to bring her back, if Freya would lend him her falcon plumes that he might disguise himself as a bird.

Thus equipped, Loki flew off to Giantland, and arrived, fortunately for him, just as Thiassi had gone out a-fishing.

High up at the window of a great stone castle fair Idun looked with tearful eyes upon the stormy sea, and, as she thought of the sunny groves of Asgard, suddenly the plumage of a great falcon almost brushed against her face. Drawing back in alarm, she saw the cunning red eyes of Loki looking at her from the bird's head.

"See how kind am I!" he jeered. "I am come to take thee back to Asgard."

Then Idun almost wept for joy, till she remembered that she was a prisoner, and so cried pitifully:

"I cannot win forth from this cold stone tower, O Loki, and even if I could, thou canst never carry me and my casket back to Asgard. And lo! I cannot outrun the wicked Storm Giant, and though the fruit be heavy, I will not leave it behind."

Then Loki soothed her, and by his magic arts he changed her into a nut, which he took up in one talon, while the casket he carried with the other, and so set off to fly back to Asgard.

Now Thiassi, the Storm Giant, was ill at ease that day, for he felt the pangs and pains of old age upon him as he went a-fishing. So he determined to return earlier than usual, in order to try once more to get the magic fruit from Idun.

Judge then of his dismay when he found his prisoner flown!

Hastily transforming himself into an eagle, Thiassi began to scour the regions of the air, looking everywhere for the maiden, and before long he noted the steady flight of a falcon towards the walls of Asgard.

Sweeping towards him through the air, the keen eyes of the eagle saw the gleam of a golden casket in his talons, and he knew that it was an Asa who had come to the rescue of Idun.

And now it seemed that Loki would be hard put to it to reach

Asgard before he was overtaken; for the eagle swept through the air with his great wings much faster than the falcon could fly, and the Asas, who had assembled on the battlements of the city to watch the race, trembled for its issue.

Then some of them remembered how once before they had played a trick upon the pursuer in a similar conflict, and they collected pine shavings in great abundance and piled them on the walls, and stood ready to fire them when the moment came.

On, on flew Loki, hard beset; and close behind him came, with steady rush, the mighty eagle Thiassi. He was almost upon his prey as they neared the walls, but Loki made a last violent effort, which was successful, and he fell exhausted into the midst of the Asas.

At the same moment the pile of fuel was lighted, and Thiassi, blinded with smoke and singed with flame, dropped over the battlements, and thus fell an easy prey to his waiting enemies. In admiration of his good race, however, the Asas placed his eyes as stars in the heavens, and there they shine to this day.

So the Apples of Youth returned to Asgard, and all the Asas hastened to eat of them and became young and beautiful again. And fair Idun once more resumed her shape, and never again was tricked by wicked Loki, but played with her magic fruit in the golden groves of Asgard till the End of All Things.

And this is how the Apples of Youth were once very nearly lost to Asgard.

From "Stories of Norse Heroes," by E. M. Wilmot-Buxton. (1909) Thomas Y. Crowell & Co. Reprinted by permission of the publishers.

How Thor's Hammer Was Lost and Found

*This is the tale the Northmen tell of how Thor's Hammer was
lost and found*

MOST precious in the eyes of Thor was his magic hammer, Miölnir,
of which even the mighty Frost Giants stood in dread.

Always he laid it by his side when he went to rest, and always
it was the first thing for which his hand was outstretched when he
awoke. Judge then of his horror and dismay when, on opening his
eyes one morning, the hammer was nowhere to be seen.

Starting up with a roar of rage, Thor commenced to search everywhere for the missing weapon. Up and down his wonderful palace,
built of the thunder clouds, he tramped, with a noise that shook the
whole city of Asgard. But the hammer was not to be found.

Then he called upon golden-haired Sif, his wife, and bade her
help in the search; and still the hammer was nowhere to be seen. It
was clear that someone must have stolen it, and, when he realized
this, Thor's wrath broke all bounds. His bristling red hair and beard
stood up on end, and from them flew a whole volley of fiery sparks.

Presently, as the angry Asa was shaking the palace with his thunderous voice, Red Loki came along to inquire into the trouble. He
was not likely to sympathize with Thor, but, always brimful of
curiosity, he loved to have a part in everything that happened.

"What's the matter, Asa Thor?" said he; and Thor replied, lower-
ing his voice as he spoke, for he did not want his loss to be too
widely known:

"Now listen to what I tell thee, Loki—'tis a thing which is known
neither on earth below nor in heaven above. My hammer's gone."

This news was most interesting to Loki, who had long owed Thor
a grudge, which he was afraid to pay openly. "Ho, ho!" said he.
"Then shall we soon have the giants turning us out of Asgard,
brother Thor."

"Not if you use your wits as you know how," growled Thor, still
in a very bad temper. "Come, you call yourself a clever fellow. Find

out for me who has robbed me of my thunderbolt, my hammer, my Miölnir."

Then Loki gave a grin and a wink, and promised to do what he could—not because he cared for Thor, but because he loved to be of importance, and was, moreover, really frightened as to what might happen to Asgard if the magic hammer was not at hand.

It was not long before he noticed that an extraordinary kind of tempest was raging in the regions below—not an orderly kind of tempest, with first some thunder, and then some rain, and then a gust of wind or two, such as Thor was wont to arrange, but a mixture of hail and wind and thunder and lightning and rain and snow, all raging together in a tremendous muddle, so that the earth folk thought the end of the world was come.

This gave Loki a hint, and he began to peer about between the clouds, until at length he saw that the trouble was coming from a certain hill which stood in the center of Giantland.

Now on the top of this hill lived a certain Thrym, prince of the Frost Giants, who for a long time past had been very envious of the might of Thor. He had, indeed, done his best to imitate him as far as he could, and had managed to get up a very good imitation of lightning and hail and rain; but he had not been able to manage the thunderbolts, for they could only be made by means of Thor's hammer, Miölnir.

All this was well known to Red Loki, and he was therefore not at all surprised to find that, somehow or other, Thrym must have got hold of the magic weapon; for here were thunderbolts crashing about the earth and sky at a terrible rate.

When informed of the discovery, Thor flew into a still more tremendous rage, and wanted to rush off at once to try conclusions with the giant. But Loki, who loved rather to get a thing by trickery and deceit, persuaded him that violence would never do.

"Remember," said he, "that Thrym *with* the hammer is much stronger than Thor without it. This is a matter which must be managed by clever wit and craft, not by force and loud talking. Leave therefore the whole matter to me."

To this Thor very reluctantly agreed.

Then Loki bethought him of some disguise wherein he might visit Giantland in safety, for he was not at all anxious to risk his life. He betook himself to the House of Maidens, over which ruled Freya, fairest of all in Asgard, she who was wont to shake the spring flowers from her golden locks as she passed over the frozen uplands, leaving behind her a region of green and smiling beauty. Loki found the goddess, and begged the loan of her magic falcon plumes, in which she was wont to flit to and fro over the earth; and when she learnt for what purpose he needed them she gladly assented.

Then Loki took the appearance of a great brown bird, and spreading his wings he flew away towards Giantland.

It was a long journey, as he already knew, and, although the tempest had now ceased to rage, he found the country of the giants darker and colder and drearier than ever.

The longest journey comes to an end, and at length Loki reached a mountain where sat the Giant Thrym, his huge legs dangling to the ground, playing with a puppy as large as an elephant.

Perching as near as he dared, Loki gazed at the giant with his bright, round eyes, and was wondering how to begin, when Thrym, who, at a glance, had seen completely through his disguise, said calmly, in a voice as much as possible like Thor's thunderous roar: "Oh, ho! Loki, what are you doing so far from Asgard? Are you not afraid, little fellow as you are, to venture alone into our country?"

Then Loki, thinking to win his way by flattery, replied: "Sad indeed is it in Asgard, now that Miölnir has vanished. Clever was that one who spirited it away from the very side of Thor. Methinks none but you could have done it, O mighty Thrym!"

Pleased with the compliment to his cleverness the giant chuckled before admitting: "Ay, Loki, the hammer is mine, 'tis very true; and now men will know who really is the Thunderer."

"Ah well!" sighed cunning Loki, "some men are strong by reason of their weapons, and some are just as strong without. Small need have you, O mighty Thrym, for hammers, but Thor is naught without it. Yet, since all the world knows that you are his master, let him have his plaything back, that we may cease to be troubled by his peevish outcry."

But though Thrym was as stupid as he was big, he was not to be caught thus.

"No, no, my little Loki," he said. "Mine is the hammer, and deep have I buried it beneath the bottom of the sea. Go, tell this to your Asa folk, and say to them that I will give it back on one condition only—and that is, that they send me Freya, that fairest of maidens, to be my wife."

At this suggestion Loki could scarcely keep from laughing, for the idea of sending the beautiful Freya, the joy and delight of Asgard, to be the wife of this ill-favored Frost Giant was too absurd for words.

It was not much to him, however, what happened to anyone except himself, so he hastened to reply: "Be sure, O Thrym, that everything I can do to further the matter shall be done. And if Freya is of the same mind as I you will soon be welcoming that most sweet maiden to Giantland—farewell!"

So saying, he spread his brown wings and flew back to Asgard, delighted to think of the mischief he could now set brewing.

First of all he visited Thor, and told him of what had passed. And the Thunderer, when he heard of Thrym's boastful words, was filled with wild wrath and wanted to start off, then and there, and wrest the hammer from the depths of the sea. But Loki pointed out the difficulties that stood in the way and, leaving the Asa to ponder over his words, he hurried off to Freya and informed her of Thrym's proposal.

The beautiful Freya was walking in her garden, and round her neck she wore her famous necklet of stars. When she heard Loki's suggestion that she should wed a hideous giant she fell into such a rage that she broke her necklace, and all the stars went falling through the sky, so that men cried: "See how the stars are shooting!"

Meantime the Asa folk had met together to consider all that had happened, and, having calmed the fury of Thor, they pointed out to him that Asgard stood in the gravest danger of an attack which would find them quite unprotected. When they had said this several times over, Thor began to weary of the subject, and he replied with great surliness: "Very well, then. Let Freya go to Thrym as his wife, and then shall we be as before, with Miölnir to defend us."

When Freya heard this, her rage turned to tears and lamentations, and she declared that it would be death to her to send her to the gloomy halls of Giantland, whence she could never hope to revisit the flowery meads and grassy slopes of Asgard. And the Asas, unable to bear the sight of her grief, with one voice declared that they would never spare her from the Home of Bliss.

Then there stepped forward Heimdall, the watchman who sits on guard over the Rainbow Bridge by night and day.

Now Heimdall had the gift of seeing into the future, and the Asas were always ready to hear his words, well knowing them to be wise.

"My plan is this," said he. "Let Thor borrow the clothes of Freya and put a thick veil over his face; and let him go thus to Thrym's castle and pass for his bride. And if he cannot by some means manage to get hold of the hammer when he is there—why, he must give it up altogether."

At this suggestion the Asas clapped their hands with approval—all, indeed, save Thor, who looked most glum, and was extremely unwilling to agree to the plan.

"Dress me as a bride!" he grumbled. "A pretty maiden I shall make. Ready enough am I to fight, but I will not make myself a laughing-stock if I know it."

But the Asas besought him to give way, while Loki twitted him with cowardice. Fair Freya, too, appealed with tearful eyes; and so at length, with great reluctance, the Thunderer agreed to do what they wished.

Fortunately the maiden Freya was very tall, but even so it was with some difficulty that they managed to cover the burly form of Thor with her robes.

He insisted, moreover, upon wearing his own shirt of mail and his girdle of strength; and these took much drapery to hide. Great was the laughter in the halls of Asgard that night as the Battle Maidens brushed and curled Thor's long yellow hair, and set a jeweled headdress upon it; and finally, when the maidens proceeded to cover up his thick beard and angry eyes with a silken veil, the mirth of the Asas was unrestrained. To complete the disguise, the maidens hung round his neck the famous necklet, which had now been re-strung, and finally Frigga, the wife of All-Father Odin, secured at his girdle the great bunch of keys proper to brides at a wedding in the Northland.

While this was being done, Loki, more than all, had been convulsed with merriment at the success of his mischief-making. The very sight of Thor's disgusted looks, and of his great hands clenched with rage under the delicate veil, nearly killed him with laughter; and when all was ready he declared himself unable to lose an atom of the fun in store.

"Let me go with you," he implored. "See, I will dress myself as your handmaiden. Ah, you had better agree, for without me to prompt you, you will never play your part."

So Loki was dressed as a waiting-maid, and took his seat very demurely by the side of Thor in the goat-car. Loud was the laughter in Asgard as the Asas watched the two drive off together and heard the roar of the Thunderer's voice issuing from the folds of a meek maiden's veil as he urged his goats upon their course. Long and stormy was that ride to Giantland, for Thor was still in the worst of tempers, and drove his chariot so furiously that

> The mountains crashed,
> The earth stood in flames,

as the hoofs of the goats clattered over mountains and waters, striking sparks wherever they touched a rock.

Thrym was much overjoyed when he heard that a chariot containing the two maidens was approaching his door. Away ran his servants in different directions, some with orders to make ready a grand banquet, some to prepare the chamber of the bride, some to receive her at the door.

The giant himself assisted them to alight, and looked with admiration at the stately figure of his bride; but he made no attempt to see her face, since it is the custom in the Northland for the bride to remain veiled until the marriage has been completed.

"A bride worthy of a giant!" murmured his servants, as he led her to a lofty seat beside his own great throne of gold; and they looked with approval also on the buxom form of the waiting-maid, who stood, closely veiled, behind her mistress' chair.

Now the journey had been long and cold, and it was with joy that the newcomers noticed that the preparations for the banquet were complete, for they were exceedingly hungry.

The giants are huge eaters, and they gathered round the board, whereon were displayed an enormous ox roasted whole, a vast dish of salmon and various other dainties. But because the bride was a woman, and modest withal, they brought her tiny morsels on a dainty golden plate.

This was too much for Thor, who had always possessed a most healthy appetite, and was now more than usually ready for his supper. Gradually drawing nearer to the table, whilst the others were busy with the meal, he managed to get hold of the dish of roasted ox, and within a few minutes the whole of the animal had disappeared.

Then he put out his hand to the platter of salmon, and in eight mouthfuls disposed of eight of the great fish. After this he noticed a large plate full of cakes and sweetmeats, which was set apart for the ladies of the party. Of these, too, he made short work. Finally, feeling thirsty after his huge meal, he took up two barrels of mead, and tossed them off, one after another, down his capacious throat. Then he sat back on his chair with a sigh of deep content.

These proceedings had been watched by Loki with uneasiness, but by Thrym with open-mouthed dismay. Was this the usual appetite of this dainty maiden, who had eaten more than the company of giants? But Loki bent towards him and whispered in his ear that the thought of marrying had so excited Freya that she had eaten nothing for eight days, and had therefore been on the point of starvation.

This reassured the giant, and being now himself filled with mead he drew nearer and, lifting a corner of the veil, tried to kiss the cheek of his future bride.

But Thor, who was longing to be at close grips with him, threw him such a fiery glance that he drew quickly back, saying: "Why does fair Freya's eye burn like a spark from a furnace?" "Pooh!" whispered Loki again, "that is nothing but her love for you, which for eight days has raged like a flaming fire."

This news was still more pleasant to hear, and Thrym, in high good humor, cried: "Bring in the hammer, my wedding gift, wherewith to plight the maid. For when I have laid it on her lap she will be my own for ever, and together we will work dire evil against the Asa folk, whom I hate with all my heart."

What was that unmaidenly sound that issued from under the silken veil at these words? But though Loki turned pale to hear it, Thrym, busy sending for the hammer, did not pay any heed.

Back came the giant's servants at length, bending under the weight of Miölnir. And as they bowed before the silent maiden, sitting with meekly bent head upon the throne, Thrym cried with a merry jest: "See, here is little Thor's tiny plaything—a pretty toy truly for his feeble hands. Take it, fair Freya, as my wedding gift."

"And take *that* as mine!" roared Thor, in a voice of thunder, as he flung off the veil and rose to his full height. And with the words he swung the hammer once—and ere the eye could follow its movement, it had crashed through Thrym's skull, and had knocked over a round dozen of his guests. Yet again did it swing in the Asa's hand, and this time it left not a giant standing in the hall.

A third time it was swung, and on this occasion the roof and walls of the palace came tumbling on every side, and only Thor and Loki were left alive amid the ruins.

"Ha! ha!" laughed Red Loki, "that was neatly done, fair Freya."

Thor, who was now busily tearing off the hated robes and veil, stayed to look threateningly at his companion. "No more of that, Loki," said he, "the thing had to be done, 'tis true, but talk not to me again of this woman's work. We will remember only that I am the Thunderer, and that my hammer that was lost is found."

So they drove back peacefully to Asgard.

BAG O' TALES

And this is the end of the tale of How Thor's Hammer Was Lost and Found.

From "Stories of Norse Heroes," by E. M. Wilmot-Buxton. (1909) Thomas Y. Crowell & Co. Reprinted by permission of the publishers.

✠

NORSE SAGAS

The Norse sagas are rich in adventure, full of action, romance and deeds of bravery. In contrast to the earlier myths they portray human conflict and their emotional appeal is adult. For these reasons they belong to the period of adolescence rather than to childhood. It is important that the versions used should reflect national ideals inherent in original sources but selection can be made which will eliminate those stories which over-emphasize as virtues trickery, bloodthirstiness and brute strength.

THE *Volsunga Saga*

The *Volsunga Saga* has its own value as literature but aside from that a knowledge of it is important since it forms the basis for other literary classics, and some of our greatest music. Sigurd, the Dragon Slayer, is echoed in the character of Beowulf, and Siegfried, the hero of the German *Nibelungenlied*, is definitely his counterpart.

Comparing the *Volsunga Saga* with the *Nibelungenlied*, Professor Sparling says of the latter: "The whole of the earlier part of the story has disappeared, and though Siegfried (Sigurd) has slain a dragon, there is nothing to connect it with the fate that follows the treasure; Andvari, the Volsungs, Fafner, and Regin are all forgotten; the mythological features have become faint, and the general air of the whole is that of mediæval romance . . . Brynhild loses a good deal and is a poor figure when compared with herself in the saga; Grimheld and the fateful drink have gone . . . but Sigurd (Siegfried), the central figure, although he has lost by the omission of so much of his life, is, as before, the embodiment of all the virtues that were so dear to the Northern hearts. Brave, strong, generous, dignified, and utterly truthful, he moves amid a tangle of tragic events, overmastered by a mighty fate and in life or death is still a hero without stain or flaw." INTRODUCTION TO TRANSLATION OF THE *Volsunga Saga* BY MAGNUSSON AND MORRIS.

There are a number of translations and adaptations of the *Volsunga Saga,* one of the finest being a metrical version, *The Story of Sigurd,* by William Morris. This is too difficult to be read generally by children but it can be read aloud to them and older children will read parts of it for themselves.

Dorothy Hosford's *Sons of the Volsungs* is a prose adaptation intended primarily for children's own reading. It is based on the first half of Morris's poem and retains some of Morris's lines. Mrs. Hosford's own style is direct and colorful.

⚔

Stories from the Volsunga Saga

Of the dwelling of King Volsung and the wedding of his daughter, Signy, and of her departure for the land of the Goths. How the feud arose between the Volsungs and the Goths.

How the Volsungs fare to the land of the Goths; Siggeir's treachery and the fall of King Volsung. Of the ending of all of Volsung's sons save Sigmund only, and of how he abideth in the wild wood.

The birth and fostering of Sinfiotli, Signy's son; the slaying of Siggeir. How Sigmund cometh again to the land of the Volsungs, and of the death of Sinfiotli, his son. Of the last battle of King Sigmund, and of the death of him.

How Queen Hiordis fares to the land of King Elf and how she abideth there. Of the birth of Sigurd. How Sigurd was nurtured. How Sigurd getteth the horse that is called Greyfell.

How Regin telleth Sigurd of his kindred, and the story of the gold that was accursed from ancient days. The forging of the sword.

Sigurd rideth to the Glittering Heath, slayeth Fafnir, and Regin, and takes the treasure of the dwarf Andvari.

How Sigurd awoke Brynhild upon Hindfell and how she sent him forth to win renown.

The story chosen for illustration is the last in the series suggested. When told separately it requires an introduction based on the events in the two preceding stories. Otherwise the references to Greyfell, and the dwarf Andvari's golden ring will lose their significance.

✵

How Sigurd Won the Hand of Brynhild

This is the tale the Northmen tell of how Sigurd braved the flames, and what befell

ON AND on, over level plain, by wild marshes, through winding ways, galloped Greyfell, until at last he brought Sigurd to the foot of a mountain that is called Hindfell. And before him, on the crest of that height, he saw a great light as of a fire burning, so that the flames seemed to touch the sky.

Riding up the slope Sigurd found himself at length face to face with a ring of lurid fire, crackling and roaring with a noise like thunder. But without a moment's hesitation he plunged into the very midst of this.

Naught did he care for peril who had come to seek such prize, and, as if daunted by the courage of the Volsung, the fierce flames shrank back as he advanced, leaving ever a magic circle in which he rode unscathed, while all around they roared like some hungry lion robbed of its prey. They rose wave upon wave to the very sky, but their fierce glare shone with glory upon Sigurd, and his form was as that of the Sun-god when he rises from the everlasting hills at the dawn of day.

And suddenly, as though their work was done, the flames flickered and fell, leaving only a broad ring of pale ashes behind the hero as he rode on to where loomed the massive shape of a great castle hung with shields.

The doors of this castle stood wide open, and not a warrior was to be seen; so, dismounting, Sigurd entered the great hall, and at first saw no one—neither man, woman, nor child. But presently he came to a room where he saw a figure, clad all in armor, lying stretched upon a couch. Approaching thither, Sigurd removed the helmet, and saw, to his astonishment, the face of a beautiful maiden fast asleep. He called to her and tried to awaken her, but in vain. Then he cut off the breastplate, which was fastened so closely that it seemed as though it had grown into her flesh, and then the sleeves and the long steel boots; and at length she lay before him in her garments of fine white linen, over which fell long, thick tresses of golden hair. Sigurd bent over her in admiration, and at that moment she opened her beautiful eyes and gazed in wonder at his face. Then she arose, and looked with joy at the rising sun, but her gaze returned to Sigurd; and they two loved each other at first sight.

When they had communed tenderly together, Sigurd told who he was and whence he came; and Brynhild rejoiced to hear the tale. "For," said she, "none but a hero might pass through that ring of fire."

Then said Sigurd: "Tell me now, fair Brynhild, how thou camest to this lonely fire-girt castle."

And she told him this tale:

"A warrior-maiden am I—chief of those Valkyrs who carry off the valiant dead to the halls of Valhalla and ply them with mead at the banquet. But many years ago I gave dire offense to All-Father Odin, as thou shalt hear.

"Two kings had a quarrel, and determined to put their feud to the issue of the sword. One was named Helm Gunnar. He was an old man and a mighty warrior, and to him had Odin promised the victory.

"But for the other, young Agnar, my heart was filled with pity; and so I disregarded the command of Odin and struck down Helm Gunnar in the fight, the victory thus going to Agnar.

"Then did All-Father Odin, in his wrath, decree that I should be cast out from Valhalla and be banished to the earth, there to find a husband like any other maiden of Midgard. But I was sore afraid, for I feared to mate with a coward—I, who had been a warrior-maiden from my birth. And All-Father Odin was pitiful, and placed me in this castle on Hindfell, and surrounded me with a barrier of flames, through which none but a hero would dare to pass. But first he pierced me with the Thorn of Sleep, that I might not grow old in the years of waiting—that I should awake, as thou seest me, just as I was when I began to sleep, at the touch of a brave man."

Then Sigurd told her all his story, and when she knew that he was bound on adventurous quest she would not let him stay long by her side, but bade him go forth and win honor for himself and afterwards return to her again. Meantime she promised to await his return in the castle, protected by the ring of flames, which should be rekindled on his departure. "For none but Sigurd," said she, "will be brave enough to make his way through such flames as these, and so shall I be safe until thy return."

So Sigurd made ready to depart; but first he took Andvari's golden ring, and placing it upon Brynhild's finger, as they stood together on the mountain crest, he vowed to love none but her as long as his life should last.

From "Stories of Norse Heroes Told by the North-men," by E. M. Wilmot-Buxton. (1909) Thomas Y. Crowell & Co. Reprinted by permission of the publishers.

The Saga of Frithiof the Bold

This is one of the most beautiful of the Northern sagas. It is a semi-mythological story with elements of adventure and romance which was put into writing in Iceland in the Twelfth or Thirteenth Century.

This saga was given the epic form in which it is best known about 1825 by Esaias Tegner, Sweden's greatest poet. It was from Tegner's masterly translation that Longfellow made his poetical English version.

In telling the story to older boys and girls, the points for emphasis are the development of the character of Frithiof, his loyalty to his friends, his devotion to his word and his desire to atone for the wrongs committed by him in his youth.

The program which follows is a series of six episodes based on Blackley's translation of the Tegner version. Fragments from Blackley's or Locock's metrical paraphrases are suggested for use if desired.

Stories from *Frithiof's Saga*

The Youth of Frithiof the Bold and Ingeborg the Fair
> Fragment-Canto 1, stanzas 1, 2, 3
> The growth of Frithiof and Ingeborg, side by side, from childhood to youth; the deaths of their fathers, King Bele and Thorsten; the parting admonitions of the two to their children; the homestead of Frithiof; his sword, his ring and his good ship, Ellida.

Frithiof's Luckless Wooing
> Frithiof woos and wins Ingeborg but is rejected by her brother, King Helga; he retires to his home in anger; he refuses to aid King Ring who declares war against Ingeborg's brothers; he refuses them his aid. Frithiof meets Ingeborg in Balder's Grove thus breaking a sacred law; they exchange betrothal rings; he bids farewell to Ingeborg.

BAG O' TALES

Frithiof's Journey to the Orkneys

Fragment-Canto 9, stanzas 1, 2, 3

Frithiof sets sail on a perilous journey for tribute; he is nearly destroyed in a storm of King Helga's seeking; reaching the Islands, he fights a duel and conquers, after which he is made welcome by Yarl Angantyr and remains with him through the winter.

Frithiof's Return

Frithiof returns full of joyous hope, to find Ingeborg married to old King Ring and his homestead burned; he challenges Helga in Balder's Temple and by accident causes its destruction; fleeing in his ship, Ellida, he is pursued by Helga; he escapes and roams the seas for three years.

Frithiof's Temptation

Frithiof again returns to spend Yuletide in the home of King Ring; he is made welcome and remains throughout the winter and spring. Although strongly tempted by his great love for Ingeborg he is loyal to his host; the King dies; his infant son is elected his successor with Frithiof as regent.

Frithiof's Reconciliation and Marriage to Ingeborg

Frithiof praying at his father's grave receives assurance of Balder's forgiveness in a vision; he rebuilds the temple; he forgives Helga, dead, and swears to aid Helga's brother whereupon the brother gives him Ingeborg in marriage.

Fragment-Canto 14, last paragraph of Locock's translation.

Frithiof's Journey to the Orkneys has been selected by way of illustration because it is somewhat more detached in the nature of its material than other parts of the saga. An introduction is given for use when the story is told separately. Both the introduction and the story are adaptations by Alice Hatch.

INTRODUCTION TO FRITHIOF'S JOURNEY

In the ancient days when Vikings ruled the seas, there lived in the Northland a noble King named Bele, whose daughter, Fair Ingeborg, was beloved by Frithiof, son of Bele's friend Thorsten.

Now the time came for the King and Thorsten to die. With his parting words the King warned his two sons who were to reign in his stead to cherish forever the family relationship with Frithiof—but all in vain. They scornfully rejected his suit for their sister's hand bidding him to serve them as friend but never to aspire to their high station.

Nevertheless the love of Frithiof for Ingeborg was so great that he sought her out in Balder's Grove where man and maid must never speak together and there they exchanged betrothal rings. To punish Frithiof for this sin, Helga, eldest son of Bele, laid upon him the task of going to the Orkneys to demand tribute money from Yarl Angantyr. So Frithiof bade Ingeborg farewell and set forth in his dragon ship, Ellida, with his foster brother, Bjorn, and twelve staunch seamen.

Frithiof's Journey to the Orkneys

KING HELGA stood on the shore and watched the striped sails of Frithiof's vessel sink behind the horizon, while his sullen anger grew apace.

"Too easily hast thou escaped my wrath, cursed Frithiof. Thou of unkingly blood who hast dared to sue for my sister; thou, not descended of gods, who hast dared profane Balder's temple. Nay, never again shall the keel of thy boat grate on the sands of thy country. Rise, storm fiends, out of the ocean's depths and drag him down to destruction."

Scarcely had Helga spoken when the sky grew dark and gloomy, and darker still grew the waters around the dragon ship. An icy breath bore down from the north and froze the sea spray on the sail ropes. From all directions swept the winds, shrieking and screaming. Great waves lifted the brave boat skyward, then plunged it headlong, quivering, into the hollows. Hailstones fell from the heavens like an onslaught of arrows, and in the boat's hold the water rose ever higher.

Now Frithiof, pitting his might against might, felt the exultant joy of battle, as with steadying hand he grasped the helm and sang aloud, undaunted,

> "Storm is coming, comrades,
> Its angry winds I hear
> Flapping in the distance
> But fearless we may be.
> Sit tranquil in the grove,
> And fondly think on me,
> Lovely in thy sorrow,
> Beauteous Ingeborg."

Yet ever ahead of the ship, unseen in the fog and the tempest, rode the storm fiends, Ham and Heyde, urging the waves to madness and the winds to greater destruction, when out of the sea, in the path of the boat, rose an island, under whose sheltering rocks the water lay smooth as a mirror. Shall the hero escape from the storm, guiding his boat into this harbor? Nay, when ever did a Northman, like a trembling coward, turn from his course in the teeth of a tempest? Better far go to one's death, than to lay down one's arms and surrender.

Now they were driven abreast of the isle; then it sank in the ocean behind them, and again they were fighting the merciless gale while the ship flew westward. Planks creaked and groaned as the waves tore over the decks, stripping the cordage loose and flinging it into the sea; the sails hung in useless tatters from the masts, and all of Frithiof's mighty strength was needed to keep the course as he steadied the cracking rudder, while his voice rose over the storm,

> "Yet longer do I find it sweet
> To battle with the breeze,
> Thunderstorm and Northmen meet,
> Exulting on the seas.
> For shame might Ingeborg blush,

If her osprey flew
Frightened by a storm stroke
Heavy winged to land."

Now darkness shrouded the ship so that the prow was lost to the stern, and out of the night rose the shrieks of Ham and Heyde, shrill above the tumult of the waves that swept over the bare deck till the pumps could no longer check the incoming torrents of water. Then Frithiof, foreseeing the end at hand, stripped from his arm his treasured betrothal ring of gold, cunningly wrought by the pygmies, and, with his magic sword, Angurvadel, he cleft it in pieces, giving a share to each man that none might start on the hazardous journey to the land of the Dead, empty-handed.

At last the storm grew so violent that Frithiof could not believe it the work of the gods alone and, calling his friend to his side, he said,

"Bjorn, come to the rudder,
Hold it tight as a bear's hug;
Valhall's power sendeth
No such storm as this.
Now at work is magic:
Coward Helga singeth
Spells above the ocean:
I will mount and see."

While Bjorn bore down on the rudder, checking the boat in its wavering course, Frithiof climbed to the top of the mast and, looking far out over the sea, he saw in front of his boat, rising on the frothy waves, a whale, on whose back sat the storm demons; Heyde in the snow garb of an icy bear, and Ham like a great storm bird, flapping loud his wings.

Now had come the time to test the magic strength of the vessel in whose frame lay hidden the power to hear and obey the master's bidding.

"Now Ellida let us see
If in truth thou bearest

213

Valor in thine iron-fastened
Breast of bended oak.
Hearken to my calling
If thou be heaven's daughter.
Up! and with thy keel of copper
Sting this magic whale."

Scarcely had Frithiof spoken when the good ship bounded forward and smote the mighty monster so that his blood spurted skyward and stained the waters red, as, deep-wounded, he sank, bellowing, to die, while the storm fiends, tasting the bitterness of blue steel hurled by a Northman's arm, received Frithiof's spears in their breasts and ceased from their shrieking incantations forever.

No sooner had the three spirits of evil sunk beneath the waves than their magic spell was broken; the winds receded to the four corners of the earth; a calm spread over the waters, and the sun, breaking through the darkness, disclosed the grassy shores of the Orkneys, whither the storm-shattered boat crawled wearily till at last her keel was checked on the sandy beach.

But the twelve valiant sailors were too weak from their battling with the gale to creep ashore. Not even the strength of their sword blades could support them, so that they lay exhausted on the deck till the sturdy Bjorn ferried four to the land on his back, while great Frithiof brought eight in safety to the green slopes of the isle.

Now it chanced that on that day Yarl Angantyr sat feasting in his banquet hall, surrounded by valiant Vikings, while his faithful old guard, Halvar, stood without the window, one watchful eye, as was his wont, turned toward the sea—the other on his ale cup which he constantly drained and passed through the window to be replenished. Suddenly he checked the hand that returned the empty goblet and, letting it fall unheeded, cried out:

"A ship upon the sea is borne,
Full heavily she goes;
Now she seemeth to tarry.

Now reacheth she the land;
Two mighty giants carry
The pale crew to the land."

The Yarl rose from his throne at the head of the banquet table
and, following the pointing finger with his eye, spake,

"Those are Ellida's pinions,
That, too, must Frithiof be.
In all the north such bearing
Belongs to him alone."

At this the Viking, Atle, sprang up in furious mood. With flashing eyes, he drew his sword and shouted,

"Now, now my hand shall show
If Frithiof, as they say,
A spell o'er steel itself can throw
And ne'er for quarter pray."

Followed by twelve warriors, swinging their clubs and eager for
battle, he rushed out of the hall and down to the grassy slope where
the weary crew rested while Frithiof stood guard over them.

"Now," shouted the jealous Atle, "I have thee at my will, and
will cleave thee with my broad sword, unless thou'lt rather sue for
peace, or flee."

"Nay," said Frithiof, "weak I be from stress of storm, but rather
than seek a craven peace, I'll prove thy mighty sword."

With that the two Vikings rushed at one another. The sword blows
fell like a hail of death strokes upon their shields, till, shattered
and useless, these were cast aside and the champions stood berserk,
sword biting sword, yet neither moving one step from his place until, by happy trick, Frithiof's magic blade, Angurvadel—the runes
on its hilt gleaming blood red—sprang up, caught Atle's blade
midway, and broke it short at the hilt leaving him defenseless.

" 'Gainst swordless man," bold Frithiof cried, "my sword I'll never use. Let's try another fight." Then throwing his good blade on the grass beside Atle's useless hilt, the mighty heroes sprang into each other's arms, breast plate clashing against breast plate, and they wrestled as two bears of the snowy north, each bent on the other's destruction. Full many a rock has tottered from its place into the sea, many an oak has been laid low in the forest by lesser shock; yet long and hard they fought, neither bending, till great drops of sweat fell from their brows, and their breath came cold and hard; till the shrubs and stones were scattered afar by the might of their wrestling.

But Frithiof felled his foe at last and, placing his knee on the vanquished one's chest, he spake in tones of wrath,

> "Oh, had I but my broadsword true,
> Black-bearded, Berserk, I
> Should drive its point triumphant through
> Your entrails, as you lie."

"Let that be no care of thine," quoth Atle. "Go get thee thy sword and slay me now. I shall not try escape. Sometime we both must pass to Valhall's joys, and if I wander there today, tomorrow may fetch thee."

Seizing his sword, Frithiof raised it high above his head to strike, but Atle watched him with calm eyes and unafraid, till anger against one so noble left the victor's heart and happily he staid the falling blade, giving instead his other hand to raise the vanquished chief.

Then old Halvar, cutting the air with his white staff, shouted, "Come, heroes, let's make all haste to Angantyr and tell this mighty tale. There, on the banquet table a feast is cooling, and for me, I die of thirst."

So, reconciled, the heroes ascended the hill arm-in-arm and passed through the portals of Angantyr's hall. Here the visitors paused in amaze. Never had they seen a place so fair. Instead of bare oaken beams, the walls were hung with gilded leather; a marble hearth leaned against the wall and glass gleamed in the windows. The noble Angantyr sat at the head of his board on a throne of silver, and down either side were ranged his warriors, each served by a maid as fair as a star gleaming behind an angry cloud.

As Frithiof stood on the threshold the Yarl rose and came three paces forward to meet him and taking his hand, led him to a seat by his side on the throne, saying,

> "Since here full many a creaming horn,
> With Thorsten emptied we,
> His son whose fame so far is borne,
> Shall not sit far from me."

Thus they sat feasting, while old Angantyr plied Frithiof with many a question concerning the land of Bele and Thorsten. And, this tale being ended, Frithiof next recounted the hazards of his journey till the table rocked with the roars of laughter and shouts of approval as he told how his dragon ship sent the whale of evil to his grave; but their mirth was stilled and the maidens sighed when he spoke of Ingeborg, so noble in her grief and care. And when at last he came to his errand hither and the cause of his coming, then indeed did Yarl Angantyr's brow darken. "I owe nothing to the sons of Bele. If they would demand tribute let them come themselves, like men, insisting with bared sword in hand, and I shall answer them with mine."

Then, calling his daughter to him, he sent her to the women's room with a whispered message and soon she returned bringing a purse of green, on which were embroidered rivers, wooded hills and moonlit seas, and having a clasp of rubies and tassels of gold. Angantyr took the purse and filled it with golden coins from many a foreign land and gave it to Frithiof, saying,

> "This gift of welcome take, oh guest,
> To do as thou mayst will,
> But for the winter stay and rest
> With us in friendship still.
> Though valor never should be scorned
> Yet now the storm rules wide;

By now again to life returned,
I'll wager Ham and Heyde.
Ellida may not always leap
So luckily again;
And whales are plenty in the deep
Though one she may have slain."

So it was that in merry mood Frithiof and his valiant crew lingered in Angantyr's safe harbor through the winter, and many a brave tale was sung over the foaming cup to pass the time till spring should bring calm seas for the journey home—and to Ingeborg.

From manuscript by Alice Hatch, and reprinted by her permission.

Beowulf

The great Anglo-Saxon epic, *Beowulf*, owes its origin to a literary fragment brought to Britain from Scandinavia about the Eighth Century. Although brief, it is dramatic in style and forceful. Its theme, which is heroic service in ridding the country of monsters, has story interest for children. It can be told in three or four episodes. When the shorter series is desired the first two listed below can be combined.

Beowulf Comes to Daneland.
He Proves His Bravery by Slaying Grendel.
Beowulf Encounters a Sea-Witch.
Beowulf Returns Home Where He Meets Heroic Death in Combat
    with a Venomous Dragon.

How Beowulf Came to Daneland

FOR twelve long years Grendel, the Ogre, warred against Hrothgar and the Dane folk. He prowled through the moorland and lay in wait in dark places, slaying young and old. Many were the grisly deeds he did, many the foul crimes. . . . And the mighty warriors, strong of heart against a mortal foe, were powerless against him.

"And now it came to pass that, across the sea in far Gothland, the songs of Grendel and his wrath were sung, until to Beowulf the Goth the tale of woe was carried. And Beowulf, when he heard of Grendel's deeds, cried that he would go across the waves to Hrothgar, the brave king, since he had need of men to help him.

"Now Beowulf was very strong in war, mighty among men. Of all the nobles of the Goths there was none so great as he. . . . And because of the love they bore him, many prayed him to bide peacefully at home, but others, knowing his prowess, bade him go forth.

"Beowulf was eager for the contest, so taking with him fifteen warriors and good comrades, he stepped into a ship and bade the captain set sail for Daneland.

"Then like a bird wind-driven upon the waves, the foam-necked ship sped forth. For two days the warriors fared on over the blue sea, until they came again to Daneland and anchored beneath the steep mountains of that far shore.

"There, lightly springing to shore, the warriors gave thanks to the sea-god that the voyage had been so short and easy for them.

"But upon the heights above them stood the warden of the shore. His duty it was to guard the sea-cliffs and mark well that no foe landed unaware. Now as the warriors sprang to shore, he saw the sun gleam upon sword and shield and coat of mail.

" 'What manner of men be these?' he asked himself. And mounting upon his horse he rode towards them.

"Waving his huge spear aloft, he cried, as he rode onward, 'What men be ye who come thus clad in mail-coats, thus armed with sword and spear, whence cometh this proud vessel over the waves? . . .'

"Then Beowulf answered him, 'We are folk of the Goths, thanes
219

of King Hygelac. In friendly guise we come to seek thy lord, King Hrothgar, the mighty chieftain. . . . Thou knowest if it be true or no, but we indeed have heard that among ye Danes there is a great and wily foe, a loather of valor, who prowleth terribly in dark nights, making great slaughter and causing much woe. Therefore have I come, for perchance I may be of succor to the noble King Hrothgar in his need.'

"Fearless and bold, facing the band of warlike men, the warden sat upon his horse, and when Beowulf had ceased speaking, he answered him.

" 'Ye come as friends, O bearers of weapons, O wearers of war garments. Follow me then, and I will lead you on. I will also give commandment to my men that they guard your ship where it lies by the shore until ye come again.'

"So following the warden they marched forward. Eager they were for battle, eager to see the far-famed Hart Hall. And as they marched, their gold-decked helmets, their steel mail-coats, their jeweled sword-hilts, flashed in the sunlight, and the clank and clash of weapons and armor filled the air.

"On and on they pressed quickly, until the warden drew rein. 'There,' he said, pointing onward, 'there lies the great Hart Hall. No longer have ye need of me. The way ye cannot miss. As for me, I will back to the sea to keep watch against a coming foe.'

"Then wheeling his horse he galloped swiftly away, while the Goths marched onward until they reached the Hart Hall. There, weary of the long way that they had come, they laid down their shields, and leaning their spears against the walls, sat upon the bench before the great door.

"And as they sat there resting, there came to them a proud warrior. 'Whence come ye with these great shields,' he asked, 'whence with these gray shirts of mail, these jeweled helmets and mighty spears? I am Hrothgar's messenger and servant, I who ask. Never saw I prouder strangers, never more seemly men. I ween it is not from some foe ye flee in fear and trouble. Rather in pride and daring it would seem ye come to visit Hrothgar.'

"Then answered Beowulf. 'My name is Beowulf, and we are

220

Hygelac's thanes. To thy lord, the mighty Hrothgar, we will tell our errand if he will deign that we do greet him.'

"The warrior bowed low, for well he saw that Beowulf was a mighty prince.

" 'I will ask my lord the King,' he said, 'if so be thou mayest come to him. And to thee right quickly will I bear his answer.'

"So saying he departed, and came to Hrothgar where he sat amongst his earls. The king was now old and gray-haired, and sat amid his wise men bowed with grief, for there was none among them mighty enough to free his land from the Ogre.

" 'My lord,' the warrior said, and knelt before the king, 'from far beyond the sea strange knights are come. They pray that they may speak with thee. These sons of battle name their leader Beowulf. Refuse them not, O King, but give them kindly answer. For by the splendor of their arms I deem them worthy of much honor. The prince who sendeth such warriors hither must be great indeed.'

" 'Beowulf!' cried Hrothgar. 'I knew him when he was yet a lad. His father and his mother have I known. Truly he hath sought a friend. And I have heard of him that he is much renowned in war, and that he hath the strength of thirty men in the grip of his hand. I pray Heaven he hath been sent to free us from the horror of Grendel. Haste thee, bid him enter, bid them all to come. I would see the whole friendly band together. Say to them that they are right welcome to the land of Danes.'

"The warrior bowed low. Then once more going to the door of the Hall, he stood before Beowulf and his knights.

" 'My lord,' he said, 'the King biddeth me to say to thee that he knoweth already of thy rank and fame. He saith to you brave-hearted men from over the sea that ye are all welcome to him. Now may ye go in to speak with him, wearing your war trappings and with your helmets upon your heads. But leave your shields, your spears, and deadly swords without here, until the talk be done.'

"Then Beowulf and his warriors rose. Some went with him to the Hall, others stayed without to guard the shields and weapons.

"Guided by the Danish warrior the knights marched right through the great Hart Hall, until they stood before the Gift-seat where sat the aged King.

" 'Hail to thee, Hrothgar,' cried Beowulf. 'I am Hygelac's friend and kinsman. Many fair deeds have I done though yet I be young. And to me in far Gothland the tales of Grendel's grim warfare were told. Seafaring men told that the great Hall so fair and well-built doth stand forsaken and empty as soon as the shades of evening fall, because of the prowlings of that fell giant.

" 'Then as we heard such tales did my friends urge me to come to thee because they knew my might. They had themselves seen how I laid low my foes. Five monsters I bound, thus humbling a giant brood. Sea-monsters I slew in the waves at night-time. Many a wrong have I avenged, fiercely grinding the oppressors.

" 'And now will I fight against Grendel. Alone against the Ogre will I wage war. Therefore one boon I crave of thee, noble prince. Refuse it not, for thereto am I come from very far. I pray thee that I alone, having with me only mine own earls and comrades, may cleanse Hart Hall.

" 'It hath been told to me that Grendel recketh not of weapons, for his hide is as of steel armor. Therefore will I bear neither sword nor shield. But I will grapple with the fiend with mine hands alone, and foe to foe we will fight for victory. And, unto whomsoever it seemeth good to the Lord of Life, unto him shall the victory be given.

" 'If Grendel win, then will he fearlessly devour the people of the Goths, my dear comrades, my noble earls, even as aforetime he hath devoured thy warriors. Then wilt thou not need to cover me with a mound, for the lone moor will be my burial-place. Where ye track the footsteps of the Ogre stained with gore, there will he with greed devour my thanes and me.

" 'But if I die, then send back to Hygelac my coat of mail, for in all the world there is no other like to it. This is all I ask.'

"Beowulf was silent, and Hrothgar the aged king answered him.

" 'O friend Beowulf,' he said, 'thou hast sought us out to help us. Yet to me it is pain and sorrow to tell to any man what shame, what sudden mischiefs, Grendel in his wrath hath done to me. See! my palace-troop, my war-band hath grown small. Grendel hath done this. In his prowlings he hath carried off my men so that my warriors are few.

" 'Full oft when the wine was red in the cup my knights did swear that they would await the coming of Grendel, to meet him with sword-thrust. So when night fell they abode in the Hall. But in the morning, when day dawned, my fair house was red with blood. And I needs must mourn the death of yet more gallant knights, must have fewer thanes to own my rule.

" 'But sit now to the feast and eat with gladness, sure that victory will come to thee.'

"So the Goths sat them down in the great Hart Hall and feasted with the Dane folk. The mead cup was carried round, the minstrel sang of deeds of love and battle. . . .

"Then Hrothgar and his band of warriors and thanes went forth from the Hall, and Beowulf with his comrades was left to guard it.

"The beds were spread around the walls, and Beowulf prepared himself strangely for battle. His coat of mail, firmly wrought with shining rings of steel, he cast aside. He took his helmet from his head, and with his sword and shield, and all his glittering war-harness, gave it to the keeping of a servant.

"And thus unarmed, clad only in his silken coat, he proudly spake:

" 'In war-craft I deem I am no worse than Grendel. Therefore not with the sword shall I put him to sleep, though that were easy. Not thus shall I take his life, for he is not learned in the use of war-weapons. So without them we twain this night shall fight. And God the all-wise shall give victory even as it shall seem best to Him.' "

From "Stories of Beowulf," by Henrietta Marshall. Published by Thomas Nelson & Sons, London, and E. P. Dutton & Co., Inc., New York, and reprinted in abridged form by permission of the publishers.

BAG O' TALES

Sources for the Story-teller

Baldwin, James. *Story of Siegfried*. Chas. Scribner's Sons. A popular children's version adapted from the Volsunga Saga and the German *Nibelungenlied*.

The Prose Edda, by Sturluson; tr. by Brodeur. American-Scandinavian Press. For student use.

The Poetic Edda, tr. by Bellows. American-Scandinavian Press. For student use.

Brown, A. F. *In the Days of Giants*. Houghton Mifflin Co. Norse myths for younger children.

Bulfinch, Thomas. *Age of Fable*. McKay. E. P. Dutton & Co., Inc. (Everyman's Library.) Gives three chapters to Norse mythology.

Colum, Padraic. *Children of Odin*. The Macmillan Company. Norse myths and Sigurd cycle stories.

Hoffman, A. S. *Book of Sagas*. E. P. Dutton & Co., Inc.

Hosford, Dorothy. *Sons of the Volsungs*. The Macmillan Company. A prose adaptation of the first half of William Morris's *Sigurd the Volsung*.

Leonard, W. E. *Beowulf*. D. Appleton-Century Co., Inc. A translation in verse.

Mabie, H. W. *Norse Stories*. Dodd, Mead and Company. Literary versions of the cycle of Norse myths.

Marshall, H. E. *Stories of Beowulf*. E. P. Dutton & Co., Inc. Simple, prose version.

Morris, William. *Story of Sigurd the Volsung and the Fall of the Nibelungs*. Longmans, Green & Co. A poetical version and an important source.

Riggs, Strafford. *Story of Beowulf*. D. Appleton-Century Co., Inc. The most attractive edition available.

Tappan, E. M. *Stories of Legendary Heroes*. Houghton Mifflin Co. Contains story of Frithiof.

Tegner, Esaias. *The Frithiof Saga*, tr. by C. D. Locock. Allen.

Wilmot-Buxton, Ethel M. *Stories of the Norse Heroes; Told by the Northmen*. T. Y. Crowell Co. Northern Myths and Sagas: Sigurd and Frithiof.

Note: The Nibelungs; tr. from the German of F. Schmidt by G. Upton, also, *Norse Mythology*, and *Viking Tales of the North* by Rasmus B. Anderson are unfortunately out of print.

Students in story-telling are advised to watch the publications of the Scandinavian Press for authoritative books on Northern Myths and Sagas.

TALES OF CHIVALRY

TALES OF CHIVALRY

KING ARTHUR LEGENDS

CHIEF among chivalric tales are the legends of King Arthur and his
Knights of the Round Table, gathered together by Sir Thomas Malory
in the Fifteenth Century from French and Welsh sources and printed
by Caxton under the title *La Morte d'Arthur*.

Malory's versions in modernized English are basic sources for
story-tellers; a favorite collection being *The Boys' King Arthur*,
edited by Sidney Lanier.

KING ARTHUR STORIES

> How Arthur Proved His Kingship
> The Winning of the Queen
> The Founding of the Round Table
> Sir Launcelot, First Champion
> Sir Tristram, Second Champion
> Sir Percival, Third Champion

Sir Galahad and the Quest of the Holy Grail
The Passing of Arthur

The story chosen for illustration follows closely Malory's text.

How Arthur Proved His Kingship

IT BEFELL in the days of the noble Utherpendragon, when he was king of England, that there was born to him a son who in after time was King Arthur. Howbeit the boy knew not he was the king's son. For when he was but a babe, the king commanded two knights and two ladies to take the child bound in rich cloth of gold, "and deliver him to what poor man you meet at the postern gate of the castle." So the child was delivered unto Merlin, and so he bare it forth unto Sir Ector, and made an holy man to christen him, and named him Arthur; and so Sir Ector's wife nourished him. Then within two years King Uther fell sick of a great malady; (and thereof he died). Then stood the realm in great (danger) a long while, for every lord made him strong, and many weened to have been king. (And so, by Merlin's counsel, all the lords of England came together in the greatest church of London on Christmas morn before it was day, to see if God would not show by some miracle who should be king.) And when the first mass was done there was seen in the churchyard, against the high altar, a great stone four-square, like to a marble stone, and in the midst thereof was an anvil of steel, a foot of height, and therein stuck a fair sword naked by the point, and letters of gold were written about the sword that said thus: WHO SO PULLETH OUT THIS SWORD OF THIS STONE AND ANVIL, IS RIGHTWISE KING BORN OF ENGLAND.

So when all the masses were done, all the (lords) went for to behold the stone and the sword. And when they saw the scripture, some assayed such as would have been king. But none might stir the sword nor move it.

"He is not yet here," said the archbishop, "that shall achieve the sword, but doubt not God will make him to be known. But this is my counsel," said the archbishop, "that we provide ten knights, men of good fame, to keep this sword."

And upon New Year's day the barons let make a tournament for to keep the lords together, for the archbishop trusted that God would make him known that should win the sword. So upon New Year's day when the service was done the barons rode to the field.

And so it happened that Sir Ector rode to the jousts, and with him rode Sir Kay, his son, and young Arthur that was his nourished brother. (But Sir) Kay had lost his sword, for he had left it at his father's lodging, and so he prayed young Arthur to ride for his sword. "I will with a good will," said Arthur, and rode fast after the sword; and when he came home, the lady and all were gone out to see the jousting. Then was Arthur wroth, and said to himself, "I will ride to the church-yard and take the sword with me that sticketh in the stone, for my brother Sir Kay shall not be without a sword this day." And so when he came to the church-yard Arthur alighted, and tied his horse to the stile, and so went to the tent, and found no knights there, for they were all at the jousting; and so he handled the sword by the handles, and lightly and fiercely he pulled it out of the stone, and took his horse and rode his way till he came to his brother Sir Kay, and delivered him the sword. And as soon as Sir Kay saw the sword, he knew well that it was the sword of the stone, and so he rode to his father, Sir Ector, and said: "Sir, lo here is the sword of the stone; wherefore I must be king of this land." When Sir Ector beheld the sword, he returned again and came to the church, and there they alighted, all three, and went into the church, and anon he made Sir Kay to swear upon a book how he came to that sword.

"Sir," said Sir Kay, "by my brother Arthur, for he brought it to me."

"How got you this sword?" said Sir Ector to Arthur.

"Sir, I will tell you. When I came home for my brother's sword, I found nobody at home for to deliver me his sword, and so I thought my brother Sir Kay should not be swordless, and so I came thither eagerly and pulled it out of the stone without any pain."

"Found ye any knights about this sword?" said Sir Ector.

"Nay," said Arthur.

"Now," said Sir Ector to Arthur, "I understand that you must be king of this land."

"Wherefore I?" said Arthur.

"Sir," said Ector, "for there should never man have drawn out this sword but he that shall be rightwise king of this land. Now let me see whether ye can put the sword there as it was and pull it out again."

"That is no mastery," said Arthur; and so he put it in the stone. Therewith Sir Ector assayed to pull out the sword, and failed.

"Now assay," said Sir Ector to Sir Kay. And anon he pulled at the sword with all his might but it would not be. "Now shall ye assay," said Sir Ector to Arthur.

"I will well," said Arthur, and pulled it out easily. And therewithal Sir Ector kneeled down to the earth, and Sir Kay.

"Alas," said Arthur, "mine own dear father and brother, why kneel ye to me?"

"Nay, nay, my lord Arthur, it is not so: I was never your father nor of your blood, but I know well ye are of an higher blood than I weened ye were." And then Sir Ector told him all. Then Arthur made great moan when he understood that Sir Ector was not his father.

"Sir," said Ector unto Arthur, "will ye be my good and gracious lord when ye are king?"

"Else were I to blame," said Arthur, "for ye are the man in the world that I am most beholding to, and my good lady and mother your wife, that as well as her own hath fostered and kept me. And if ever it be God's will that I be king, as ye say, ye shall desire of me what I may do, and I shall not fail you."

"Sir," said Sir Ector, "I will ask no more of you but that you will make my son, your foster brother Sir Kay, seneschal of all your lands."

"That shall be done, sir," said Arthur, "and more by the faith of my body; and never man shall have that office but he while that he and I live."

Therewithal they went unto the archbishop, and told him how the sword was achieved, and by whom.

Adapted from several sources but chiefly from version in "Boys' King Arthur," ed. by Sidney Lanier. Copyright, 1908, by Mary Day Lanier, published by Charles Scribner's Sons.

✷

CHARLEMAGNE AND ROLAND LEGENDS

So great was the fame of the historic Charlemagne that he became the hero of the romantic legends of several centuries following his reign. He lived before the days of chivalry, but it was only natural that the bards who sang of his brave deeds in feudal halls should invest him with knighthood.

Roland, or Orlando as he is known in Italian literature, is not known to history. In the legends of the age of chivalry he is the favorite nephew of Charlemagne and one of the noblest of his Peers. The legendary Charlemagne and Roland were Christian knights whose stories are those of bloody wars against pagan hosts. As legendary heroes they are enshrined in the national life of France, Italy and Spain, and in the chivalric literature of the world.

The list of stories which follows is intended for use with boys and girls of ten years and older.

Roland's Youth.
A Roland for an Oliver.
Charlemagne Answers the Message of King Marsilius.
Ganelon's Treason.
Roland's Pride.
The Death of Roland.

Charlemagne's Conquest and his Return to France.
The Story of Ogier the Dane.

Brief outlines of two of the above stories are followed by a more complete version of *The Death of Roland.*

Roland's Youth

"THE twelve most illustrious knights of Charlemagne were called Peers, for the equality that reigned among them; while the name of Paladins, also conferred on them, implies that they were inmates of the palace and companions of the king."

One of the most illustrious of the Peers was Orlando, or Roland.

"Milon, or Milone, a knight of great family, and distantly related to Charlemagne, having secretly married Bertha, the Emperor's sister, was banished from France. . . . After a long and miserable wandering on foot . . . Milon and his wife arrived at Sutri, in Italy, where they took refuge in a cave, and in that cave Orlando was born. There his mother continued, deriving a scanty support from the compassion of the neighboring peasants; while Milon, in quest of honor and fortune, went into foreign lands. Orlando grew up among the children of the peasantry, surpassing them all in strength and manly graces. Among his companions in age, though in station far more elevated, was Oliver, son of the governor of the town. Between the two boys a feud arose that led to a fight, in which Orlando thrashed his rival; but this did not prevent a friendship springing up between the two, which lasted through life.

"Orlando was so poor that he was sometimes half naked. As he was a favorite of the boys, one day four of them brought some cloth to make him clothes. Two brought white and two red; and from this circumstance Orlando took his coat-of-arms, or *quarterings.*

"When Charlemagne was on his way to Rome to receive the im-

232

perial crown, he dined in public in Sutri. Orlando and his mother that day had nothing to eat, and Orlando coming suddenly upon the royal party, and seeing abundance of provisions, seized from the attendants as much as he could carry off, and made good his retreat in spite of their resistance. The Emperor, being told of this incident, was reminded of an intimation he had received in a dream, and ordered the boy to be followed. This was done by three of the knights, whom Orlando would have encountered with a cudgel on their entering the grotto, had not his mother restrained him. When they heard from her who she was they threw themselves at her feet, and promised to obtain her pardon from the Emperor. This was easily effected. Orlando was received into favor by the Emperor and returned with him to France. . . ."

*Adapted from version in "Legends of Charlemagne,"
by Thomas Bulfinch.*

A Roland for an Oliver

"GUERIN DE MONTGLAVE held the lordship of Vienne, subject to Charlemagne. He had quarreled with his sovereign, and Charles laid siege to his city, having ravaged the neighboring country. Guerin was an aged warrior, but relied for his defense upon his four sons and two grandsons, who were among the bravest knights of the age. After the siege had continued two months, Charlemagne received tidings that Marsilius, king of Spain, had invaded France, and, finding himself unopposed, was advancing rapidly in the Southern provinces. At this intelligence Charles listened to the counsel of his peers, and consented to put the quarrel with Guerin to the decision of Heaven, by single combat between two knights, one of each party, selected by lot. The proposal was acceptable to Guerin and his sons. The names of the four, together with Guerin's own, who would not be excused,

233

and of the two grandsons, who claimed their lot, being put into a helmet, Oliver's was drawn forth, and to him, the youngest of the grandsons, was assigned the honor and the peril of the combat. He accepted the award with delight, exulting in being thought worthy to maintain the cause of his family. On Charlemagne's side Roland was the designated champion, and neither he nor Oliver knew who his antagonist was to be.

"They met on an island in the Rhone, and the warriors of both camps were ranged on either shore, spectators of the battle. At the first encounter both lances were shivered, but both riders kept their seats, immovable. They dismounted, and drew their swords. Then ensued a combat which seemed so equal, that the spectators could not form an opinion as to the probable issue. Two hours and more the knights continued to strike and parry, to thrust and ward, neither showing any sign of weariness, nor ever being taken at unawares. At length Orlando struck furiously upon Oliver's shield, burying Durindal in its edge so deeply that he could not draw it back, and Oliver, almost at the same moment, thrust so vigorously upon Orlando's breastplate that his sword snapped off at the handle. Thus were the two warriors left weaponless. Scarcely pausing a moment, they rushed upon one another, each striving to throw his adversary to the ground, and failing in that, each snatched at the other's helmet to tear it away. Both succeeded, and at the same moment they stood bareheaded face to face, and Roland recognized Oliver, and Oliver Roland. For a moment they stood still; and the next, with open arms, rushed into one another's embrace. 'I am conquered,' said Orlando. 'I yield me,' said Oliver.

"The people on the shore knew not what to make of all this. Presently they saw the two late antagonists standing hand in hand, and it was evident the battle was at an end. The knights crowded round them, and with one voice hailed them as equals in glory. If there were any who felt disposed to murmur that the battle was left undecided they were silenced by the voice of Ogier the Dane, who proclaimed aloud that all had been done that honor required, and declared that he would maintain that award against all gainsayers.

"The quarrel with Guerin and his sons being left undecided, a truce was made for four days, and in that time, by the efforts of Duke Namo on the one side, and of Oliver on the other, a reconciliation was effected. Charlemagne, accompanied by Guerin and his valiant family, marched to meet Marsilius, who hastened to retreat across the frontier."

From "Legends of Charlemagne," by Thomas Bulfinch.

The Death of Roland

"Over the plain fled the heathen, and Roland could no more pursue them. His good horse lay dead beside him, and he, all weary and worn, bent to aid his dear friend Turpin. Quickly he unlaced his helmet, drew off his shirt of mail, now all stained and rent with many a sword-cut, and tearing his silken vest in strips, he gently bound his wounds. Then tenderly lifting him in his arms he laid him on a grassy bank.

"Kneeling beside the dying Archbishop, Roland whispered softly, 'Father, our comrades, whom we loved, are all slain, but we should not leave them thus. Give me leave to go, and I will seek them and bring them here, that thou mayest bless them once more.'

" 'Go, friend,' said Turpin, 'but return right soon. Thanks be to God, the field is ours. We have won it, thou and I alone.'

"So all alone Roland went across the dreadful field. One by one he found the Peers of France. One by one he tenderly raised them in his arms, and brought them to the Archbishop, laying them at his feet.

"As Turpin gazed upon them lying there so still and quiet, tears started to his eyes and trickled down his pale worn cheeks. 'My lords,' he cried, raising his hand in blessing, 'may the Lord of all glory receive your souls! In the flower-starred meadows of Paradise may ye live for ever!' And there on the battle-field he absolved them from all their sins, and signed them with the sign of the Cross.

"Once again Roland returned to search the plain for his friend Oliver. At last, under a pine tree, by a wild-rose bush, he found his body. Very tenderly he lifted him, and faint and spent, staggering now beneath his burden, he carried him, and laid him with the other Peers, beside the Archbishop, so that he too might receive a last blessing.

" 'Fair Oliver, my comrade,' said Roland, kneeling beside him, 'to break a lance and shatter in pieces a shield, to counsel loyally and well, to punish traitors and cowards, never was there better knight on earth.' Then, fainting, Roland fell forward on the ground.

"When Turpin saw Roland swoon, he stretched out his hand and took his ivory horn from his neck. Through Roncesvalles there flowed a stream, and the Archbishop thought that if he could but reach it, he would bring from it some water to revive Roland.

"With great difficulty he rose, and with trembling footsteps, staggering as he went, he dragged himself a little way. But his strength was gone. Soon he stumbled and fell upon his knees, unable to rise again. Turning his eyes to heaven he clasped his hands together, 'May God take me to His Paradise,' he cried, and so fell forward dead. Thus died the Archbishop in the service of his Emperor. He who both by word and weapon had never ceased to war against the heathen was now silent and still forever.

"When Roland came to himself he saw Turpin kneel upon the ground a little way off and then fall forward dead. Again Roland rose, and going to the Archbishop crossed his beautiful white hands upon his breast. 'Ah! Father,' he said, 'knight of noble lineage, I leave thee in the hands of the Most Glorious. Never man served Him more willingly. Nay, never since the Holy Apostles hath such a prophet been. To win man and to guard our faith thou wert ever ready. May the gates of Paradise be wide for thee.'

"Then lifting his hands to heaven, Roland called aloud, 'Ride! oh Karl of France, ride quickly as thou mayest. In Roncesvalles there is great sorrow for thee. But the King Marsil too hath sorrow and loss, and for one of us there lie here forty of the heathen.'

"Then faint and weary Roland sank upon the grass. In one hand he clasped his ivory horn which he had taken again from the fingers of the dead Archbishop, in the other he held his sword Durindal. As he sat there still and quiet, a Saracen who had lain among the dead, pretending to be dead also, suddenly rose. Stealthily he crept towards Roland. Nearer and nearer he came, until when he was quite close, he stretched out his hand and seized Durindal. 'Vanquished, he is vanquished, the nephew of Charlemagne is vanquished!' he shouted. 'Behold his sword, which I will carry with me into Arabia!'

"But even as the Saracen seized Durindal, Roland opened his eyes. 'Thou art none of our company, I ween,' he cried, and raising his ivory horn he brought it crashing down upon the head of the Saracen. Helmet and skull-bone cracked beneath the blow, and the heathen fell dead at Roland's feet.

" 'Coward,' he cried, 'who made thee so bold that thou didst dare to lay hand upon Roland? Whoever hears of it will deem thee a madman.' Then looking sadly at his horn, he said, 'For thee have I broken the mouthpiece of my horn, and the gold and gems about the rim are scattered on the ground.'

"And now, fearing that some one might again steal his sword when he was no longer able to resist, Roland gathered all his strength together. Taking Durindal in his hand he went to where a bare brown rock rose out of the plain. With mighty blows he dashed the blade against the rock again and again. But it would not break. The steel grated and screeched upon the stone, but no scratch or dent was seen upon the blade, no notch upon the edge. 'Oh, Holy Mary, Mother of Heaven, come to my aid!' cried Roland. 'Oh my good Durindal, what misfortune! When I am parted from thee I shall no longer be able to take care of thee. We together have gained many battles; we together have conquered many realms, which now own Charlemagne as King. As long as I live, thou shalt never be taken from me, and when I am dead thou shalt never belong to one who shall flee before the foe, thou, who hast so long been borne by a valiant warrior.'

"Again Roland struck upon the rock. Again the steel grated and screeched, but the sword would not break. When the knight saw that he could not break the blade he became very sad. 'Oh my good Durindal,' he cried, 'thou who hast shone and flamed in the sunshine

237

many a time and oft to my joy, now givest thou me pain and sorrow lest I leave thee in the hands of the heathen?'

"A third time Roland struck upon the rock and beat the blade with all his might. But still it would not break. Neither notch nor scratch was to be seen upon the shining steel. Then softly and tenderly he made moan, 'Oh, fair and holy, my Durindal, it is not meet that the heathen should possess thee. Thou shouldst ever be served by Christian hand, for within thy hilt is many a holy relic. Please Heaven thou shalt never fall into the hands of a coward.' Thus spoke he to his sword, caressing it as some loved child.

"Then, seeing that by no means could he break his sword, Roland threw himself upon the grass with his face to the foe, so that when Charlemagne and all his host arrived they might know that he had died a conqueror. Beneath him, so that he guarded them with his body, he laid his sword and horn.

"Clasping his hands, he raised them to heaven. 'Oh God,' he cried, 'I have sinned. Pardon me for all the wrong that I have done both in great things and in small. Pardon me for all that I have done from the hour of my birth until now when I am laid low.'

"So with hands clasped in prayer, the great warrior met his end. Through the quiet evening air was heard the rustle of angels' wings. And St. Raphael, St. Michael of Peril, and the angel Gabriel swept down upon the dreadful battle-field, and taking the soul of Roland, bore it to Paradise."

From "Stories of Roland," by Henrietta Marshall. Published by Thomas Nelson & Sons, London, and E. P. Dutton & Co., Inc., New York, and reprinted by permission of the publishers.

TALES OF CHIVALRY

Sources for the Story-teller

Baldwin, James. *Story of Roland.* Chas. Scribner's Sons. The best version for children's own reading.

Bulfinch, Thomas. *Legends of Charlemagne.* McKay. E. P. Dutton & Co., Inc.

Clay, Beatrice. *Stories of King Arthur and the Round Table.* E. P. Dutton & Co., Inc. Use for outlines.

Echols, U. W. *Knights of Charlemagne.* Longmans, Green & Co.

Greene and Kirk. *With Spurs of Gold.* Little, Brown & Company. Short Stories of the Cid, Bayard, Roland and Oliver and other knights of old.

Hyde, M. P. *The Singing Sword.* Little, Brown & Company. A story of Ogier the Dane.

Macleod, Mary. *Book of King Arthur and His Noble Knights.* Frederick A. Stokes Co. A very readable, condensed version adapted from Malory.

Malory, Sir Thomas. *Boys' King Arthur,* ed. by Sidney Lanier, il. by N. C. Wyeth. Chas. Scribner's Sons. Abridged only.

Pollard, Alfred W., ed. *Romance of King Arthur and His Knights of the Round Table.* The Macmillan Company. Follows Malory closely.

Pyle, Katherine. *Charlemagne and His Knights.* J. B. Lippincott & Co. A good version for children's own reading.

Pyle, Howard. *Story of King Arthur and His Knights. Story of Sir Launcelot and His Companions. Story of the Champions of the Round Table. Story of the Grail and the Passing of Arthur.* Chas. Scribner's Sons. Independent, charming, somewhat lengthy treatment.

Roland. *Song of Roland,* newly translated into English with an introduction by Jessie Crosland. Chatto and Windus, London. A prose version from manuscripts, in the form of a personal narrative.

Roland. *Chanson de Roland,* tr. by Charles Scott Moncrief. Chapman and Hall, London. A metrical translation from the original.

Tennyson, Alfred Lord. *Idylls of the King.* Houghton Mifflin Co. Modernized poetical versions of some of the King Arthur legends.

Wilmot-Buxton. *Stories from Old French Romance.* Frederick A. Stokes & Co. Includes the Story of the Enchanted Knight (Ogier the Dane).

IRISH HERO TALES

IRISH HERO TALES

GENIUS for story-telling is an inheritance of the Irish. There is a legend that in the mythical period of Ireland's history, Saint Finnen, an Irish abbot, asked for hospitality from a Donegal chief named Tuan mac Carell and was refused. Nothing dismayed, the saint sat on the surly leader's doorstep, fasting, until he relented and invited him in, whereupon they became great friends through Tuan's prowess in telling tales of old Ireland.

This human interest in the myths and legends of the country has never been lost and the hero tales of ancient Ireland have remained authorless, and a living literature to the present century. The fact that they took form in manuscripts between the Seventh and Twelfth Centuries did not affect the bards.

They continued to tell their tales on the hills and by lake and wood, in the halls of early kings, and by peat firesides, expanding and altering the old legends at will, to suit their own poetic feelings and the emotions of their listeners.

These hero tales fall into several distinct cycles of which two, the Ultonian, and the Ossianic (or Fenian), are favorites among the present-day children who are fortunate enough to know them.

The hero of the earliest, or Ultonian cycle, is Cuchulain, nephew of Conar mac Nessa, King of Ulster and of the Red Branch Order of chivalry. Many stories are told of Cuchulain's prodigious size and strength. As a boy he strangled a hound that attacked him, for which act he pledged himself to guard his host's house in its stead and thereby won the name of The Hound of Cullan. Later, when he became a leader, his band called him The Hound of Ulster. It was prophesied at his birth: he would win praise from all men; charioteers, kings and sages would recount his deeds; he would win the love of many; give combat at the fords; decide the people's quarrels. Great and many were the deeds of Cuchulain.

The tales of the Ossianic Cycle cluster about Finn mac Cumhal, who is supposed to have lived in the Third Century, some two or three hundred years after the death of Cuchulain, but neither the deeds of Cuchulain or Finn are sober history. Finn's exploits take their name from his son, Oisin, a legendary poet and warrior who related them. Oisin is the traditional narrator of many hundred Irish stories in epic form.

Like many of the Irish heroes Finn had a partly faërie ancestry. In his youth he won a treasure bag filled with magic weapons and jewels, after which he went to Finegan, a Druid, who lived on the river, Boyne, to learn poetry and science.

In a pool in this river, under boughs of hazel from which dropped the Nuts of Knowledge, there lived a salmon of which it was said that whosoever ate of him would gain the wisdom of the ages. Now it happened that after much effort Finegan caught the salmon and gave it to Finn to cook, bidding him to eat none of it. When the cooked salmon was brought to Finegan he noticed that Finn's countenance was changed. "Hast thou eaten of the salmon?" he asked. "Nay," answered Finn, "but when I turned it on the spit my thumb was burned and I put it in my mouth." "Take the Salmon of Knowledge and eat it," said Finegan, "for in you a prophecy has been fulfilled. I can teach you no more." After that Finn became as wise as he was strong, and great were his deeds. It was said of him that he could divine what would happen by putting his thumb in his mouth and biting it.

IRISH HERO TALES

Finn was valorous, gentle, generous and greatly loved by his comrades, the Fianna. It is told of the Fianna that each man was required to know The Twelve Books of Poetry and to be able to make rhymes; to draw a thorn from his foot while running without slackening his speed. He must prove his valor in personal combat; he must take no dowry with a wife.

IRISH HERO TALES

Cuchulain's Youth

How Conar became king; The faërie prophecy; Cuchulain and the Boy Corp; How Cuchulain got his name; How he took arms; His first feats of championship.

Cuchulain's Wooing

Emer in her home; The youth, Cuchulain; The quest of the King's heralds; Cuchulain's first visit to Emer; His return and seizure of Emer; "Nor were they henceforth parted until death."

The Strife for the Brown Bull of Cooley

The wrath of Queen Meave; Her march against Ulster; Her theft of the Bull; Her enchantments against Cuchulain; The fight at the Ford; The last great battle of the Tain; Cuchulain's death.

Deidre, or the Fate of the Three Sons of Usna

The birth of Deidre; The prophecy; Her life in the fortress; Her rescue by the three sons of Usna; Her love for Naoise; Their escape to Alba; Their luckless return; Naoise blinds the eye of the King's messenger; The sons of Usna are overcome and killed; Deidre's lament; Deidre's death.

The Boyhood of Finn mac Cumhal

His life in the forest; His feats of strength; His winning of the Treasure Bag of Cumhal; Finegan and his teachings.

Finn and the Fianna

Conn of the Hundred Battles makes Finn captain; The maxims of the Fianna; The tests of the Fianna; Their exploits; The chase of the Gilla Dacar; Oisin in the Land of Youth.

245

Cuchulain's Wooing

IT WAS on a day of the days of summer that Emer, daughter of For-gall the Wily, sat on a bench before her father's door, at his fort that is called Lusk today, but which in olden days men spoke of as the Gardens of the Sun-god Lugh, so sunny and so fair and fertile was that plain, with waving meadow-grass and buttercups, and the sweet May-blossom girdling the fields. Close all about the fort the gardens lay, with apple-trees shedding their pink and white upon the playing fields of brilliant green; and all the air was noisy with the buzz of bees, and with the happy piping of the thrush and soft low cooing of the doves. And Emer sat, a fair and noble maid, among her young companions, foster-sisters of her own, who came from all the farms and forts around to grow up with the daughters of the house, and learn from them high-bred and gentle ways, to fashion rich embroideries such as Irish women used to practice as an art, and weaving, and fine needlework, and all the ways of managing a house. And as they sat round Emer, a bright comely group of busy girls, they sang in undertones the crooning tender melodies of ancient Erin; or one would tell a tale of early wars, and warrior feasts or happenings of the gods, and one would tell a tale of lover's joys or of the sorrows of a blighted love, and they would sigh and laugh and dream that they too loved, were wooed, and lost their loves.

And Emer moved about among the girls, directing them; and of all maids in Erin, Emer was the best, for hers were the six gifts of womanhood, the gift of loveliness, the gift of song, the gift of sweet and pleasant speech, the gift of handiwork, the gifts of wisdom and of modesty. And in his distant home in Ulster, Cuchulain heard of her. For he was young and brave, and women loved him for his nobleness, and all men wished that he should take a wife. But for a while he would not, for among the women whom he saw, not one of them came up to his desires. And when they urged him, willfully he said: "Well, find for me a woman I could love, and I will marry her." Then sent the King his heralds out through every part of Ulster and the south to seek a wife whom Cuchulain would care to woo. But still

246

he said the same, "This one, and this, has some bad temper or some want of grace, or she is vain or she is weak, not fitted as a mate to such as I. She must be brave, for she must suffer much; she must be gentle, lest I anger her; she must be fair and noble, not alone to give me pleasure as her spouse, but that all men may think of her with pride, saying, 'As Cuchulain is the first of Ulster's braves, the hero of her many fighting-fields, so is his wife the noblest and the first of Erin's women, a worthy mate for him.'"

So when the princely messengers returned, their search was vain; among the daughters of the chiefs and noble lords not one was found whom Cuchulain cared to woo. But one who loved him told him of a night he spent in Forgall's fort, and of the loveliness and noble spirit of Forgall's second girl Emer, the maiden of the waving hair, but just grown up to womanhood. He told him of her noble mien and stately step, the soft and liquid brightness of her eyes, the color of her hair, that like to ruddy gold fresh from the burnishing, was rolled around her head. Her graceful form he praised, her skillfulness in song and handiwork, her courage with her father, a harsh and wily man, whom all within the house hated and feared but she. He told him also that for any man to win the maiden for his wife would be a troublesome and dangerous thing, for out of all the world, her father Forgall loved and prized but her, and he had made it known that none beneath a king or ruling prince should marry her, and any man who dared to win her love, but such as these, should meet a cruel death; and this he laid upon his sons and made them swear to him upon their swords, that any who should come to woo the girl should never leave the fort alive again.

All that they said but made Cuchulain yet the more desire to see the maid and talk with her. "This girl, so brave, so wise, so fair of face and form," he pondered with himself, "would be a fitting mate for any chief. I think she is the fitting mate for me."

So on the very day when Emer sat upon her playing-fields, Cuchulain in the early morn set forth in all his festal garb in his chariot with his prancing steeds, with Laeg before him as his charioteer, and took the shortest route towards the plain of Bray, where lie the Gardens of the Sun-god Lugh. The way they went from Emain lay between the Mountains of the Wood, and thence along the High-road of the Plain, where once the sea had passed; across the marsh that bore the name the Whisper of the Secret of the Gods. Then driving on towards the River Boyne they passed the Ridge of the Great Sow, where not far off is seen the fairy haunt of Angus, God of Beauty and of Youth; and so they reached the ford of Washing of the Horses of the Gods, and the fair, flowering plains of Lugh, called Lusk today.

Now all the girls were busied with their work, when on the high-road leading to the fort they heard a sound like thunder from the north, that made them pause and listen in surprise.

Nearer and nearer yet it came as though at furious pace a band of warriors bore down towards the house. "Let one of you see from the ramparts of the fort," said Emer, "what is the sound that we hear coming towards us." Fiall, her sister, Forgall's eldest girl, ran to the top of the rath or earthen mound that circled round the playing-fields, and looked out towards the north, shading her eyes against the brilliant sun. "What do you see there?" asked they all, and eagerly she cried: "I see a splendid chariot-chief coming at furious pace along the road. Two steeds, like day and night, of equal size and beauty, come thundering beneath that chariot on the plain. Curling their manes and long, and as they come, one would think fire darted from their curbed jaws, so strain and bound they forward; high in the air the turf beneath their feet is thrown around them, as though a flock of birds were following as they go. On the right side the horse is gray, broad in the haunches, active, swift and wild; with head erect and breast expanded, madly he moves along the plain, bounding and prancing as he goes. The other horse jet-black, head firmly knit, feet broad-hoofed, firm, and slender; in all this land never had chariot-chief such steeds as these."

"Heed not the steeds," the girls replied, "tell us, for this concerns us most, who is the chariot-chief who rides within?"

"Worthy of the chariot in which he rides is he who sits within. Youthful he seems, as standing on the very borders of a noble manhood, and yet I think his face and form are older than his years. Gravely he looks, as though his mind revolved some serious thought,

248

and yet a radiance as of the summer's day enfolds him round. About his shoulders a rich five-folded mantle hangs, caught by a brooch across the chest sparkling with precious gems, above his white and gold-embroidered shirt. His massive sword rests on his thigh, and yet I think he comes not here to fight. Before him stands his charioteer, the reins held firmly in his hand, urging the horses onward with a goad."

"What like is he, the charioteer?" demanded the girls again.

"A ruddy man and freckled," answered Fiall; "his hair is very curly and bright-red, held by a bronze fillet across his brow, and caught at either side his head in little cups of gold, to keep the locks from falling on his face. A light cloak on his shoulders, made with open sleeves, flies back in the wind, as rapidly they course along the plain." But Emer heard not what the maiden said, for to her mind there came the memory of a wondrous youth whom Ulster loved and yet of whom all Erin stood in awe. Great warriors spoke of him in whispers and with shaking of the head. They told how when he was a little child, he fought with full-grown warriors and mastered them; of a huge hound that he had slain and many feats of courage he had done. Into her mind there came a memory, that she had heard of prophets who foretold for him a strange and perilous career; a life of danger, and an early death. Full many a time she longed to see this youth, foredoomed to peril, yet whose praise should ring from age to age through Erin; and in her mind, when all alone she pondered on these things, she still would end: "This were a worthy mate! This were a man to win a woman's love!" And half aloud she uttered the old words: "This were a man to win a woman's love!"

Now hardly had the words sprung to her lips, when the chariot stood before the door, close to the place where all the girls were gathered. And when she saw him Emer knew it was the man of whom she dreamed. He wished a blessing to them, and her lovely face she lifted in reply. "May God make smooth the path before thy feet," she gently said. "And thou, mayest thou be safe from every harm," was his reply. "Whence comest thou?" she asked; for he had alighted from his seat and stood beside her, gazing on her face. "From Conor's court we come," he answered then; "from Emain, kingliest of Ulster's forts, and this the way we took. We drove between the Mountains of the Wood, along the High-road of the Plain, where once the sea had been; across the Marsh they call the Secret of the Gods, and to the Boyne's ford named of old the Washing of the Horses of the Gods. And now at last, O maiden, we have come to the bright flowery Garden-grounds of Lugh. This is the story of myself, O maid; let me now hear of thee." Then Emer said: "Daughter am I to Forgall, whom men call the Wiley Chief. Cunning his mind and strange his powers; for he is stronger than any laboring man, more learned than any Druid, more sharp and clever than any man of verse. Men say that thou art skilled in feats of war, but it will be more than all thy games to fight against Forgall himself; therefore be cautious what thou doest, for men cannot number the multitude of his warlike deeds nor the cunning and craft with which he works. He has given me as a bodyguard twenty valiant men, their captain Con, son of Forgall, and my brother; therefore I am well protected, and no man can come near me, but that Forgall knows of it. Today he is gone from home on a warrior expedition, and those men are gone with him; else, had he been within, I trow he would have asked thee of thy business here."

"Why, O maiden, dost thou talk thus to me? Dost thou not reckon me among the strong men, who know not fear?" "If thy deeds were known to me," she said, "I then might reckon them; but hitherto I have not heard of all thy exploits." "Truly, I swear, O maiden," said Cuchulain, "that I will make my deeds to be recounted among the glories of the warrior-feats of heroes." "How do men reckon thee?" she said again. "What then is thy strength?" "This is my strength," he said. "When my might in fight is weakest, I can defend myself alone against twenty. I fear not by my own might to fight with forty. Under my protection a hundred are secure. From dread of me, strong warriors avoid my path, and come not against me in the battle-field. Hosts and multitudes and armed men fly before my name."

"Thou seemest to boast," said Emer, "and truly for a tender boy those feats are very good; but they rank not with the deeds of chariot-chiefs. Who then were they who brought thee up in these deeds of which thou boastest?"

"Truly, O maiden, King Conor is himself my foster-father, and not as a churl or common man was I brought up by him. Among chariot-chiefs and champions, among poets and learned men, among the lords and nobles of Ulster, have I been reared, and they have taught me courage and skill and manly gifts. In birth and bravery I am a match for any chariot-chief; I direct the counsels of Ulster, and at my own fort at Dun Dalgan they come to me for entertainment. Not as one of the common herd do I stand before thee here today, but as the favorite of the King and the darling of all the warriors of Ulster. Moreover, the god Lugh the Long-handed is my protector, for I am of the race of the great gods, and his especial foster-child. And now, O maiden, tell me of thyself; how in the sunny plains of Lugh hast thou been reared within thy father's fort?" "That I will tell thee," said the girl. "I was brought up in noble behavior as every queen is reared; in stateliness of form, in wise, calm speech, in comeliness of manner, so that to me is imputed every noble grace among the hosts of the women of Erin."

"Good, indeed, are those virtues," said the youth; "and yet I see one excellence thou hast not noted in thy speech. Never before, until this day, among all women with whom I have at times conversed, have I found one but thee to speak the mystic ancient language of the bards, which we are talking now for secrecy one with the other. And all these things are good, but one is best of all, and that is, that I love thee, and I think thou lovest me. What hinders, then, that we should be betrothed?" But Emer would not hasten, but teasing him, she said, "Perhaps thou hast already found a wife?" "Not so," said he, "and by my right-hand's valor here I vow, none but thyself shall ever be my wife." "A pity it were, indeed, thou shouldst not have a wife," said Emer, playing with him still; "see, here is Fiall, my elder sister, a clever girl and excellent in needlework. Make her thy wife, for well is it known to thee, a younger sister in Ireland may not marry before an elder. Take her! I'll call her hither." Then Cuchulain was vexed because she seemed to play with him. "Verily and indeed," he said, "not Fiall, but thee, it is with whom I am in love; and if thou weddest me not, never will I, Cuchulain, wed at all."

251

Then Emer saw that Cuchulain loved her, but she was not satisfied, because he had not yet done the deeds of prime heroes, and she desired that he should prove himself by champion feats and deeds of valor before he won her as his bride.

So she bade him go away and prove himself for a year by deeds of prowess to be indeed a worthy mate and spouse for her, and then, if he would come again she would go with him as his one and only wife. But she bade him beware of her father, for she knew that he would try to kill him, in order that he might not come again. And this was true, for every way he sought to kill Cuchulain, or to have him killed by his enemies, but he did not prevail.

When Cuchulain had taken farewell of Emer and gained her promise, he returned to Emain Macha. And that night the maidens of the fort told Forgall that Cuchulain had been there and that they thought that he had come to woo Emer; but of this they were not sure, because he and Emer had talked together in the poet's mystic tongue, that was not known to them. For Emer and Cuchulain talked on this wise, that no one might repeat what they had said to Forgall.

And for a whole year Cuchulain was away, and Forgall guarded the fort so well that he could not come near Emer to speak with her; but at last, when the year was out, he would wait no longer, and he wrote a message to Emer on a piece of stick, telling her to be ready. And he came in his war-chariot, with scythes upon its wheels, and he brought a band of hardy men with him, who entered the outer rampart of the fort and carried off Emer, striking down men on every side. And Forgall followed them to the earthern outworks, but he fell over the rath, and was taken up lifeless. And Cuchulain placed Emer and her foster-sister in his chariot, carrying with them their garments and ornaments of gold and silver, and they drove northward to Cuchulain's fort at Dun Dalgan, which is Dundalk today.

And they were pursued to the Boyne, and there Cuchulain placed Emer in a house of safety, and he turned and drove off his enemies who followed him, pursuing them along the banks and destroying them, so that the place, which had before been called the White Field, was called the Turf of Blood from that day. Then he and Emer

252

reached their home in safety, nor were they henceforth parted until death.

> *From "Boys' Cuchulain," by Eleanor Hull. Reprinted by permission of Thomas Y. Crowell & Co., publishers.*

Other tales of heroes and the many kings of Ireland and their sons will be found in the books listed as sources for story-tellers.

Three of the many charming romances preserved by the Irish bards are: The Fate of the Children of Lir; The Quest of the Sons of Turenn; King Iubdan and King Fergus. These are lovely tales of magic and enchantment in the Land of the Wee People, which may be told preceding or following the hero sagas.

Sources for the Story-teller

Colum, Padraic. *King of Ireland's Son.* The Macmillan Company.

Dunbar, Aldis. *The Sons o' Cormac.* E. P. Dutton & Co., Inc.

Gregory, Augusta, Lady. *Cuchulain of Muirthemne.* John Murray, London.

Hull, Eleanor. *Cuchulain, the Hound of Ulster.* George G. Harrap & Co., Ltd. (Out of print.)

Hyde, Douglas. *Literary History of Ireland.* Chas. Scribner's Sons.

Joyce, P. W. *Old Celtic Romances.* Longmans, Green & Co.

Rolleston, T. W. *High Deeds of Finn.* George G. Harrap & Co., Ltd. (Out of print.) Myths and Legends of the Celtic Race. T. Y. Crowell Co.

Young, Ella. *The Tanglefooted Horse.* Longmans, Green & Co. The Fionn Saga. *The Wonder-Smith and His Son.* Longmans, Green & Co. Stories of the Gubbaun Saor.

PERSIAN HERO TALES

PERSIAN HERO TALES

THE Persian hero tales which follow are from the great national epic of Persia, the *Shah Nameh,* written by the poet, Firdausi, in the Eleventh Century. The *Shah Nameh* is a poet's interpretation of the deeds and achievements of the ancient kings of Iran (Persia) as recounted in earlier manuscripts or passed down from reign to reign through oral tradition.

The chief hero is Rustem, son of Zal of the White Hair. Rustem, a Persian Hercules in bravery and power, is portrayed as having lived during several centuries and is the center of a cycle of stories abounding in wild and romantic description and exploits of strength and valor. There are heroines, also, in these tales by the Persian bard, as intrepid and beautiful as ever vanquished hearts in other great world literature.

The author of the *Shah Nameh* has been called the Homer of the East; he is the father of Persian poetry as Homer is of the Greek. His treatment by the Shah Mahmud for whom he composed his work during thirty years has gained for him sympathetic interest. This is told in the prefaces to the various editions listed as sources for the stories to be told.

BAG O' TALES

It is evident from these tales that the old Persian heroes admired courage, loyalty and the primitive virtues which mark the heroes of all great epics and their world was a very colorful one of shady trees, cool streams, bright gardens, sunshine, rich fabrics and flashing jewels. There is a glamour surrounding the exploits of war in some of the Persian tales that limits their use; and situations of deep pathos such as the tragic moment when Rustem discovers that he has unknowingly killed his own son.

The selection of stories given is intended for reading aloud or for telling to girls and boys of nine years and older.

Stories of Persian Heroes

Zal, the White-Haired

To Sahm, paladin of the Shah, is born a white-haired son. Persuaded it is a demon child, Sahm exposes the babe to die on Mount Elburz. The Simurgh, bird of marvel, rescues the boy and raises him in her nest. Reproached in a dream, Sahm seeks his son. Simurgh gives Zal three of her feathers and restores him to his father. Zal becomes enamored of the lovely princess Rudabah, daughter of an enemy of Persia. Overcoming all obstacles, their romantic courtship terminates in marriage. Rudabah falls ill and Zal burns one of the Simurgh's feathers. The bird appears and heals her.

Rustem, the Wonder Child

Rustem is born. Wise men prophesy his greatness. Sahm journeys to see his grandson. Rustem slays the white elephant. Rustem chooses his horse, Rakush. King Kai Kaoos goes to the enchanted country of Mazinderan and becomes a captive of the White Demon. Rustem goes to his aid. Rakush kills a lion, Rustem kills a dragon. Aulad becomes Rustem's guide and leads the way to the Seven Mountains. Rustem overcomes the demons, slays the White Terror and saves the king and his warriors. The King of Mazinderan is defeated and Aulad placed on the throne.

258

PERSIAN HERO TALES

Sohrab and Rustem

Rustem goes hunting and Rakush is stolen. In his search Rustem comes to the palace of a king. Tamineh, fearing her son will be taken from her, sends word to Rustem the child is a daughter. Sohrab learns Rustem is his father. Sohrab chooses a horse and marches against Persia. Tartars join forces of Sohrab. Kai Kaoos sends for Rustem. The armies meet. Sohrab's search is for his father. Sohrab challenges the Persians to send a champion to meet him in single combat. Rustem takes up the challenge, hides his identity from Sohrab, and slays his unknown son.

(Omit details of quarrel between King and Rustem, Sohrab's fight with Gurdafrid. Soften the tragedy of Sohrab's death.)

Kai Khosroo

Siawush, the Shah's son, trained by Rustem, leads Persians against Afrasiab. Siawush's quarrel with his father and friendship with Afrasiab. Siawush is slain. Kai Khosroo is born and Peran Wisa hides him with peasants. His identity is discovered, he is taken to king, returned to Ferangis. Rustem leads an army against Afrasiab. Kai Khosroo and Ferangis flee into a far country. Afrasiab hides and Rustem rules the country. Gew goes in search of Kai Khosroo. Kai Khosroo wins his horse. Kai Khosroo, Gew and Ferangis flee before Afrasiab. Gew proves himself a mighty warrior. They swim a river and escape into Persia. Kai Khosroo made Shah.

(Use the story of Siawush merely as an introduction to the story of Kai Khosroo.)

Gushtap and Isfendiyar

Gushtap leaves his father's court. Lives in disguise in a far country. Wins the princess, is driven from court, kills fierce wolf and fiery dragon. He is reconciled with father and becomes Shah. Isfendiyar, his son, conquers many nations for Persia. Influenced by jealous warrior, Gushtap refuses Isfendiyar the throne and binds him with chains. Isfendiyar defeats Arjasp and

rescues his sisters. Again refused throne. Sent to bring Rustem
to court in chains. Isfendiyar and Rustem meet in combat. Simurgh is called to heal Rakush and Rustem. Death of Isfendiyar. Rustem's death.

✻

Zal, the White-Haired

LONG, long ago, in the land named Persia, there ruled a great king.
Wise he was and powerful, and all men bowed before him. Now at
the king's court lived Sahm. He was the strongest of the Shah's
warriors and was both fierce and brave. Sahm lived in a large castle
surrounded by gardens filled with beautiful trees and flowers and
pools. His food he ate from silver plates and his wine he drank from
golden cups. And over all ruled his beautiful wife veiled in rose and
saffron. She waited longingly while he fought the king's battles in
distant lands and welcomed him with joy when he returned.

But none of these things brought happiness to this great warrior.
He had no son. He alone of all the warriors and the greatest of them,
was without a child. Always he thought of this and it grieved him
deeply. After many years of longing, it came to pass that a son was
born to him, a baby with a beautiful face, but strange to say, with
hair entirely white like that of an old man.

Now the slaves were afraid and for a week no one told Sahm of
the birth of his son. No one dared to tell him the baby had white
hair. At last the child's nurse summoned her courage and going before the warrior said:

"May the Lord keep and guard thee. May thy enemies be utterly
destroyed; may the days of Sahm the hero be happy; for the Al-
mighty hath given him an heir. A son is born unto the mighty warrior, a moon-faced boy, beautiful of face and limb, in whom there is
neither fault nor blemish, save that his hair is like unto that of an

aged man. I beseech thee, O my master, bethink thee that this gift is from God nor give place in thine heart to ingratitude."

When Sahm saw the child, he said to himself, "When people see my son's white hair, they will laugh at me. Now this child may have come from the devil. People may say it will bring evil on the land." Calling his trusted servants to him, he told them to take the child and carry it out of the land to a far distant mountain. Now this mountain was so high that it touched the stars and no man had ever climbed its steep sides. The servants left the child on the rocks at the foot of the mountain to be devoured by wild beasts.

Now upon this mountain had the Simurgh, the bird of marvel, builded her nest, a nest made of ebony and sandalwood and studded about with precious stones until it was fit for a king's throne. Her feathers were as yellow as though they had been hammered out of gold. She was as strong as the steeds in Sahm's stables and more swift.

Flying about in search of food to feed her young ones, Simurgh came upon the baby as it lay naked among the rocks, sucking its fingers in hunger. She darted to the earth, seized the baby in her talons and took him to her nest. When she saw the tears rolling down its cheeks, she felt sorry and bade her young ones not to eat him, but to treat him as a brother. She brought choice bits of meat for him and at night he crept under her wings.

Years went by. The child grew as tall as a young cypress tree. Wise was he, for the Simurgh had taught him much. He knew the language of the birds and trees; he understood the mountain streams as they leaped from rock to rock; he knew the hidden secret of the sky, the wheeling circle of the stars. But, save for the language, he knew nothing of the world where men walked as he did and could not fly. Nor did he know of the great warrior, his father, who had cast him out.

Meanwhile Sahm had passed through years of miserable longing for his only son. One night he had a strange dream. It seemed to him that a man came to his tent riding upon an Arab steed and said, "Oh thou ungrateful father, who left thy son to perish because his hair was white, and thought a bird was good enough to nurse a son as beautiful as a poplar tree, wilt thou let another day go by before thou claimest him for thine own?" Then Sahm awoke and began to question his wise men as to whether his son could be yet alive. And they answered him, "Oh thou who wast ashamed of the white hair given thy son by God, search the world for him."

So Sahm and all his army set out on the quest and hearing of a boy who had been seen in the Simurgh's nest, they turned their steps to Mount Elburz. Far above his head Sahm caught sight of the great nest of the Simurgh and on the edge, shading his eyes with his hand, stood a noble boy. He was strong and straight and as the rays of the noonday sun fell upon his hair, it shone like snow. Sahm sought to find any path or track by which to scale the mighty mountain. But he tried in vain, for the mountain in that place was as smooth as glass. He fell upon his knees and begged God to forgive his past cruelty and to help him now.

When the Simurgh saw the army and heard Sahm's prayer, she knew the time had come to take the boy to his father. She called him to her and said, "I have been thy nurse all these years. I have shared my nest with thee and been to thee a mother, for thy father cast thee out. It is time for us to part. Yonder, at the foot of the mountain, is your father Sahm, the hero, the greatest warrior in the world. He has come for thee and great things await you at his court."

When the youth had heard her words his eyes filled with tears. "Art thou tired of me? Am I no longer fit to live with thee? Why should I go to my father when to thee I owe all that I am, for thou wast my friend in need." And the Simurgh answered, "I would keep thee with me always. But a great destiny is yours. Go therefore and seek thy fortune in the world. But that thou may never forget thy nurse, take these feathers from my breast and guard them with care. If thou art ever in danger or need help, throw one upon the fire and it will bring me to thy aid at once." Then the golden bird raised the boy in her talons and carried him to where his father still knelt and prayed.

The warrior blessed and thanked the bird and watched her soar heavenward. Trembling Sahm turned his eyes upon his son. He gazed on the youth from head to foot and saw that he was fit for a throne. He had a lion's breast and limbs, a strong hand to seek the scimitar, eyes pitch-colored, coral lips and blood-red cheeks. Except for his hair, there was no fault at all. "Have no hard thoughts oh my son, forget the past and try to learn to love me; never again will I wrong thee and I will grant thee all thy wishes."

He dressed his son in handsome clothes and because of his snow-white hair he named him Zal, which means the aged. He placed him on a royal elephant and with the army returned to the warrior's castle.

When the king heard the news, he sent for Zal and gave him rich gifts, horses and jewels and swords. He bade his wise men foretell the future and they announced the white-haired boy would become a brave paladin and the father of the mightiest warrior the world had ever known.

Glad were the days that followed for Sahm and the white-haired Zal. When Sahm went forth to fight the king's enemies, he gave his whole kingdom to his son. And Zal ruled with wisdom and kindness and all men marveled that a boy raised in a bird's nest should be so courteous.

Anon it came about that Zal desired to see all the kingdoms of Persia. He set off with a great train of followers and presently came to a city named Cabul. This city was governed by good King Mihrab.

Mihrab was descended from a very cruel tyrant who because of his wickedness was called the Serpent King. All Persians hated him, therefore Zal would not go into the palace. But Mihrab did him honor and gave him gifts and feasted him in his tents. And as they feasted, one of the nobles began to tell Zal about King Mihrab's daughter, whose name was Rudabah.

"The king hath a daughter whose face is fairer than the sun. Her skin is white as ivory; her eyes are soft as narcissus; her lashes like the raven's wing; her brows are like an archer's bow; her hair is musky nights. From head to foot she is as Paradise, all music, charm and beauty."

That same day Mihrab went into his palace and spoke of Zal to his queen and his daughter, "He is a lion in his heart and in strength an elephant. When he is on the throne, he scattereth gold. On horseback in battle he is brave and fearsome. His hair is white, yet it is becoming and thou wouldst say: 'He fascinates hearts.' " So well did the king speak of the stranger, that even before she had seen Zal, Rudabah knew she loved him and could neither eat nor sleep for thinking of him, but the two lovers could not meet because of the ancient feud between their countries. The Persians would never forgive Zal if he entered the courts of Mihrab who was descended from the wicked Serpent King.

Now just outside the city Zal was encamped beside a stream. Rudabah's maidens-in-waiting were on the farther bank near Mihrab's palace. They gathered roses along the river's side, filling their arms with blossoms. Zal saw them and said to his servants, "Who are yonder flower worshipers?" And his servants answered, "They are damsels of Rudabah, daughter of Mihrab." Zal called a slave boy and walked to the river's side. Spying a strange bird flying over the water, he took an arrow and shot it through the heart and it fell among the rose-gatherers. "Row across the stream and bring yonder bird to me." And the slave returned smiling and Zal asked, "What was it the maids did say to thee to make thee smile?" "They told me of the moon within the palace of Mihrab who would look with jewel bright eyes upon Zal the beautiful." The heart of Zal was glad and he sent presents of gold and pearls to the maidens. One came to the brink of the stream and spoke to Zal of Rudabah and her beauty, so that he longed still more to wed her and casting all caution to the winds, he bade the maiden ask her mistress to meet him.

So at evening time the slave appeared and took him to a garden in which stood a tower and presently, Rudabah, fairest of maidens, appeared upon the roof top and said, "I bid thee welcome, O young man!" Not content that such a distance should separate him from his love, he cried, "Oh find some way for me to look on thee! For why shouldst thou be on the tower and I here far below?" Rudabah heard his words and doffing her scarlet veil let fall her hair, coil on coil, strand on strand and it was so long it reached from the battlements and fell upon the ground. And she said, "Here thou hast a rope; seize my tresses and climb up to me." But Zal said, "Not so, fair one; never would I do you hurt." And because he would not touch her hair so roughly, he swung his lasso around a battlement and so ascended to the beautiful maiden. Then they gazed upon each other and knew they truly loved. And there in her rich room, adorned like Paradise, the two did plight their troth.

When the moonlight meeting of Zal and Rudabah became known, Sahm was flaming with wrath and he determined to destroy the whole country rather than allow his son to marry a daughter of his ancient enemy. So with a mighty army of the Persians, Sahm started for the city of Cabul where Rudabah lived.

When Zal heard his father was coming with an army to destroy the land, he hastened to him and said, "I was a child, left on the rocks until the mighty Simurgh took me to her nest. Thou didst cast me out and deprived me of a home. Now you would destroy my happiness. I love Rudabah. Behold I stand before thee and expose my body to thy wrath. Kill me if you choose, but utter not a word against my love nor her country."

When Sahm heard these words, he made peace with his son and sent a message to his king to know what to do with the boy. The king replied, "I will have my wise men put to Zal some riddles. If he can answer these ancient runes, he will prove himself wise beyond mortals and so master his fortune. He shall then marry Rudabah, daughter of mine ancient enemy." For the king thought to himself, "No mortal can answer these riddles and I shall still have Mihrab for mine enemy." The wise men put to Zal seven riddles but to each he gave much thought and answered them so wisely that all the people wondered. Then the king said, "My word shall stand. Zal, son of Sahm shall have the beautiful princess for his wife."

Together Zal and Sahm journeyed forth to the kingdom of Mihrab. As they neared the city and heard the bells and harps and pipes, one would have said, "The very roofs and doors make music." Zal and Rudabah were placed on a throne from which they scattered emeralds and diamonds. Rudabah's crown was wrought of gold and Zal's of royal gems. After a joyous celebration Zal did travel with his bride unto the city of Sahm. And his father said, "I give to thee, O Zal, this state, this realm and glorious crown." And when Rudabah sat beside the white-haired one, Sahm placed the wreath of all his land upon her brow.

Only once did sorrow cross their path and that was when Rudabah fell ill. In his despair Zal remembered the feathers given him by the bird who had been his nurse. He cast one upon the fire; soon the sky grew dark; there came the sound of rushing wings and the Simurgh alighted at his feet. On hearing his troubles this bird of marvel gave Zal a remedy which cured Rudabah of her illness and caused them to rejoice.

And not long after a son, called Rustem, was born to them, of whom we have much to hear.

From manuscript by Katherine Moorhead, and reprinted by her permission.

Sources for the Story-teller

Coit, Dorothy. *Ivory Throne of Persia.* Frederick A. Stokes Co. For younger children.

Firdausi. *Shahnama of Firdausi;* done into English by A. G. and Edmund Warner. 9 vols. Kegan Paul, Trench, Trubner & Co. A complete translation for student use.

Renninger, Elizabeth. *Story of Rustem and other Persian Hero Tales from Firdausi.* Chas. Scribner & Sons.

Wilmot-Buxton, Ethel M. *Book of Rustem.* T. Y. Crowell Co. George G. Harrap & Co., Ltd., London.

Zimmern, Helen. *Epic of Kings; Hero Tales of Ancient Persia.* The Macmillan Company.

BALLADS

BALLADS

IN BALLAD literature there are many stories of simple romance which
satisfy girls who are seeking for love stories beyond those found in
their fairy tales. The old ballads run the gamut of human emotions,
but because they are frank and outspoken and deal with situations
removed from present-day environment they are usually far more
wholesome than the majority of modern love stories which are scattered about so widely.

The original versions sung by minstrels of old, present difficulties
in form and language but there are many excellent prose adaptations
which are in themselves good stories and which can be used to introduce girls and boys to modernized metrical versions.

By far the most popular ballad hero is Robin Hood of Sherwood
Forest about whom entire volumes have been written. The following
series of stories is suggested for telling:

ROBIN HOOD STORIES

How Robin Hood Became an Outlaw.
How Robin Hood Gained His Right Good Man, Little John.
The Shooting Match in Nottingham Town or The Silver Arrow.
How Will Gamwell became Will Scarlet.

Robin Hood Aids a Knight in Distress.
Robin Hood and His Men Shoot for Queen Eleanor.
King Richard in Sherwood Forest.

✖

The Silver Arrow

AFTER the proud sheriff of Nottingham had been outwitted time and
again by Robin Hood and his band of merry foresters he went to
London and complained to King Edward. But he said too much. He
wearied the king with all his complaints, and the king at last broke
out with, "Well, well! what can I do? Art thou not sheriff? Must I
myself go into the greenwood and seize these men? Art thou not
there to do this very work for me? The law is still in force by which
thou mayst have redress of those that injure thee. Get thee gone, and
set thy wits to work to devise some trick by which thou mayst get
these men into thy hands."

Then back the sheriff went, rather crestfallen, but turning over
things in his mind. The best way that he could devise to get at the
outlaws was to hold another shooting contest. He knew that would
draw them out of the greenwood, and he was determined not to trust
himself in there again. So he proclaimed that the best archers of the
north should meet one day and shoot at the butts, and he that shot the
best should bear away the prize, which was a right good arrow made
of silver, the head and feathers being of rich red gold, and there was
none like it in England.

Tidings of this came to Robin, who told his men, "Make ye ready,
ye doughty men, for I would be at that shooting. Busk ye, then, and
ye shall go with me, and I will prove whether the proud sheriff be as
good as his word."

Then there was mighty preparation of bows and strings and feath-
ering of arrows, and when all was ready one hundred and forty bowmen stood awaiting the order to start. But now stepped forth a brave

and cunning young man, called David of Doncaster. He placed himself before his captain and bowing low said, "Good master, wilt thou be ruled by my advice? Let us not stir from the greenwood, for I trow well that yon shooting match is but a cunning wile of the sheriff's to beguile us into his hands."

"Good David," said Robin, "I thank thee for thy care and wisdom, but to go not to the archery would smack of cowardice. Come what will, I must win the sheriff's silver arrow."

Then up spake Little John. "Listen to me, master and men. We will not go in our mantles of Lincoln green lest they should know us at a glance. We must e'en leave those behind and put on divers colors. One shall wear white, another red, another yellow, another blue. Once there we will mix with the throng and no one shall know us." This counsel was hailed and acted upon. Quickly the stores were ransacked for all the odd clothing they had, and when all was ready they set forth in little knots of three and four. Arrived at Nottingham they found the butts good and the range long. There sat the sheriff in state looking eagerly around to espy his enemies; but amongst as many as eight hundred people he looked in vain for the mantle and hood of the man he wanted.

Robin told off six of his men to join in the shooting with him, but all the rest he commanded to stand near him in case of an attack.

Many archers had tried their skill when at last Robin's men stepped up. First came Gilbert of the white hand, and he was followed by Little John and Scathelock. They shot so well that all the people cheered. Some cried, "Hurrah, Blue jacket!" some "Hurrah, Brown coat!" others, "Yellow! Yellow!" but when Robin shot a great shout went up for Red, for that was the color he wore, and so sure was he that he missed nothing at all, but hit the mark every time. Next followed Mutch and one Reynolde, and they did well too, much better than the bowmen who were not outlaws. Some one said to the sheriff, "If Robin Hood and all his men were here they could not have surpassed these men who shoot so bravely."

"Ay!" quoth the sheriff, "I hoped he would be here; but thou seest that for all his boldness he dare not come."

Robin overheard this and it made his blood boil. "Wait, my fine fellow," thought he, "thou shalt soon discover that Robin Hood hath been here."

At the end Robin was declared to have done best and thus to have won the prize. So he stepped up to the sheriff and received the silver and gold arrow with much courtly grace, and at that the sheriff had his doubts for he thought any one but a nobleman born would have received it differently. Robin got outside the inclosure as soon as he could and his men rallied round him; but no sooner had they taken a few steps homeward than they heard blasts on the great horns. "Ah! treason!" cried Robin. "Close up, my men, and woe be to thee, evil sheriff! Is this the way thou speedest thy guest? In yonder forest thou promised me otherwise. Had I thee now in the greenwood, thou shouldst leave me a better pledge than a false oath."

Robin's men closed all around him and a great fight commenced. No man could get near Robin without a broken head. The outlaws shot so fiercely that their enemies could not stand up against them, and the sheriff's men soon ran away. This broke up the ambush and the foresters retreated into the greenwood. But Little John could not go far, for he had an arrow wound in his knee. "Master," he said, "if thou lovest me, and for our Lord's love, and for my service to thee these years, I pray thee never let me fall into the hands of the sheriff alive; but take thy sword and smite off my head rather."

"I would not that thou wert slain, John," said Robin, "for all the gold in merry England, were it now in a heap before me."

"God forbid that thou shouldst part company from us, Little John," said little Mutch, and with these words he hoisted the wounded man on his back and bore him away. Many a time he put him down while he joined in shooting at the pursuers.

It happened now that they were near to the castle of that very knight whom Robin had helped, Sir Richard-at-the-Lee, so they repaired thither and sought admittance. It was on the skirts of the wood, strongly walled and double-ditched about. The knight flung open his gates when he saw who was there and took them all in. "Welcome!" he cried. "Welcome, Robin Hood! I remember well thy great courtesy and kindness under the greenwood tree. No man in the world is so dear to me as thou art, and thou shalt be safe here in spite of the

272

sheriff of Nottingham." Then he ordered the gates to be shut, and the drawbridge to be drawn up, and the men posted themselves on the battlements and soon drove off those who were come up to take them.

From "Robin Hood and His Merry Outlaws," retold by F. C. Tilney. Published by J. M. Dent & Sons, London, and E. P. Dutton & Co., Inc., New York, and reprinted by permission of the publishers.

OTHER ENGLISH AND SCOTTISH BALLADS

The ballads which follow are modern versions in prose and verse. They illustrate two types; the humorous and the romantic. Both types are well adapted to story-telling to adult groups.

Saddle to Rags

"WIFE," said the simple old man, "it's time to pay the rent. How many pounds have we in the house? I must get on old Tib and hobble along the way to see the landlord."

"There's the forty pounds that we saved for the last half-year's rent, and that's under the stone in the fireplace; and there's the five shillings and three-pence that's in the pocket of my best church gown; and there's nineteen shillings and five-pence and one farthing that's put up in the hole in the chimney; and there's a penny that I found in the road as I was coming home from the fair; and there's twenty pounds and one shilling and four-pence that we got for the butter and the eggs, only they brought two-score of the eggs back again after

273

they had kept them so long that they were addled; and there's the money for the sheep's wool, and that's out in the corner of old Tib's stall under a wisp of hay, lest thieves should come upon us of a sudden. It's all put convenient and near to hand, so that if the house was afire we could find it in the wink of a cat's eye and take care of it. That's not all, for under the head of the bed in the west room there's a box, and in the box there's a wooden bucket, and in the bucket there's six pounds and eleven shillings and ten-pence; and under the front doorstep—" But the simple old man looked bewildered, and began to shake his head and rub his eyes.

"Wife," said he, "couldn't you get it together and heap it up and tell me if it's all right? Then I'll get on old Tib and go to the landlord, and I'll say, 'Here's the forty pounds for the last half-year, and here's the forty pounds for this half-year. I'm not very good at the learning, but my wife says it's all right.'"

"I do believe," rejoined the wife rather sharply, "that I'd better get on old Tib and go myself."

"I wish you would, I wish you would," pleaded the simple old man meekly. "I'm always afeard I'll lose some of the money and be hanged for it."

"No, I'll not go either," said his wife. "What's the use of having a man if he can't do what you tell him?" And so the simple old man got on old Tib and started out of the gate.

"Now, if you meet a thief on the highway, remember to tell him that you're going to pay the landlord, and that you have four-score pounds in your leather saddle. You're so simple that I really believe it's just what you would do," she said to herself as she shut the door with a slam. She would have been more anxious if she had heard the old man's humble promise, "Yes, wife, I'll do just what you tell me," as he went out of the gate and into the road.

As he was jogging along the highway, who should come up to him but a fine gentleman riding on a noble black horse, with silver mountings to his saddle and a handsome black portmanteau with silver at the corners.

"Good morning," said the fine gentleman, and the simple old man answered humbly:—

"Good morning, and thank you kindly, sir, for speaking so friendly like to a plain old man like me."

"How far are you going?" asked the fine gentleman; and the old man smiled and answered with a good deal of pride for so humble an old man:—

"I'm going to pay my rent, sir. It's only two miles away, sir, where my landlord lives. I didn't pay him the last half-year, but, indeed, sir, it wasn't my fault, for he was away."

"And so you're going to pay him now, are you?"

"Yes," said the simple old man, "I have forty pounds for the last half-year's rent and forty pounds for this half-year's rent. My wife says it's all right, and she's good at the counting, my wife is; and she told me that's what I must say if any one asked me. Some of it's from the butter and some of it's from the wool, and there's a penny that my wife picked up in the road when she came from the fair, but she says it is all right."

"Then it must be," declared the fine gentleman, "but there's many a thief going about these days, and you ought not to tell any one about your money; you might be robbed."

"Oh no, my wife is far wiser than that," said the simple old man, "for she put all the money in my saddle, where no one would look for it."

So the two jogged pleasantly along together, and the old man said to himself that he had never before seen a fine gentleman who was so gracious to him. The fine gentleman asked him about his sheep and how he cared for them, and about his old horse, Tib, and how long he had had her. The old man was just telling about what a fine colt she was only twenty-nine years ago, when the road made a sharp turn down a hill, with a brook at the bottom and trees growing thickly all around, and the fine gentleman pulled out a pistol and pointed it full at the simple old man and said:—

"Stand still and give me your money," but the simple old man hesitated and asked:—

"Please tell me, sir, are you a thief?" and the fine gentleman answered:—

"There's better names for it than that, but what do you want to know for?" and the simple old man replied:—

"My wife told me that if I met a thief on the highway, I was to tell him that I was going to pay the rent, and that I had four-score pounds in my saddle; but she did not tell me what to do if he told me to give it to him. I'll have to follow my own wit, and indeed, I haven't much; so I'll just fling the saddle over the hedge and be rid of it."

The thief threw back his head and laughed.

"Your wife will never find any fault with you if you mind her like that; and yet you never know what a woman will like," he added meditatively, for he was a philosopher as well as a thief. "Now see how well you can mind me," he said. "Stand here and hold my horse while I go over the hedge, and take good care of my portmanteau."

It was not easy to climb through the hedge, for it was all thorns and briers, but the very moment that the thief was through it, the simple old man put his foot in the stirrup of the thief's noble horse and rode away like the wind chasing a hat.

"Hold on!" shouted the thief.

"Yes, sir, I am a-holding on," he cried, "and I'm a-taking care of the portmanteau, sir, just as you told me to. I'm a-minding, sir."

"Stay," called the thief, "and I'll give you half of all I've got."

"My wife didn't tell me to," said the simple old man, "and I don't think she'd like it if I did. She told me to go to the landlord and pay the rent."

There was nothing for the thief to do but to sit down on the ground and cut open the old man's saddle. The leather was hard, and his sword was rusty, for he was more accustomed to frightening people with it than to cutting their heads off, and it was full three hours by the sun that he worked to get the saddle open; and after all, there was nothing in it but rags, for when the simple old man had once made his way out of his wife's sight, he had taken the money out of the saddle and put it into his bosom, for he said to himself:—

"A man ought to be at the head of his own house, and I'm going to do what I like with it. I'm not one bit afraid."

The old man had never sat on so noble a horse before, and had never had such a gallop in all his life as he had that morning. When he came to his landlord's house, he opened the portmanteau, and the landlord stared in surprise, for there was five hundred pounds in silver and five hundred pounds in good yellow gold.

"And where did you get the silver money, and where did you get the gold?" asked the landlord; and the simple old man answered:—

"I met a man by the way, and he and I swapped horses, and he gave me the silver money and the gold money to boot."

"I don't believe that you ought to go about by yourself with all that money," said the landlord; and the simple old man answered:—

"I don't think any one would hurt such a simple old man as I am; and besides, I always do what my wife tells me to, for she has learning and she can count. Maybe the fine gentleman that I met didn't mind his wife."

The simple old man did not go home by the highway, but by a narrow lane; and far down the road he spied old Tib feeding under a tree, for the fine gentleman had found that he could get on faster without her. So the simple old man and Tib and the fine gentleman's horse and the fine gentleman's portmanteau with the gold and the silver all went home together; and when his wife saw it, she danced for joy, and she said:—

"Now, old man, see what you get by minding your wife!"

The King of France's Daughter

A LONG time ago, there ruled in France a famous monarch, called "Charles the Bald," who had a fair daughter named Judith, the only child of his dead queen. She was a very sweet young princess; graceful and beautiful, as only a princess in a ballad or a fairy story can be. The king doted on her with all his heart, was proud of her beauty and accomplishments, and resolved to wed her to some rich and powerful prince. But unfortunately for his ambitious plans, there came to his court a young prince of England, named Ethelwulph, brave and renowned, but, because of a revolution in his native land, an exile, poor and powerless. He was handsome and amiable, and, falling in love with the princess of France, had little difficulty in winning her love in return. This was not at all pleasing to the king, her father; indeed was so displeasing that he frowned on his young guest in awful indignation and reproach. This made Ethelwulph's residence at court very uncomfortable, as all the courtiers—who copied after their liege lord so servilely that to the youngest they shaved their crowns, in imitation of the royal baldness—frowned with double blackness on the unlucky stranger; and all the fair ladies of the court, except the princess, looked most ungracious, or coolly turned their backs upon him.

The king reproved his daughter sternly, and commanded her to think no more of that penniless and proscribed young Englishman. A great king was Charles, but his power did not reach quite so far as that; Judith thought of her lover more than ever, pitied him, and resolved to cling to him all the more for his misfortunes.

At length her father began to treat her severely, and wished to marry her to a gray-headed old royal suitor, whom she detested; and, getting very desperate, she agreed to escape from court with her lover, to some safe refuge, where they could wed and live in peace. So she disguised herself in humble attire, and, taking only, of all her royal goods, a casket of jewels and gold, stole forth, one summer night, from her father's stately palace, away to the great hunting

278

forest, on the borders of which her English lover had promised to meet her.

The young prince reached the spot agreed upon for the meeting before his fair lady, and sat down under an oak-tree, to wait her coming. But most unluckily, as he waited there, all fond impatience, he was attacked by outlaws, robbed, and mortally wounded by dagger-strokes.

The princess came to the wood, yet could not for a long time find the spot where he lay, but wandered about, listening for his voice, and calling him softly, for fear of being overheard by robbers, or some of the king's foresters. At length she was startled by hearing piteous sobs and groans, and then a mournful voice, saying, "Farewell, my beloved, whom I must never more see! My days are at an end, and for thy love I die. While I lie here, bleeding all my brave young life away, I think only of my beautiful lady, and I am not sorry that I loved her. Ah, little knows she that my heart's blood is flowing on the ground!"

At these words, the princess, struck with a sad foreboding, rushed forward to the side of the dying man. The robbers had dragged him out from under the oak-tree's shadow into an open glade, where the full moon shone down on his ghastly face. It was, indeed, her beloved prince. She flung herself down by him, raised his head on her knee, and called him by his name very tenderly and sorrowfully. Alas! he could not answer her. Once he looked at her; then with a low, sad sigh, his life fled away forever.

For a long time the princess would not believe Prince Ethelwulph dead, but continued to call on his name more and more wildly, striving to rouse him from his deep swoon, and to stanch his bleeding wounds. At last she resigned all hope, and, lying down by his side, with his cold hand pressed close to her heart, she wept bitterly till morning. Then she rose up and looked about her, wearily and desolately. "Alas!" she murmured, "what will become of me? I cannot bear to return to the court of my father;—my father, who scorned *him*,—my gracious and right royal love, the princeliest man under the sun,—and drove him forth to die in this savage wood! Rather will I seek a servant's lowly place, in some stranger's family, and, all

279

unknown, live out my few sad days,—my woeful widowed days."
Then she fell to weeping again very drearily, and calling on the name
of her dead love.

It happened that a forester—a very brave and comely youth—was
that morning ranging the wood, and came suddenly upon the maiden.
Seeing that he looked gentle and full of pity, she told him a part of
her sorrowful story, and showed him her dead lover, but did not re-
veal his rank or her own. Her distress moved him to tears. He comforted her all he could; he took up the body of the prince, and bore it
tenderly to his cottage, where he washed its wounds, composed its
limbs, and laid it to rest in the flowery earth, under an old forest-tree.

Then, as the princess had spoken to him of wishing to go to service,
he placed her with his mother, who was very kind to her, and soon
grew to love her very dearly. And not alone did that good old dame
love the fair and sorrowful stranger, but all her household; and most
of all, the handsome young forester. He had never beheld a maiden
of such refined beauty, such grace, and such gentle manners; and he
thought it would be the happiest thing in the world if he could win her
for his wife.

It was a long time before the princess would consent to marry him.
Her love and her joy seemed all buried with her murdered prince.
But the forester was so kind and generous, and she was so grateful to
him, and honored him so sincerely, that she finally granted him her
hand; and he proved so good a husband that at last she grew very
happy and contented, and almost forgot the lofty rank to which she
was born, and the bitter sorrow of her girlhood.

It was not till after years had gone by, and she was the mother of
seven children, that the Princess Judith revealed the secret of her
royal birth to her husband. He was greatly astonished; and, though he
did not love his beautiful wife any better than before, he wondered
that she could have ever loved him and married him,—a man of
low degree. He besought her to allow him to proclaim her rank to the
world; and from that time he clothed his children in a very curious
manner. He had made for them parti-colored garments,—the right
side of cloth of gold, the left of gray frieze, as emblematical of the
rank of the mother and of the father. When he next heard that the

king was coming to chase the deer in the forest, he persuaded Judith to place herself and her children near a path along which his majesty must ride.

The princess was dressed in robes of crimson velvet, and wore the royal jewels she had secretly treasured through all these years. Her husband stood beside her, dressed all in sober gray, but a right gallant figure to behold; and the seven beautiful children, in their parti-colored dress,—half cloth of gold, half gray frieze, like sunshine and shadow,—were grouped around their parents.

Judith started and turned pale when she heard the horn of the hunters, and the dull sound of their horses' hoofs on the grassy forest paths. Her heart yearned lovingly toward her father, as it had often done since she had been a mother; but she feared to meet him face to face,—feared that he would reproach and disown her; or, what would be far worse, treat with lofty scorn her good and noble husband.

At length the monarch came in sight, followed by a long cavalcade of knights and gentlemen. Judith looked at him eagerly. He did not seem greatly changed; he had grown a little stouter and ruddier, a little more bald, and his face seemed somewhat softened, as by sorrow and regret.

Charles was a keen-eyed monarch, who saw everything in his way; so that singular group by the roadside did not escape his notice. He checked his horse, and looked at them curiously for a few moments; then, calling the forester to him, asked how he dared to dress his wife in such a royal way, and to put cloth of gold on his children.

"Because, sire," replied the forester, "she hath, by birth, as well as by sovereign beauty, the right to be so arrayed; and the children, through her, are entitled to cloth of gold and pearls; she being a princess—the highest in the land."

On hearing this reply, the king looked more earnestly at Judith, and his stern face lighted up with a great joy, as he said to the forester, "The more I look at thy wife, the more it seems to me that she is my long lost daughter, whom I have mourned as dead."

At these words the princess sprang forward, and, kneeling before him, cried, "I am thy daughter,—once thy little Judith. Pardon me, my dear father and sovereign liege!"

The king at once dismounted and raised her in his arms, kissed her, and wept over her. Then he embraced her husband, and kissed and blessed her children—all seven of them—right tenderly and joyfully.

After this glad meeting, the king gave up hunting for the day; and, turning about with all his train, went home with the forester and his family. There, in that rustic cottage, which, though not very small, quite overflowed with all that gay retinue, Charles the Bald—no longer the proud and ambitious monarch who frowned on poor Ethelwulph, and so cruelly treated his only daughter—dubbed the lowly-born forester knight, and made him Earl of Flanders, and chief of all the royal forces.

Soon after this time, the earl and the princess went to live in a royal castle, and had hosts of servitors; and, though they saw less of each other than formerly, they saw a great deal of good company, to make up for it. Their seven children no longer wore parti-colored clothes, but dressed in velvet and cloth of gold every day, and had tutors and governesses, and were taught to behave like fine ladies and gentlemen.

But I doubt if they were, any of them, happier than in the old days, before the princess revealed that she was a princess, and when the children ran free about the forester's cottage, and grew strong and beautiful in the breezy old wood; when they gathered wild flowers, waded in the brook, and tumbled in the grass, without fear of soiling their clothes,—their gray peasant gowns, jerkins, and hose,—and without fear of tiresome reproofs for their merry frolics and joyous laughter. But people can't be great princes and princesses without paying for their grandeur, in quiet ease, healthy sport, and careless happiness.

From "Stories of Famous Ballads," by Grace Green-wood, ed. by Caroline Burnite. Copyright, 1906, by Ginn & Co. Reprinted by the H. R. Huntting Co., 1929.

BALLADS

Forester Etin

"WHAT is that bird-song that I hear far away in the forest?" said Lady Margaret to her bower-maiden; and the bower-maiden answered:—

"Never did I hear such a bird-note before. O my lady, do not go to the forest," she pleaded, for Lady Margaret half rose from her seat, and the pearls that she was sewing to her silken mantle fell to the floor and rolled about the room. One of them rolled out of the open door, and it did not stop, but rolled on and on, and ever it went toward the forest.

"Do you see the pearl?" asked Lady Margaret. "It is rolling toward Elmond Wood. Look, it is waiting for me. Now it goes on. We will go, the pearl and I, and we will listen to all the birds that sing on all the trees, and by and by we shall surely find the bird that sings the wonderful new song."

"Oh, do not go, my lady," said the bower-maiden. "The wise woman in the little house by the hazel said there was no good to be got by following strange guides."

"Call you my own pearl a strange guide, you foolish maiden?" queried Lady Margaret, with a smile.

"I do not know," answered the bower-maiden meekly, "but the wise woman once said that sometimes one's own were strange to one. The bird is not one of our own birds, my lady; it is not the mavis nor the laverock, and I am afraid. Do not go."

"Silly little maiden," laughed Lady Margaret. "I am going to Elmond Wood—no, you shall not go with me, because you were afraid of my pretty bird-song; but I will come again before the sun is behind the hill where the pine-trees stand, and I will bring you a handful of brown nuts, and I will tell you where my pretty bird lives, foolish child as you are." And Lady Margaret dropped her needle and her silken mantle, and kissed lightly the little bower-maiden; and then she sped away out of the open door, and followed the pearl down the winding path, along the lane, over the stepping-stones in the brook, up the little hill, and into Elmond Wood.

283

The shade was green, and there was long, pale moss on the trees, and here and there the sun glinted down between the branches, and the brown water of the little pools in the forest was touched with gold. The pathway was all of bright green moss, and she wandered along happily, sometimes singing little snatches of old songs, and sometimes she stood with her lily-white hand behind her rosy ear, listening for the song of the wonderful bird-note; and whenever she heard it, it seemed to come from farther away in the forest.

"I thought the forest was full of the nut bushes," said Lady Margaret to herself, "but any way, I will not go back without my handful of nuts, or my silly little maiden will laugh at me."

But there was no nut bush to be seen, and before she had found one, the rays of the sun that made their way into the forest were pale and dim, and the gold had faded from the brown water.

"Here is my nut bush at last!" cried Lady Margaret, and she broke off a tiny branch. But hark! What was that? for she heard the bird-song, and it came out of the bush. No, it was not a bird-note, it was a human voice, and it said gently:—

"And do you pick the nuts without asking leave of the forester, Lady Margaret?"

"My father is earl of all the land," said Lady Margaret. "May I not pick a nut in my father's woods without asking any forester?"

"This is not the earl's nut bush, Lady Margaret; it is my own. A wise woman gave it me, but I'll gladly give it to you, my love, if you'll only bide in the forest here with me."

There was something of the bird-note in the pleading voice; and when the nut bush suddenly sank into the ground and disappeared, and he stood before her, a comely youth wearing the green of the forester, she said to herself:—

"He is taller and straighter than the men of my father's court; his eyes are clearer and brighter, and if he was in the great hall of the castle, he would be the best man of them all."

"I know I'm only your father's forester, Lady Margaret," said he, with the same bird-note in his voice, "but if you'll be my own sweetheart and bide with me in the forest, I'll build you a fairer bower than ever you saw.'

Lady Margaret looked upon him again, and again she said to herself:—

"His eyes are true, and his voice is true, and if he was in the great hall of the castle, he would be the best man of them all."

And this is why the little bower-maiden wept for her lost lady until her pretty eyes were all red with the salt tears; and this is why the pearls still lay on the floor of the bower, and why the door of the bower was never closed by day or by night, for the maiden liked to fancy that her lady was coming in at any moment and would say to her:—

"Little maiden, why do you not pick up the pearls that lie all about the floor?"

And so it was that Lady Margaret became the sweetheart of Forester Etin. Far in the depths of the forest he built the beautiful bower. It was made of boughs on which the green leaves never withered, and over it ran many vines, and all about it were bright flowers whose colors never faded. Around it Forester Etin built a high stone wall to keep his lady safe from any harm; and beside the wall was a thorn-tree, and whenever anything came near that might hurt her, the thorn-tree would stoop down and catch it up on its sharp thorns.

Twelve long, happy years they lived together, Forester Etin and his dear Lady Margaret, in the beautiful bower among the flowers that never faded, and seven fair sons she bore under the green leaves that never withered. On the day when the eldest son was just ten years old, Forester Etin said:—

"My bonny lad is almost a man now, and he shall go to the hunting with me this day."

So Forester Etin and his eldest son set out to wander through the gay greenwood. All around them was merry and glad. The mavis was singing overhead; the trees were murmuring quietly together, and all among the grass and the flowers were soft, sweet little voices, so gentle that the boy could not always hear them, but he was so happy that he knew they were there. All at once he heard a music that he had never heard before.

"What is it, my father?" he asked, "the strange, new music? I never heard a bird like that."

Then the father said that it was a church bell, and somehow the sound of it made the boy think of his mother, and he said:—

"Shall you be angry, Father, if I ask you something?" and Forester Etin smiled and answered:—

"Say on, say on, my bonny boy. You may always ask your own father what you will," and the boy said:—

"What makes my mother's cheeks so wet, and why does she sometimes sob so bitterly when you are away at the hunting?"

Then the father put his arm about the boy, and they sat under an oak-tree, and the sun glinted down through the branches and made the water in the little brown pools all golden; and the father spoke very sadly:—

"No wonder is it that she pines and grieves, for it is twelve long years and more since she has seen either kith or kin. She was the daughter of an earl, a lady of high degree. She might have wedded the first in all the land, but I loved her so with all my heart that she could not help loving me. I was only her father's forester, but for twelve long years she has abode with me in the forest."

"I'm sorry," said the little boy. "I'll shoot the laverock in the lift and the bunting on the tree, and I'll carry them home to my mother, and I'll say, 'Mother, do not grieve any more,' and then perhaps she will be merrier."

But Lady Margaret was no merrier, and one day Forester Etin took his little son aside and whispered:—

"I'm going far away into the greenwood, my eldest son; and if I do not come back when the sun shines no more through the thorn-tree, then I shall not come again, and you must go to your mother and say, 'Mother, let us all go away from the forest, and let us seek your own father in the land where one hears the church bells ring.' " Then Forester Etin took his bow and arrows and went far away into the greenwood; but every few steps he stopped, and looked back to see his wife's face once more before she should go to the land where the church bells ring.

All day long the little boy stayed under the thorn-tree outside the high stone wall and watched for his father. When the sun no longer shone through the thorns, he went in to his mother and said:—

"Mother, should you be angry with me if I asked you something?" and his mother smiled and answered:—

"Say on, say on, my bonny boy. You may always ask your own mother what you will," and the boy pleaded:—

"You're grieving, Mother, and your cheeks are wet with tears, and when you kiss me at night they drop on my face and wake me. Won't you tell me why you grieve?"

Then the mother answered:—

"It is because I have seven fair sons and not one of them has ever had christening, for I have stayed away from my father, the earl of all the land, twelve long years for the love of Forester Etin."

"Could you not go back to the earl, and take my father and me and my six brothers?"

"Alas, no, for your father is an outlaw, and if he should go to the castle of the earl without a pardon, he would be hanged on the gallows-tree."

"Would you go if my father told you to go?" asked the boy; and then he repeated what his father had said. His mother wept more bitterly than ever, and she answered:—

"If your father has left us, then we must go."

So in the morning the eldest son took his mother by the hand, and they two and the six little brothers went to find the castle of the earl. It was a long way and they were weary, and the little brothers were afraid, for they had never before been so far away from the bower where the flowers never faded. The rough stones cut their feet, and the sharp briers scratched their little fingers, and when they were out of the cool shade of the forest, the hot sun burned their cheeks. At last the mother stopped and pointed to a gray cloud on a hill and said:—

"That is my father's castle"; and when they had come nearer, she pointed to a heavy iron gate set in a high stone wall, and said:—

"That is the gate of my father's castle. Stop by the little brook and bathe the sun-burn from your cheeks and the touch of the briers from your fingers and the bruises of the rough stones from your feet, and then, my own eldest son, we will wait here beside the little brook, and you must go alone to the earl and tell him that you are the son of his own daughter Margaret."

"But there is a man at the gate, my mother, and will he let me in?"

"He'll let you in for a fee, my son. No money have I, but I have three jewel rings. Give the ruby to the proud porter, and he will let you through the gate. Then give the emerald to the butler boy, and he will take you to the door of the hall; but save the diamond to give to the minstrel that's harping in the hall, for he is the one that can turn the hearts of the earl and all his men to joy or woe as he will."

So the little boy did as his mother bade him, and before long he was within the door of the hall, and far up at the other end sat the earl on the high seat. The boy looked timidly at the minstrel, for he thought:—

"To turn one's heart to joy or to woe, that is greatest of all." But when he shyly held out the ring with its flashing diamond, the minstrel looked upon him kindly and shook his head and said:—

"Something tells me that my song may be for love and not for reward." Then he began to play on his harp, and somehow every note gave the boy new courage. He was no longer afraid, but he stood erect and walked up the hall till he came before the earl. Then he fell on one knee and was silent. The earl looked at him and turned pale. Then he put his hand over his eyes and moaned:—

"Go away, child, or my heart will break, for you are so like to my own dear Margaret"; but the boy only bowed lower and kissed the hand of the earl and said:—

"But your own dear Margaret stands at your castle gate, and with her are my six little brothers, for I am her oldest son."

Then the earl stalked down the hall and called out angrily:—

"Where are my porters that I pay good silver and good gold? How dare they leave Lady Margaret outside my castle gate?"

Then the little eldest son ran so joyfully to tell his mother that he was beside her before the proud porter could take his eyes from the ruby ring long enough to see who it was that ran past him.

And so Lady Margaret was with her father again; but when it was time for the feast, a great longing to see Forester Etin came over her, and she said:—

"My heart aches, Father, to see my own Etin. No bit can I eat and no drop can I drink till he is by my side."

Then the earl called out angrily:—

"Where are all the bold rangers that I pay good silver and good gold? Why do they not search the woods and bring Forester Etin home to us?" But the little boy shook his head and said:—

"He cannot come without a free pardon, or he would be hanged on the gallows-tree."

Then the earl declared:—

"Here is a pardon all sealed with my own hand. Let every ranger go to the forest and search till he finds the husband of Lady Margaret."

So the rangers searched the forest, and when they found Forester Etin, he lay on the ground under the thorn-tree, and he was groaning and tearing his yellow hair.

"Take me to hang on the gallows-tree, if you will," he said. "My lady's gone, and my life is nothing to me."

"But it is your lady that has sent for you," they answered, "and here's a free pardon for you from the earl of all the land."

And so it came to pass that they all sat at the feast together and when the earl asked the little oldest son what gift he would have for himself, the little boy remembered what his mother had said and answered:—

"Will you and my mother and my father take me and my six brothers to the holy church and let us get our christening? for it's only once that I have even heard the sound of a church bell."

"That's not so hard a boon, my boy, and this very day you shall go to the holy church and get your christening, and you shall all live here in the castle with me, and when I die, the brave Forester Etin shall rule the land for the love that he has borne to my dear Lady Margaret these twelve long years and more."

When Lady Margaret went into her own bower again, there was the little bower-maiden, and Lady Margaret smiled and asked:—

"Little maiden, why do you not pick up the pearls that lie all about the floor?" and the bower-maiden smiled in answer and said:—

"But, Lady Margaret, where is the handful of nuts that you promised to bring me from Elmond Wood?"

From "Old Ballads in Prose," by E. M. Tappan.
Copyright, 1901, 1929, by Houghton Mifflin Co.,
and reprinted by permission of the publishers.

Muckle Mou'ed Meg

"O wha hasna heard o' the bauld Juden Murray,
The Lord o' the Elibank Castle sae high?
An' wha hasna heard o' that notable foray,
Whan Willie o' Harden was catched wi' the kye?"

EARLY one evening Sir Juden Murray was walking in the low meadows which lay along the banks of the River Tweed that flowed close by his Old Tower. His hands were clasped behind his back and his head was sunk low on his breast. There was a matter that had been pressing heavily on his mind and it troubled him more and more. It was a sore anxiety to him how he was going to provide for his three daughters who were so plain looking that it was very unlikely that any gay wooers would ever stop at their door.

Meg, the eldest, was especially plain. She was pale and thin; her eyes were colorless, and to make matters worse, her mouth was so wide that she was known throughout the length and breadth of four counties as "Muckle Mou'ed Meg o' Elibank."

Sir Juden was roused from his thoughts by a shout from the hill above where he was walking. It was one of his men-at-arms who called to him that young Will o' Harden and some of his wild companions were driving a herd of Elibank cattle down the glen.

BALLADS

Now Will o' Harden was one of the bold sons of Walter Scott o' Harden of Teviotdale. In those days all the people who lived on the borderland between Scotland and England were fond of rieving, and the sons of Harden were no exception to the rule. Besides, it is not unlikely, that the very cattle which young Will was stealing had been taken in the same manner from the Harden hills by Sir Juden's men.

Be that as it may, Sir Juden was wise enough to know that his men were no match for Will o' Harden and his companions. So instead of meeting them in the open, he bade his men to lie down in the grass on the hillside, and in order that they should not shoot one another, each man was bidden to place a white feather in his cap. Thus they lay quietly in the dusk and when Will o' Harden came down the glen behind his men with the cattle, they seized him, stifled his cries, and carried him away to the deepest dungeon in Elibank Castle.

When Will o' Harden's men discovered that their leader was gone, they got together and rode to the castle gate. They reached it at dawn only to find that the stout ash door to the prison had been closed against them and then they knew that bold Willie would see the light of day but once, and that when he was brought out to be hanged under the dule tree on the green.

"Juden, Juden," called the Lady o' Elibank to her husband, early the next morning. Sir Juden answered drowsily and looked across the room to where his wife Margaret, already dressed, was looking out of the narrow casement. "What are you going to do with that poor young man?" she said. Sir Juden stared at his wife in amazement at the question, for she was not wont to be so pitiful toward any of his prisoners. "By'r our Lady, but there is but one thing to do. Hang the rogue, and that right soon," he answered. "What," said the Lady o' Elibank, "hang the young Knight o' Harden, when I have three ill-favored daughters to marry off on my hands. I wonder at ye, Juden."

Sir Juden looked at his wife for full three minutes then burst into a hearty laugh. "By my soul, thou art right, Margaret," he said. "Thou wert born with the wisdom of Solomon, though men would scarce think it to look at thee," and he began to dress himself, without more ado.

Less than two hours afterwards the door that led to the dungeon was opened. Three men-at-arms appeared and young Will o' Harden, bound as he was, was ordered to follow them. He obeyed without a word. He had had his adventure and failed. He would pay the penalty that the times required without complaining but as he climbed those steps I doubt not but that his thoughts turned to the bonny braes that lay around Harden and to his Mother, the gentle Flower of Yarrow, whom he would never see again.

To his great surprise instead of being taken at once to the dule tree on the green he was led into a large hall, where a strange sight met his eyes. The room was filled with men-at-arms laughing and talking together. Across the hall on a raised dais, seated in an arm chair, was his captor of the night before, and beside him in another chair, sat a stern-faced lady in a wondrous headdress and a stiff silk dress whom he took to be his wife. Between them, blushing and hanging her head as though the ordeal was too much for her was the plainest looking maiden he had ever seen. She was thin and ill-thriven, her nose was long and pointed, her eyes were colorless, and the size of her mouth alone proclaimed her at once as the worthy couple's eldest daughter, "Muckle Mou'ed Meg."

Her two sisters stood near by laughing and whispering. They were plain looking but not so plain looking as Meg.

Sir Juden crossed one thin leg over the other and looked at the prisoner from under his bushy eyebrows. "Good morrow, young sir," he said. "So you and your friends thought you would steal some of my cattle. By whose warrant did you ride?" "I rode at my own peril," answered the young man haughtily, for he did not like to be questioned in this manner. "Thou knowest that right well, Sir Juden, and it is a waste of words to parley here."

"So thou knowest the fate that thy rash deed brings on thee," said Sir Juden, his temper rising, "and by my faith I am inclined to hang thee right soon. But thou art young, William, and young blood is ever roving, that I would fain remember, and so I offer you another chance."

Here the Lord of Elibank looked at his wife to see if he had said the right thing for it was she who had schooled him. Meanwhile, young Harden happening to meet Meg Murray's eyes was puzzled by the look, half wistful, half imploring, which she gave him. He turned to the window and received somewhat of a shock when he saw a strong rope with a noose at the end dangling from a tree while a man at arms stood idly by waiting his turn as executioner.

"So the old rascal is going to hang me after all," he said to himself. "But if so, what means all this mummery and why does that poor maiden look at me as though her life depended on mine?"

The Lady Margaret having nodded her head in approval, Sir Juden went on with his speech, "I will offer you another chance, I say, and moreover, I will throw a herd of the cattle which thou wert so anxious to steal into the bargain, if thou wilt promise on thy part, to wed my daughter, Meg, within the space of four days."

For the moment young Harden was too astonished to speak. So this was the meaning of it all. He was to be forced to wed the ugliest maiden in the south of Scotland to save his life. The vision of his Mother's beauty rose before him and the contrast between the Flower of Yarrow and Muckle Mou'ed Meg o' Elibank struck him so sharply that he cried out in anger, "By my troth, but this thing can never be, do your worst, Sir Juden."

"Think well before ye choose," said that knight, "there are better things in the world than beauty, young man. Hast thou not read in the good book, if ever ye find time to read it, which I doubt, that a prudent wife is more to be sought after than a bonnie one?"

Young Harden glanced from the lady, who, poor thing, had hidden her face in her hands, to the gallows and back again to the lady. Was ever mortal man in such a plight? Here was he, young, handsome, rich and little more than four and twenty, and he must either lose his life on yonder green or marry a maiden whom everyone mocked at for her looks.

"If I could only be alone with her for a few minutes," he thought to himself, "to see what she looks like when no one is peering at her. The maiden hath no chance in the midst of this mannerless crowd, and methought her eyes were honest and true when they looked into mine a little while ago."

At that moment Meg Murray raised her head and looked about her like a stag at bay. Poor lassie, it had been bad enough to be jeered at by her Father and scolded by her Mother because of her unfortunately large mouth without being put up for sale, as it were, before all her Father's retainers: and now the young man to whom she had been offered chose to suffer death rather than have her for his bride.

It was the bitterest moment in Meg Murray's life and had she known it, it was the moment that fixed her destiny. For young Willie o' Harden saw that look and something in it stirred his pity. Besides he noticed that her pale face was sweet and confiding and her gray eyes clear and true.

"Hold," he cried, "I have changed my mind and I accept the conditions. But I call all men to witness that I accept not the hand of this maiden of necessity or against my will. I am a Scot, and had I minded to I could have faced death. But I now crave the honor of her hand from her Father, in humility, and here I vow, before ye all, to do my best to be to her a loyal and a true husband."

There was laughter in the hall, and men would have crowded around the young knight and made much of him, but he would have none of it. He forced his way across the room to where Meg stood trembling and took her hand. She greeted him with a look that set him thinking of a bird set free from its cage, and I wot, that though he did not know it, from that moment he began to love her.

His words to Sir Juden were short and gruff. "Sir," he asked, "hast thou a priest in this castle? If so, let him come hither and finish what we have begun for I would fain spend this night in my own Tower of Oakwood."

"There is no need for such haste," said Lady Margaret to her husband. "The lassie's providing must be gathered together for I would not have it said that a bride went out of Elibank with only the clothes she stood in."

But young Harden interrupted her with, "Let her be married now or not at all," and as the heir of Harden as a prospective son-in-law was very different from the heir of Harden as a prisoner, a priest was called and in great haste William Scott of Harden was married to

Margaret Murray of Elibank, and then they two set out alone over the hill to the old Tower of Oakwood—he with high thoughts of anger and revenge for the trick that had been played on him and she wondering wistfully what the future held for her.

The day was cold and wet and halfway over the Hangingway Heights he heard a stifled sob and turning saw his little woebegone bride trying in vain with numbed fingers to guide her palfrey to firmer footing.

The sight would have touched a harder heart than Willie of Harden's, but after all, he was a true son of the Flower of Yarrow who was aye kind-hearted. "God save us, lassie, but there's nothing to grieve about. 'Tis not thy fault that things have fallen out thus, and if I be angered, 'tis not at thee. Come," and as he spoke he lifted her from her saddle and placed her on his horse before him. "Leave that stupid horse of thine to find its way home. We will go over the hill quicker in this fashion, and thee wilt have more shelter from the rain. There is many a good nag on the hills at Harden and my Mother will soon have one trained for thee."

Poor Meg caught her breath. "Thy Lady Mother, she is very beautiful," she faltered. "And doubtless she looked for beauty in her sons' wives?" Then forever and a day all resentment went out of Willie o' Harden's heart and love and pity entered it. "If her sons' wives are but good women, my Mother will be well content," he said, and with that he kissed her.

That kiss marked the beginning of Meg Scott's happiness. For happy she always was. She was always plain looking, for nothing could alter her features, but great happiness brings with it a look of contentment which can beautify the most homely face, and she was such a good housekeeper (no one could salt beef as she could), and so modest and gentle, that her handsome husband came to love her more and more, and I wot that her face became to him the bonniest and sweetest face in the whole world.

Sons and daughters were born to them, strapping lads and fair faced lassies. And in after years when old Wat o' Harden died and Sir William reigned in his stead, he was wont to declare that for prudence and virtue and honor there was no woman on earth to be compared with his good wife Meg.

Freely adapted from version in "Tales from Scottish Ballads," by E. W. Grierson, n. d. London, Black. First edition ("Children's tales from Scottish Ballads,") published September, 1906. Imported by The Macmillan Co. under both titles.

Get Up and Bar the Door

IT FELL about the Martinmas time,
    And a gay time it was then,
When our good wife got puddings to make,
    And she's boild them in the pan.

The wind sae cauld blew south and north,
    And blew into the floor;
Quoth our goodman to our goodwife,
    "Gae out and bar the door."

"My hand is in my hussyfskap,
    Goodman, as ye may see;
And it shoud nae be barrd this hundred year,
    It's no be barrd for me."

They made a paction tween them twa,
    They made it firm and sure,
That the first word whaeer shoud speak,
    Shoud rise and bar the door.

Then by there came two gentlemen,
    At twelve o clock at night,

And they could neither see house nor hall,
   Nor coal nor candle-light.

"Now whether is this a rich man's house,
   Or whether is it a poor?"
But neer a word wad ane o them speak,
   For barring of the door.

And first they ate the white puddings,
   And then they ate the black;
Tho muckle thought the goodwife to hersel,
   Yet neer a word she spake.

Then said the one unto the other,
   "Here, man, tak ye my knife;
Do ye tak aff the auld man's beard,
   And I'll kiss the goodwife."

"But there's nae water in the house,
   And what shall we do than?"
"What ails ye at the pudding-broo,
   That boils into the pan?"

O up then started our goodman,
   An angry man was he:
"Will ye kiss my wife before my een,
   And scad me wi pudding-bree?"

Then up and started our goodwife,
   Gied three skips on the floor:
"Goodman, you've spoken the foremost word,
   Get up and bar the door."

*From "English and Scottish Popular Ballads," ed.
from the collection of Frances James Child, by
Helen Child Sargent and George Lyman Kittredge,
Houghton Mifflin Co., publishers.*

BAG O' TALES

Sources for the Story-teller

Bates, Katherine L. *Ballad Book.* Benjamin H. Sanborn & Co. Poetical versions.

Greenwood, Grace. *Stories from Famous Ballads,* ed. by Caroline Burnite. Huntting.

Grierson, E. W. *Tales from Scottish Ballads.* Frederick A. Stokes Co.

Macleod, Mary. *Book of Ballad Stories.* Frederick A. Stokes Co.

McSpadden, J. W. *Stories of Robin Hood and His Merry Outlaws.* T. Y. Crowell Co.

Percy, Thomas. *Boy's Percy,* ed. by Sidney Lanier. Chas. Scribner's Sons.

Olcott, F. J. *Story-Telling Ballads.* Houghton Mifflin Co. Modern metrical versions of old ballads.

Perkins, L. F. *Robin Hood.* Houghton Mifflin Co. In verse.

Pyle, Howard. *Merry Adventures of Robin Hood.* Chas. Scribner's Sons. Independent, literary versions. Very popular with children.

Tappan, E. M. *Old Ballads in Prose.* Houghton Mifflin Co. Excellent versions and wide variety.

Tappan, E. M. *Robin Hood.* Little, Brown & Company.

Tilney, F. C. *Robin Hood and His Merry Outlaws.* E. P. Dutton & Co., Inc. A good selection of stories and a re-telling which is faithful to the original ballads.

FANCIFUL STORIES AND FAMILY BOOKS

FANCIFUL STORIES AND FAMILY BOOKS

FANCIFUL STORIES

THE modern fanciful tales that count for full value have in most cases been produced by artists who have met with success in other fields of writing. The ability to enter the imaginative life of children and relate it in terms which children accept, requires not only gifts of mind and heart but literary skill as well. To adapt stories of this literary type requires creative ability second only to authorship, and for this reason, literary stories when used for story-telling, should usually be made word-perfect.

A short selected list from approved sources is given.

"The Princess on the Pea."

"The Nightingale."

"Ole Shut-Eye."

"The Snow Queen," from *Fairy Tales* by Hans Christian Andersen.

"The Seller of Dreams," from *The Firelight Fairy Book* by Henry Beston.

"The Rabbit Sends In a Little Bill."

"The Mad Tea Party," from *Alice in Wonderland* by Lewis Carroll.

"A Roundabout Turn," by Robert H. Charles (Story poem).

"Shen of the Sea," by Arthur Bowie Chrisman.

"Knock at the Door," by Elizabeth Coatsworth.

"Truce of the Wolf," by Mary G. Davis. A version of the story of St. Francis and the Wolf of Gubbio.

"The Open Road," from *The Wind in the Willows* by Kenneth Grahame.

"The Tar Baby," from *Uncle Remus, His Songs and His Sayings,* by Joel Chandler Harris. A modernized version of a very old folk tale.

"The Rat-Catcher's Daughter," from Lawrence Housman's *A Doorway in Fairy-land.*

"The Elephant's Child."

"How the Camel Got His Hump," from *Just So Stories* by Rudyard Kipling.

"Rikki-Tikki-Tavi," from *The Jungle Book* by Rudyard Kipling.

"Clever Peter and the Two Bottles," from *Pepper and Salt* by Howard Pyle.

"Peterkin and the Little Grey Hare," from *The Wonder Clock* by Howard Pyle.

"How They Broke Away to Go to the Rootabaga Country."

"How to Tell Corn Fairies If You See Them," from *Rootabaga Stories* by Carl Sandburg.

"Old Pipes and the Dryad," from *Bee Man of Orn and Other Fanciful Tales* by Frank Stockton.

"Poor Count's Christmas," by Frank Stockton.

"A Christmas Star," from *Birch and the Star,* by Mrs. Gudrun Thorne-Thomsen.

"Where Love Is, There God Is Also," by Count Tolstoi from *Christmas in Legend and Story* by Smith and Hazeltine.

"How the Son of Gubbaun Met with Good Luck," from *The Wonder Smith and His Son* by Ella Young. Irish legends.

A few examples of types of literary stories follow:

Ole Shut-Eye

IN THE whole world there is nobody who knows so many stories as Ole Shut-Eye; he can tell capital ones!

As evening comes on, when the children still sit nicely at table or on their stools, then comes Ole Shut-Eye. He comes up the stairs quite softly, for he walks in his stockinged feet; he opens the door noiselessly, and st! he syringes sweet milk in the children's eyes, a small, small stream, but enough to prevent them from keeping their eyes open; and thus they cannot see him. He creeps just among them, and blows softly upon their necks, and this makes their heads heavy. O yes, but it doesn't hurt them, for Ole Shut-Eye is very fond of the children; he only wants them to be quiet, and that they are not until they are taken to bed: they are to be quiet that he may tell them stories.

When the children sleep, Ole Shut-Eye sits down upon their bed. He is well dressed: his coat is of silk, but it is impossible to say of what color, for it shines red, green, and blue, according as he turns. Under each arm he carries an umbrella: the one with pictures on it he spreads over the good children, and then they dream all night the most glorious stories; but on his other umbrella nothing at all is painted, and this he spreads over the naughty children, and these sleep in a dull way, and when they awake in the morning they have not dreamed of anything.

Now we shall hear how Ole Shut-Eye came to a little boy named Hjalmar, and what he told him.

MONDAY

"Listen," said Ole Shut-Eye in the evening, when he had put Hjalmar to bed; "now I'll clear up."

And all the flowers in the flower-pots became great trees, stretching out their long branches under the ceiling of the room and along the walls, so that the whole room looked like a beauteous bower; and all the twigs were covered with flowers, and each flower was more beautiful than a rose, and smelt so sweet that one wanted to eat it;

it was sweeter than jam. The fruit gleamed like gold, and there were cakes bursting with raisins. It was splendid. But at the same time a terrible wail sounded from the table-drawer, where Hjalmar's school-book lay.

"Whatever can that be?" said Ole Shut-Eye; and he went to the table, and opened the drawer. It was the slate which was suffering from convulsions, for a wrong number had got into the sum, so that it was nearly falling in pieces; the slate pencil tugged and jumped at its string, as if it had been a little dog who wanted to help the sum; but he could not. And thus there was a great lamentation in Hjalmar's copy-book; it was quite terrible to hear. On each page the great letters stood in a row, one underneath the other, and each with a little one at its side; that was the copy; and next to these were a few more letters which thought they looked just like the first; and these Hjalmar had written; but they lay down just as if they had tumbled over the pencil lines on which they were to stand.

"See, this is how you should hold yourselves," said the Copy. "Look, sloping in this way, with a powerful swing!"

"O, we should be very glad to do that," replied Hjalmar's Letters, "but we cannot; we are too weakly."

"Then you must take medicine," said Ole Shut-Eye.

"O no," cried they; and they immediately stood up so gracefully that it was beautiful to behold.

"Yes, now we cannot tell any stories," said Ole Shut-Eye; "now I must exercise them. One, two! one, two!" and thus he exercised the Letters; and they stood quite slender, and as beautiful as any copy can be. But when Ole Shut-Eye went away, and Hjalmar looked at them next morning, they were as weak and miserable as ever.

TUESDAY

As soon as Hjalmar was in bed, Ole Shut-Eye touched all the furniture in the room with his little magic syringe, and they immediately began to talk together.

Over the chest of drawers hung a great picture in a gilt frame—

it was a landscape. One saw therein large old trees, flowers in the grass, and a broad river which flowed round about a forest, past many castles, and far out into the wide ocean.

Ole Shut-Eye touched the painting with his magic syringe, and the birds began to sing, the branches of the trees stirred, and the clouds began to move across it; one could see their shadows glide over the landscape.

Now Ole Shut-Eye lifted little Hjalmar up to the frame, and put the boy's feet into the picture, just in the high grass; and there he stood: and the sun shone upon him through the branches of the trees. He ran to the water, and seated himself in a little boat which lay there; it was painted red and white, the sails gleamed like silver, and six swans, each with a gold circlet round its neck, and a bright blue star on its forehead, drew the boat past the great wood, where the trees tell of robbers and witches, and the flowers tell of the graceful little elves, and of what the butterflies have told them.

Gorgeous fishes, with scales like silver and gold, swam after their boat; sometimes they gave a spring, so that it splashed in the water; and birds, blue and red, little and great, flew after them in two long rows; the gnats danced, and the cock-chafers said, "Boom! boom!" They all wanted to follow Hjalmar, and each one had a story to tell.

That was a pleasure voyage. Sometimes the forest was thick and dark, sometimes like a glorious garden full of sunlight and flowers; and there were great palaces of glass and of marble; on the balconies stood princesses, and these were all little girls whom Hjalmar knew well; he had already played with them. Each one stretched forth her hand, and held out the prettiest sugar heart which ever a cake-woman could sell; and Hjalmar took hold of each sugar heart as he passed by, and the Princess held fast, so that each of them got a piece—she the smaller share, and Hjalmar the larger. At each palace little princes stood sentry. They shouldered golden swords, and caused raisins and tin soldiers to shower down: one could see that they were real princes. Sometimes Hjalmar sailed through forests, sometimes through great halls, or through the midst of a town.

And all the birds sang, the flowers danced on their stalks, and the old trees nodded, just as if Ole Shut-Eye had been telling stories to *them*.

THURSDAY

"I tell you what," said Ole Shut-Eye, "you must not be frightened. Here you shall see a little Mouse," and he held out his hand with the pretty little creature in it. "It has come to invite you to a wedding. There are two little Mice here who are going to enter into the marriage state tonight. They live under the floor of your mother's store-closet: that is said to be a charming dwelling-place!"

"But how can I get through the little mouse-hole in the floor?" asked Hjalmar.

"Let me manage that," said Ole Shut-Eye. "I will make you small."

And he touched Hjalmar with his magic syringe, and the boy began to shrink and shrink, until he was not so long as a finger.

"Now you may borrow the uniform of a tin soldier: I think it would fit you, and it looks well to wear a uniform when one is in society."

"Yes, certainly," said Hjalmar.

And in a moment he was dressed like the spiciest of tin soldiers.

"Will your honor not be kind enough to take a seat in your mamma's thimble?" asked the Mouse. "Then I shall have the honor of drawing you."

"Will the young lady really take so much trouble?" cried Hjalmar.

And thus they drove to the Mouse's wedding. First they came into a long passage beneath the boards, which was only just so high that they could drive through it in the thimble; and the whole passage was lit up with rotten wood.

"Is there not a delicious smell here?" observed the Mouse. "The entire road has been greased with bacon rinds, and there can be nothing more exquisite."

Now they came into the festive hall. On the right hand stood all the little lady mice; and they whispered and giggled as if they were making fun of each other; on the left stood all the gentlemen mice, stroking their whiskers with their fore paws; and in the center of the hall the bridegroom and bride might be seen standing in a hollow cheese rind, and kissing each other terribly before all the guests; for this was the betrothal, and the marriage was to follow immediately.

More and more strangers kept flocking in. One mouse nearly trod another to death; and the happy couple had stationed themselves just in the doorway, so that one could neither come in nor go out. Like the passage, the room had been greased with bacon rinds, and that was the entire banquet; but for the dessert a pea was produced, in which a mouse belonging to the family had bitten the name of the betrothed pair—that is to say, the first letter of the name: that was something quite out of the common way.

All the mice said it was a beautiful wedding, and that the entertainment had been very agreeable. And then Hjalmar drove home again.

Abridged from "Fairy Tales," by Hans Christian Andersen.

Pies of the Princess

THREE plump mandarins hid behind a single tiny rose bush. The chancellor crawled under a chair. All courtiers fell upon their chins, and shivering, prayed that soft words might prevail.

For no slight reason did they shiver and hide and pray. King Yang Lang was angry. And he was an old-fashioned monarch, living in the long ago. Nowadays, any greasy kitchen lout may tweak a King's beard, and go forth to boast of his bravery. But then-a-days, Kings were Kings, and their swords were ever sharp.

King Yang Lang was such a ruler—and more angry than is good to see. His face was purple, and his voice boomed like a battle drum. "Keeper of the Treasury, has all my gold been used to make weights for fishing lines?"

307

Time after time the treasurer knocked his head against the paving. "Most Glorious and Peaceful Monarch, your gold is so plentiful that seven years must pass before I can finish counting the larger bars—ten years more for the smaller."

That was rather pleasant news. The King's voice lost some of its harshness. "What of ivory? Has all my ivory been burned for firewood, a pot to boil?"

The treasurer continued to knock his head. "Supreme Ruler of The World and The Stars, your ivory completely fills a hundred large and closely guarded vaults."

The King hadn't dreamed that his wealth was so vast. His voice was not more than moderately furious as he asked: "For what reason have you disposed of my jade? Do you mean to say that my jade has been used to build a stable for donkeys?"

Tap, tap, tap, went the treasurer's head on marble paving: "Oh, Powerful Potentate, the store of green jade grows larger each day. Your precious white jade is worth more than green, and gold, and ivory combined. It is all quite safe, under lock and key and watchful spears."

The King was astonished and put in somewhat better humor. His voice was no louder than thunder as he again questioned the treasurer. "Then why, tell me why is my daughter, the Princess Chin Uor, not given suitable toys? If the treasury holds gold and ivory and jade, why is my daughter compelled to use toys of common clay?"

The treasurer could not explain: "Monarch whose word compels the sun to rise, we have pleaded with the wee Princess Chin Uor. We have given her a thousand dolls of solid gold, with silver cradles for each, cradles set with rubies—and the dolls have eyes of lustrous black pearl. For the princess we have made ivory cats, and ivory mice for the cats to catch—two thousand of each. For the princess we have fashioned from jade, lovely tossing balls, wonderful dishes, and puppy dogs that bark and come when called. Yet, the princess ignores these things . . . and makes mud pies—MUD PIES. Mightiest Majesty, I do not know why, unless it may be that the princess is a girl, as well as a princess."

A trifle relieved, King Yang Lang passed into the garden. Beside the river bank he found his daughter, the Princess Chin Uor, or Princess Many Dimples—for that is the meaning of Chin Uor. Nurses standing near kept watch upon wheelbarrows spilling over with golden dolls. But Chin Uor had no thought for such toys. Her royal hands shaped the tastiest of mud pies. Very pretty pies they were—made of white clay.

The King said: "Littlest and most beautiful daughter, the golden dolls are longing for your touch. Why do you not please them? It is not seemly for a princess to dabble in clay. Then why do you make pies?"

The princess had a very good answer ready. "Because, Daddy, I want to make pies. This nice large one is for your dinner."

The King was so shocked that he could say nothing more. Mud pies for a King's dinner? Such nonsense. His Majesty was scandalized at the thought. He departed in haste.

But the Princess Chin Uor smiled and kneaded more and more pies. And when she had made enough she placed them in a wheelbarrow and trundled them to the palace.

And now the story changes. Far away to the west, in a mountain named Huge Rocks Piled, the famous dragon, Oo Loong, made his home. This fierce dragon was a creature of consuming greed. He was ever hungry and anxious to dine. A rabbit or an elephant—nothing was too large, nothing too small. A turtle or a jellyfish—nothing was too hard, nothing too soft. A man he considered fine eating. Boys he liked somewhat better. Girls? Girls were far superior to boys—in the dragon's opinion.

Much sorrow this ferocious *loong* had created in His Majesty's kingdom. A reward of one hundred silver pieces had been offered for the dragon's horns. Two hundred for his ears. Magicians had worked charms to slay him—only themselves to be slain. Hunters had loaded their jingals with yellow paper, and had fired where the dragon was thickest, fired where he was thinnest—only to be eaten —their guns with them. Made angry by the loss of so many people, King Yang Lang marched an army into the Mountain of Huge Rocks Piled. And the army was well armed with thumping drums and fifes and smoking guns.

Then the dragon became doubly furious and ferocious. To punish King Yang Lang, he resolved to visit the palace. That, he knew, would cause the army to be withdrawn. Accordingly, at the hour of deepest slumber, darksome mid of night, he prowled round Yang Lang's palace, seeking entrance. He had no easy task. Upon the King's door were pictures, also the word "Chi," written in gold. And so that door was well protected. The Queen's door likewise was dragon proof. It was covered with whole sentences taken from the black book of Hu Po, master magician. The door that led to where Princess Chin Uor slept was made strong by magic words and symbols. More of Hu Po's sorcery. Useless to prowl there. Dangerous to prowl there. The dragon was a knowing beast and prudent. The signs were against him. Hence, he tarried not, but crawled down the hallway in leaving.

A wheelbarrow stood in his path. He could not pass to the right. To the left he could not pass. Nor could he leap over the obstruction. But the dragon was not one to be baffled by such a weak and wooden contrivance. His huge mouth opened and his white hot breath rushed forth. In a twinkling the wooden barrow vanished. Like a butter cake dropped upon the summer sun it melted, burned to a cinder of nothingness.

Now the wheelbarrow thus destroyed was property of the little Princess Chin Uor. In it had been golden dolls, dolls of the princess. The dolls were dolls no longer. Under the dragon's fiery breath they changed to a pool of liquid gold. The hard gold became soft and flowing.

In the barrow had been pretty mud pies, pies of the princess. Under the dragon's burning breath they were changed to disks of stony hardness. The soft clay took on a hardness as of flint. The princess had wished her pies to dry. And her wish had been granted.

Next morning, the palace, from presence room to pantry, buzzed with excitement. Oo Loong had dared intrude within the royal dwelling. It could not be doubted. He had left his footprints in the molten gold, and the gold, in hardening, had preserved his tracks.

Witches and wizards came to make more able charms. Messengers galloped away to summon the distant army. The King raged and roared. Said His Majesty: "Let that reprobate dragon return, if he dares. If he dares, let that reprobate dragon return." The courtiers trembled and gasped: "Pray may the wicked *loong* never return. Never, never return." But little Princess Many Dimples played with her pies and was happy. Her pies had been baked to a queen's taste— or rather to the taste of a princess. Beside the river she worked faithfully in wet white clay. Such beautiful pies. "I do hope that the nice *loong* will return," said Princess Chin Uor. "He is such a fine oven. I shall make a hundred more pies for his baking."

Pie after pie. Even the nurses helped. Instead of saying, "Please, will your Royal Highness not play with this lovely doll?" they said, "Please, is this one rounded enough?" and "Please, shall I scallop the edges a trifle deeper?" and "Shall I imagine that this one contains cherries, or radishes?" or whatever it may be that makers of pies would say in a royal kitchen. So, a hundred pies were made and wheeled to the palace. In reality, they numbered a hundred and one, but the odd one was so thick that it must be called a cake. Howbeit, that is not so important as you might think.

Night followed day—a habit that most nights have. The soldiers slept—as they had been ordered not to do. The hour approached when clock hands point to the highest sky. Midnight came, and with it the mountainous mountain *loong*. Unseen by those whose duty was seeing, the dragon entered King Yang Lang's courtyard. And there he was perplexed and paused. The King's door was a hodgepodge of magic signs, plastered with yellow paper. Vain to think of entering there. The Queen's door was upside down—best charm of all. To think of entering was vain. The door that led to Princess Chin Uor's sleeping chamber was written thick with words to still a dragon's heart, circles to dizzy his head. Say what you please, the witches and wizards had done good work upon that door. Their charms were written with clearness and force. The *loong* dared not take a second glance. He felt his limbs grow weak. Wisely hastened he from the spell-guarded threshold.

Now in the reign of the Emperor Ming, a crazed and knavish fellow, known to the world as Wing Dow, invented a contrivance called by him "Look-through-the-wall," but which we of today call a "Window." His invention gave the Emperor Ming a severe cold, and

Wing Dow came within a sword's width of losing his ears—but more of that later. Here it is necessary to say only that Look-through-the-walls became popular, and many such were to be found in King Yang Lang's palace. In the Princess Chin Uor's room were many wing-dows (or windows), and—hard to believe—those wing-dows were unguarded either by charm or by apple wood beam, which is as good as a charm. Could the dragon pass by such a fine chance? Could he pass the wing-dow and not have a try? When he had come with purpose to do harm? It is easy to imagine the thing that happened. And yet not so easy as may seem.

The dragon's lumpish head entered the wing-dow. His deer horns, his rabbit eyes, his snake tongue, all entered, and easily enough. A ponderous sofa-cushion foot he placed upon the window ledge . . .

Crash, and smash, and clatter. . . .

The nurses awoke and screamed, "Save us."

The Princess Chin Uor awoke and said, "Shoo."

Soldiers in the courtyard awoke and lighted green fires as they smote their drums, saying: "Come if you dare. Help. Help."

The dragon was already awake—awake to the danger. Promptly he vanished. Such noise he could not abide.

King Yang Lang came with a golden torch. Greatly he was pleased that the *loong* had been routed.

But Princess Chin Uor was far from pleased. Indeed, she was fretful. From the floor she took a sliver of flint-hard clay. "My pies are all broken. All. All are broken," mourned Princess Many Dimples. "I had placed them in the wing-dow. And the dragon knocked them down and broke them." And beyond doubt so had he done. There were the pieces.

Still the King remained cheerful. His little daughter's sadness passed unnoticed. His Majesty said: "Your pies, my daughter, are excellent food—let no one deny it—but even better are they to give warning of the dragon's nearness. Your pies have provided me with a wonderful idea. Hereafter we need have no more fear of the *loong*. . . . Ho. General. Awaken your soldiers again. Let them march to the river."

For a week the King's army did no other labor than make mud

pies. And liked it. The pies were given heat in giant ovens, were baked into stony hardness. Then they were placed throughout the palace, in windows, upon tables, chairs, upon chests and shelves, high and low and everywhere. Even on the chimney tops were rows of glistening pies. The slightest misstep by a prowling dragon would have caused a din most tremendous.

The royal dining table was a shining whiteness, covered with mud pies. So numerous were the pies of the princess that no room remained for food. But that was no cause for worry. The King merely ordered that his rice be placed upon a baked clay pie. Mandarins who visited the palace were much surprised at what they saw—a King eating from common clay. Nevertheless, their own tables were soon covered with Princess Chin Uor's pies. For the King, of course, set all fashions.

And so, we modern peoples speak of our plates and cups and saucers as "China." China? Is it? Yes, and no. China is merely our way of pronouncing Chin Uor. Our plates are merely thin copies of Princess Chin Uor's pies.

From "Shen of the Sea," by Arthur Bowie Chrisman. Copyright, 1925, by E. P. Dutton & Co., Inc., and reprinted by permission of the publishers.

Ladders to Heaven

A LEGEND

THERE was a certain valley in which the grass was very green for it was watered by a stream which never failed. And here it was that once upon a time certain pious men who had withdrawn from the world and formed a brotherhood made a sheltered home for themselves.

The world outside was very rough and full of wars; but the little world in the Green Valley was quiet and full of peace. And most of these men who had taken each other for brothers, and had made one home there, were happy, and being good deserved to be so.

Brother Benedict was so named, because where he came blessings followed. This was said of him, from a child, when the babies stopped crying if he ran up to them, and when on the darkest days old women could see sunbeams playing in his hair. He had always been fond of flowers, and as there were not many things in the Brotherhood of the Green Valley on which a man could full-spend his energies, when prayers were said, and duties done, Brother Benedict spent the balance of his upon the garden. And he grew herbs for healing, and plants that were good for food, and flowers that were only pleasant to the eyes; and where he sowed he reaped, and what he planted prospered, as if blessings followed him.

In time the fame of his flowers spread beyond the valley, and people from the world outside sent to beg plants and seeds of him, and sent him others in return. And he kept a roll of the plants that he possessed, and the list grew longer with every autumn and every spring; so that the garden of the monastery became filled with rare and curious things, in which Brother Benedict took great pride.

The day came when he thought that he took too much pride. For he said, "The cares of the garden are, after all, cares of this world, and I have set my affections upon things of the earth." And at last it so troubled him that he obtained leave to make a pilgrimage to the cell of an old hermit, whose wisdom was much esteemed, and to him he told his fears.

But when Brother Benedict had ended his tale, the old man said, "Go in peace. What a man labors for he must love, if he be made in the image of his Maker; for He rejoices in the works of His hands."

So Brother Benedict returned, and his conscience was at ease till the autumn, when a certain abbot, who spent much care and pains upon his garden, was on a journey, and rested at the Monastery of the Green Valley. And it appeared that he had more things in his garden than Brother Benedict, for the abbey was very rich, and he had collected far and near. And Brother Benedict was jealous for the garden of the monastery, and then he was wrath with himself for his jealousy; and when the abbot had gone he obtained leave, and made a pilgrimage to the cell of the hermit and told him all. And the old man, looking at him, loved him, and he said:

"My son, a man may bind his soul with fine-drawn strands till it is either entangled in a web or breaks all bonds. Gird thyself with one strong line, and let little things go by."

And Benedict said, "With which line?"

And the hermit answered, "What said Augustine? 'Love, and do what thou wilt.' If therefore thy labors and thy pride be for others, and not for thyself, have no fear. He who lives for God and for his neighbors may forget his own soul in safety, and shall find it hereafter; for such a spirit—of the toils and pains and pleasures of this life—grace shall build Ladders unto Heaven."

Then Benedict bowed his head, and departed; and when he reached home he found a messenger who had ridden for many days, and who brought him a bundle of roots, and a written message, which ran thus:

"These roots, though common with us, are unknown where thou dwellest. It is a lily, as white and as fragrant as the Lily of the Annunciation, but much smaller. Beautiful as it is, it is hardy, and if planted in a damp spot and left strictly undisturbed it will spread and flourish like a weed. It hath a rare and delicate perfume, and having white bells on many footstalks up the stem, one above the other, as the angels stood in Jacob's dream, the children call it Ladders to Heaven."

And when Brother Benedict read the first part of the letter he laughed hastily, and said, "The abbot hath no such lily." But when he had finished it, he said, "God rid my soul of self-seeking! The children shall have them, and not I."

And, seizing the plants and a spade, he ran out beyond the bounds of the monastery, and down into a little copse where the earth was kept damp by the waters of the stream which never failed. And there he planted the roots, and as he turned to go away he said, "The blessing of our Maker rest on thee! And give joy of thy loveliness, and pleasure of thy perfume, to others when I am gone. And let him who enjoys remember the soul of him who planted thee."

And he covered his face with his hands, and went back to the monastery. And he did not enter the new plant upon his roll, for he had no such lily in his garden.

Brother Benedict's soul had long departed, when in times of turbulence and change, the monastery was destroyed, and between fire and plunder and reckless destruction everything perished, and even the garden was laid waste. But no one touched the Lilies of the Valley in the copse below, for they were so common that they were looked upon as weeds. And though nothing remained of the brotherhood but old tales, these lingered, and were handed on; and when the children played with the lilies and bickered over them, crying, "My ladder has twelve white angels and yours has only eight," they would often call them Brother Benedict's flowers, adding, "but the real right name of them is Ladders to Heaven."

And after a time a new race came into the Green Valley and filled it; and the stream which never failed turned many wheels, and trades were brisk, and they were what are called black trades. And men made money soon, and spent it soon, and died soon; and in the time between each lived for himself, and had little reverence for those who were gone, and less concern for those who should come after. And at first they were too busy to care for what is only beautiful, but after a time they built smart houses, and made gardens, and went down into the copse and tore up clumps of Brother Benedict's flowers, and planted them in exposed rockeries, and in pots in dry hot parlors, where they died, and then the good folk went back for more; and no one reckoned if he was taking more than his fair share, or studied the culture of what he took away, or took the pains to cover the roots of those he left behind, and in three years there was not left a Ladder to Heaven in all the Green Valley.

The Green Valley had long been called the Black Valley, when those who labored and grew rich in it awoke—as man must sooner or later awake—to the needs of the spirit above the flesh. They were a race famed for music, and they became more so. The love of beauty also grew, and was cultivated, and in time there were finer flowers blossoming in that smoky air than under many brighter skies. And with the earnings of their grimy trades they built a fine church, and adorned it more richly than the old church of the monastery, that had been destroyed.

The parson who served this church and this people was as well-beloved by them as Brother Benedict had been in his day, and it was in striving to link their minds with sympathies of the past as well as hopes of the future, that one day he told them the legend of the Ladders to Heaven. A few days afterwards he was wandering near the stream, when he saw two or three lads with grimy faces busily at work in the wood through which the stream ran. At first, when he came suddenly on them, they looked shyly at one another, and at last one stood up and spoke.

"It's a few lily roots, sir, we got in the market, and we're planting them; and two or three of us have set ourselves to watch that they are not shifted till they've settled. Maybe we shall none of us see them fair wild here again, any more than Brother Benedict did. . . . But maybe we can take a pride too in thinking that they'll blow for other folk and other folk's children when we are gone."

So once more the Lilies of the Valley spread, and the memory of Brother Benedict lingered by the stream, and was doubly blessed.

Slightly adapted from Juliana Horatia Ewing.

The Lepracaun; or, Fairy Shoemaker

LITTLE Cowboy, what have you heard,
　Up on the lonely rath's green mound?
Only the plaintive yellow bird
　Sighing in sultry fields around,
Chary, chary, chary, chee-ee!—
Only the grasshopper and the bee?—
　"Tip tap, rip-rap,
　Tick-a-tack-too!

317

Scarlet leather, sewn together,
   This will make a shoe.
Left, right, pull it tight
   Summer days are warm;
Underground in winter,
   Laughing at the storm!"
Lay your ear close to the hill.
Do you not catch the tiny clamor,
Busy click of an elfin hammer,
Voice of the Lepracaun singing shrill
   As he merrily plies his trade?
     He's a span
     And a quarter in height.
Get him in sight, hold him tight,
     And you're a made
      Man!

You watch your cattle the summer day,
Sup on potatoes, sleep in the hay;
   How would you like to roll in your carriage,
   Look for a duchess's daughter in marriage?
Seize the Shoemaker—then you may!
   "Big boots a-hunting,
     Sandals in the hall,
   White for a wedding-feast,
     Pink for a ball.
   This way, that way,
     So we make a shoe;
   Getting rich every stitch,
     Tick-tack-too!"
Nine-and-ninety treasure-crocks
This keen miser-fairy hath,
Hid in mountains, woods, and rocks,
Ruin and round-tow'r, cave and rath,
   And where the cormorants build;
     From times of old

Guarded by him;
Each of them fill'd
Full to the brim
    With gold!

I caught him at work one day, myself,
    In the castle-ditch, where foxglove grows,—
A wrinkled, wizen'd, and bearded Elf,
Spectacles stuck on his pointed nose,
Silver buckles to his hose,
Leather apron—shoe in his lap—
    "Rip-rap, tip-tap,
    Tick-tack-too!
(A grasshopper on my cap!
    Away the moth flew!)
Buskins for a fairy prince,
    Brogues for his son,—
Pay me well, pay me well,
    When the job is done!"
The rogue was mine, beyond a doubt.
    I stared at him; he stared at me;
"Servant, Sir!" "Humph!" says he,
    And pull'd a snuff-box out.
He took a long pinch, look'd better pleased,
    The queer little Lepracaun;
Offer'd the box with a whimsical grace,—
Pouf! he flung the dust in my face,
    And, while I sneezed,
        Was gone!

WILLIAM ALLINGHAM

319

Christian and Hopeful in Doubting Castle

CHRISTIAN and Hopeful were on their way to the Celestial City. Now a little before them, there was on the left hand of the road a meadow and a stile, and that meadow was called By-path Meadow. When they were gone over, and were got into the path, they found it very easy for their feet. They met Vain-confidence and asked him whither the path led. He said, To the Celestial Gate. Look, said Christian, did not I tell you so! But behold the night came on, it grew dark, the waters had risen, and the way of going back was very dangerous.

Wherefore, at last lighting under a little shelter, they sat down there till the day brake; but, being weary, they fell asleep. Now there was, not far from the place where they lay, a castle, called Doubting Castle, the owner whereof was Giant Despair, and it was in his grounds they now were sleeping: wherefore he getting up in the morning early, and walking up and down in his fields, caught Christian and Hopeful asleep in his grounds. Then with a grim and surly voice he bid them awake, and asked them whence they were and what they did in his grounds. They told him they were pilgrims, and that they had lost their way. Then said the Giant, You have this night trespassed on me, by trampling in and lying on my grounds, and therefore you must go along with me. So they were forced to go, because he was stronger than they. They also had but little to say, for they knew themselves in a fault. The giant therefore drove them into his castle, into a very dark dungeon, here then they lay, from Wednesday morning till Saturday night, without one bit of bread, or drop of drink, or light, or any to ask how they did. Now in this place, Christian had double sorrow, because 'twas through his unadvised counsel that they were brought into this distress.

Now Giant Despair had a wife, and her name was Diffidence. So when he was gone to bed, he told his wife what he had done, to wit, that he had taken a couple of prisoners, and cast them into his dungeon, for trespassing on his grounds. So she asked him whence they came, and whither they were bound; and he told her. Then she counseled him, that when he arose in the morning he should beat them, without any mercy. So when he arose, he getteth him a grievous crab-tree cudgel, and goes down into the dungeon to them, and there first falls to rating of them as if they were dogs. Then he falls upon them, and beats them fearfully, in such sort, that they were not able to help themselves, or to turn them upon the floor. This done, he withdraws and leaves them, there to condole their misery: so all that day they spent the time in nothing but sighs and bitter lamentations. When morning was come, he goes to them in a surly manner as before, and perceiving them to be very sore with the stripes that he had given them the day before, he told them, that since they were never like to come out of that place, their only way would be, forthwith to make an end of themselves. For why, said he, should you choose life, seeing it is attended with so much bitterness? But they desired him to let them go. With that he looked ugly upon them, and rushing to them had doubtless made an end of them himself, but that he fell into one of his fits (for he sometimes in sunshiny weather fell into fits), and lost (for a time) the use of his hand; wherefore he withdrew, and left them (as before), to consider what to do. Then did the prisoners consult between themselves, whether 'twas best to take his counsel or no; and thus they began to discourse:

Brother, said Christian, what shall we do? The life that we now live is miserable: for my part I know not whether is best, to live thus, or to die out of hand. "My soul chooseth strangling rather than life," and the grave is more easy for me than this dungeon: Shall we be ruled by the Giant?

Said Hopeful, Indeed our present condition is dreadful, and death would be far more welcome to me than thus for ever to abide: But yet let us consider, the Lord of the country to which we are going hath said, Thou shalt do no murder, no, not to another man's person; much more then are we forbidden to take his counsel to kill ourselves. Who knows, but that God that made the world, may cause that Giant Despair may die; or that at some time or other he may forget to lock us in; or but he may in a short time have another of his fits before us, and may lose the use of his limbs; and if ever that should come to pass again, for my part I am resolved to pluck up the heart of a man, and to try my utmost to get from under his hand. With these words Hopeful did moderate the mind of his brother; so they continued together that day, in their sad and doleful condition.

Well, towards evening the Giant goes down into the dungeon again, to see if his prisoners had taken his counsel; but when he came there, he found them alive, and truly, alive was all; for now, what for want of bread and water, and by reason of the wounds they received when he beat them, they could do little but breathe: But, I say, he found them alive; at which he fell into a grievous rage, and told them, that seeing they had disobeyed his counsel, it should be worse with them that if they had never been born.

At this they trembled greatly, and I think that Christian fell into a swoon; but coming a little to himself again, they renewed their discourse about the Giant's counsel, and whether yet they had best to take it or no. Now Christian again seemed to be for doing it, but Hopeful made his second reply as followeth:

My brother, said he, rememberest thou not how valiant thou hast been heretofore? Apollyon could not crush thee, nor could all that thou didst hear, or see, or feel in the Valley of the Shadow of Death. Remember how thou playedst the man at Vanity Fair, and wast neither afraid of the chain nor cage; nor yet of bloody death?

Now night being come again, and the Giant and his wife being in bed, she asked him concerning the prisoners, and if they had taken his counsel. To which he replied, They are sturdy rogues, they choose rather to bear all hardship, than to make away themselves. Then said she, Take them into the castle-yard tomorrow, and show them the bones and skulls of those that thou hast already dispatched, and make them believe, ere a week comes to an end, thou also wilt tear them in pieces, as thou hast done their fellows before them.

So when morning was come, the Giant goes to them again, and takes them into the castle-yard, and shows them as his wife had bidden him. These, said he, were pilgrims as you are, once, and they trespassed in my grounds, as you have done; and when I thought fit, I tore them in pieces, and so within ten days I will do you. Go, get you down to your den again; and with that he beat them all the way thither. They lay therefore all day on Saturday in lamentable case, as before.

Well, on Saturday about midnight they began to pray, and continued in prayer till almost break of day.

Now a little before it was day, good Christian, as one half amazed, brake out in this passionate speech: What a fool, quoth he, am I thus to lie in a stinking dungeon, when I may as well walk at liberty! I have a key in my bosom called Promise, that will, I am persuaded, open any lock in Doubting Castle. Then said Hopeful, That's good news; good brother, pluck it out of thy bosom and try.

Then Christian pulled it out of his bosom, and began to try at the dungeon door, whose bolt (as he turned the key) gave back, and the door flew open with ease, and Christian and Hopeful both came out. Then he went to the outward door that leads into the castle-yard, and with his key opened that door also. After he went to the iron gate, for that must be opened too, but that lock went damnable hard, yet the key did open it; then they thrust open the gate to make their escape with speed, but that gate, as it opened, made such a creaking, that it waked Giant Despair, who hastily rising to pursue his prisoners, felt his limbs to fail, for his fits took him again, so that he could by no means go after them. Then they went on, and came to the King's highway, and so were safe, because they were out of his jurisdiction.

Now when they were gone over the stile, they began to contrive with themselves what they should do at that stile, to prevent those that should come after from falling into the hands of Giant Despair. So they consented to erect there a pillar, and to engrave upon the side thereof this sentence, "Over this stile is the way to Doubting Castle, which is kept by Giant Despair, who despiseth the King of the Celestial Country, and seeks to destroy his holy pilgrims." Many therefore that followed after, read what was written, and escaped the danger.

From "Pilgrim's Progress," by John Bunyan.

FAMILY BOOKS

By family books is meant those which are sufficiently attractive in style and subject matter to appeal to both young and old in a home group; books such as *Alice in Wonderland,* and the *Nonsense Songs* by Lear, which bring their fullest pleasure when read aloud in congenial company.

Family enjoyment of reading is far-reaching and permanent in results. Children will read and re-read classic literature for themselves after they have been won to it by an appreciative older person whose taste they have learned to trust. And there are parents who need to discover through children's enthusiasms, that there is a literature for children and not merely children's books.

Whether the book chosen for reading aloud is dramatic or discursive in style will depend upon the occasion and the moods of the listeners. It may be mere nonsense to enliven an hour and encourage good humor; it may be a hero tale, a story-telling picture book or serious poetry. But whatever its form, it should present beauty of thought in language above the commonplace. Too many stories of home and school life, a type of book which children greatly enjoy hearing and sharing with one another, are written in children's vernacular.

Story-telling Picture Books

BY STORY-TELLING picture books is meant those in which the illustrations follow closely the text and help to tell a good story. The selection which follows is intended for use with children from three to six years old. The text is child-like and well-written; the illustrations are attractive to children as well as artistic.

FANCIFUL STORIES AND FAMILY BOOKS

d'Aulaire, Ingri & Parin. *Ola and Blakken.* Doubleday, Doran & Co.

Baker, Margaret. *Black Cats and the Tinker's Wife.* Duffield and Green.

Bannerman, Helen. *Little Black Sambo.* Frederick A. Stokes Co.

Beskow, Elsa. *Pelle's New Suit. Tale of the Little Old Woman.* Harper & Brothers.

Brock, Emma. *One Little Indian Boy. To Market to Market.* Alfred A. Knopf.

Brooke, Leslie. *Johnny Crow's Garden. Three Little Pigs.* Frederick Warne & Co., Ltd.

Caldecott, Randolph. *Hey Diddle Picture Book. The Farmer's Boy.* Frederick Warne & Co., Ltd.

Donaldson, Lois. *Karl's Wooden Horse.* Albert Whitman.

Flack, Marjorie. *Angus and the Cat.* Doubleday, Doran & Co.

Flack, Marjorie & Wiese, Kurt. *Story about Ping.* Doubleday, Doran & Co.

Gag, Wanda. *Funny Thing. Millions of Cats. Snippy and Snappy.* Coward-McCann, Inc.

Hader, Berta and Elmer. *Farmer in the Dell.* The Macmillan Company.

Kuebler, Katherine. *Hansel the Gander.* Wm. Morrow & Co.

Le Fevre, Felicite. *The Cock, the Mouse and the Little Red Hen,* il. by Tony Sarg. Macrae Smith.

Moe, Louis. *Raggle Taggle Bear.* Longmans, Green & Co.

Moore, Clement. *The Night before Christmas,* il. by Elizabeth MacKinstry. E. P. Dutton & Co., Inc.

Morrow, Elizabeth. *The Painted Pig,* il. by Rene d'Harnoncourt. Alfred A. Knopf.

Nicholson, William. *Clever Bill. The Pirate Twins.* Coward-McCann, Inc.

Orton, Helen. *Little Lost Pigs.* Frederick A. Stokes Co.

Petersham, Maud and Miska. *Miki. The Christ Child.* Doubleday, Doran & Co.

Potter, Beatrice. *Peter Rabbit. Benjamin Bunny.* Frederick Warne & Co., Ltd.

Sewell, Helen. *Head for Happy.* The Macmillan Company.

Stoney, T. Butler. *The Old Woman Who Rode on a Broom.* E. P. Dutton & Co., Inc.

Wiese, Kurt. *Liang and Lo.* Doubleday, Doran & Co.

Williamson, Hamilton. *A Monkey Tale.* Doubleday, Doran & Co.

BAG O' TALES

Books for Family Reading

THE list of books for family reading which follows, supplements those listed elsewhere in this volume as sources for story-tellers. Only a few titles are repeated.

Poetry is indicated when not suggested by the title.

Andersen, H. C. *Fairy Tales*, tr. by Lucas. E. P. Dutton & Co., Inc.

Arabian Nights Entertainments, ed. by Olcott (Henry Holt & Co.), or Wiggin & Smith (Chas. Scribner's Sons).

Aspinwall, Alicia. *Short Stories for Short People*. E· P. Dutton & Co., Inc.

Armer, Laura A. *Waterless Mountain*. Longmans, Green & Co.

Auslander and Hill. *The Winged Horse*. Doubleday, Doran & Co. An introduction to poetry.

Barrie, Sir James M. *Peter and Wendy*. Chas. Scribner's Sons.

Bennett, John. *Master Skylark*. D. Appleton-Century Co., Inc.

Bianca, Margery. *The Little Wooden Doll*. The Macmillan Company. *Poor Cecco*. Doran.

Bjornsen, B. *A Happy Boy*. The Macmillan Company.

Bullen, Frank. *Cruise of the Cachelot*. D. Appleton-Century Co., Inc.

Burroughs, John. *Birds, Bees and Sharp Eyes*. Houghton Mifflin Co. *Squirrels and Other Fur Bearers*. Houghton Mifflin Co.

Caldecott, Randolph. *Picture Books* (poems). Frederick Warne & Co., Ltd.

Coit, Dorothy. *Ivory Throne of Persia*. Frederick A. Stokes Company. Stories from the Persian epic, the *Shah-Nameh* of Firdausi.

Carroll, Lewis. *Alice in Wonderland*. The Macmillan Company. *Through the Looking Glass*. The Macmillan Company.

Cervantes. *Don Quixote*, ed. by Judge Parry. Dodd, Mead and Company.

Chaucer, Geoffrey. *Tales from Chaucer*, retold by Eleanor Farjeon. Hale Cushman & Flint, Inc.

Chrisman, A. B. *Shen of the Sea*. E. P. Dutton & Co., Inc.

Clark and Quigley. *The Poppy Seed Cakes*. Doubleday, Doran & Co.

Collodi, C. *Pinocchio*. Ginn & Company.

Colum, Padraic. *The King of Ireland's Son*. The Macmillan Company.

Cooper, J. F. *Last of the Mohicans*. Macrae Smith.

Defoe, Daniel. *Robinson Crusoe*. Houghton Mifflin Co.; Macrae Smith.

De la Mare, Walter, ed. *Come Hither* (poems). Alfred A. Knopf.

De la Mare, Walter. *Child's Day* (poem). Henry Holt & Co.

De la Mare, Walter. *Poems for Children*. The Macmillan Company.

Dickens, Charles. *David Copperfield*. Dodd, Mead and Company. *Cricket on the Hearth*. E. P. Dutton & Co., Inc.

Dickens, Charles. *The Magic Fishbone*. Frederick Warne & Co., Ltd. A nonsense tale.

Dodge, M. M. *Hans Brinker*. Chas. Scribner's Sons.

Edgar, M. G. *Treasury of Verse for little Children*. T. Y. Crowell & Co.

Ewing, J. H. *Jan of the Windmill*. Harcourt, Brace & Company.

Farjeon, Eleanor. *Martin Pippin in the Apple Orchard*. Frederick A. Stokes Company.

Field, Rachel. *Hitty*. The Macmillan Company. *Taxis and Toadstools* (poems). Doubleday, Doran & Co.

Finger, Charles J. *Tales from Silver Lands*. Doubleday, Doran & Co.

Fyleman, Rose. *Fairies and Chimneys* (poems). Doubleday, Doran & Co.

Gag, Wanda. *Millions of Cats*. Coward-McCann, Inc.

Golding, Vautier. *Story of David Livingstone*. E. P. Dutton & Co., Inc.

Grahame, Kenneth. *The Wind in the Willows*, il. by Ernest Shepard. Methuen & Company, London. Chas. Scribner's Sons.

Harris, Joel Chandler. *Uncle Remus, His Songs and His Sayings*. D. Appleton-Century Co., Inc.

Hodgkins, Mary D. *Atlantic Treasury of Childhood Stories*. Atlantic Monthly Press.

Hudson, W. H. *A Little Boy Lost*. Alfred A. Knopf.

Hull, Eleanor. *Cuchulain, the Hound of Ulster*. T. Y. Crowell Co.

Irving, Washington. *Tales of the Alhambra*. Houghton Mifflin Co.

Kelly, Eric P. *Trumpeter of Krakow*. The Macmillan Company.

Kipling, Rudyard. *The Jungle Book*. Doubleday, Doran & Co. *Just So Stories*. Doubleday, Doran & Co.

La Fontaine, Jean de. *Hundred Fables*. Dodd, Mead & Company.

Lagerlof, Selma. *The Wonderful Adventures of Nils*. Doubleday, Doran & Co.

Lear, Edward. *The Complete Nonsense Book* (Prose and verse). Frederick Warne & Co., Ltd.

Lofting, Hugh. *Story of Dr. Dolittle*. Frederick A. Stokes Co.

Lownsberry, Eloise. *Boy Knight of Reims*. Houghton Mifflin Co.

Lucas, E. V. *The Slow Coach*. The Macmillan Company.

Macdonald, George. *The Princess and the Goblin*. The Macmillan Company.

Macdonald, Greville. *Billy Barnicoat*. E. P. Dutton & Co., Inc.

Masefield, John. *Jim Davis*. Grosset & Dunlap, Inc.

Milne, A. A. *When We Were Very Young* (poems). E. P. Dutton & Co., Inc. *Winnie the Pooh*. E. P. Dutton & Co., Inc.

Moore, Anne Carroll. *Nicholas; a Manhattan Christmas Story*. G. P. Putnam's Sons. *Nicholas and the Golden Goose*. G. P. Putnam's Sons.

Morrow, Elizabeth. *The Painted Pig*. Alfred A. Knopf.

Mukerji, Dhan Gopal. *Kari, the Elephant.* E. P. Dutton & Co., Inc.

Nesbit, Edith. *Bastable Children.* Coward-McCann, Inc.

Nordhoff, Charles. *Pearl Lagoon.* Little, Brown & Company.

Paine, A. B. *Arkansaw Bear.* Altemus.

Parkman, Francis. *The Oregon Trail.* Farrar & Rinehart.

Parrish, Anne. *Floating Island.* Harper & Brothers.

Plutarch. *Plutarch's Lives for Boys and Girls*, retold by W. H. Weston. Thomas Nelson & Sons.

Potter, M. C. *Sally Gabble and the Fairies.* The Macmillan Company.

Pyle, Howard. *Pepper and Salt.* Harper & Brothers. *Twilight Land.* Harper & Brothers. *Wonder Clock.* Harper & Brothers.

Pyle, Howard. *Men of Iron.* Harper & Brothers. *Otto of the Silver Hand.* Chas. Scribner's Sons.

Ransome, Arthur. *Swallows and Amazons.* J. B. Lippincott & Co.

Repplier, Agnes. *A Book of Famous Verse.* Houghton Mifflin Co. Stirring, narrative poems.

Rossetti, Christina. *Sing-song* (poems). The Macmillan Company.

Rowe, Dorothy. *Rabbit Lantern.* The Macmillan Company.

Royde-Smith, N. G. *Una and the Red Cross Knight*, from Spenser's *Faerie Queene.* E. P. Dutton & Co., Inc.

Sandburg, Carl. *Rootabaga Stories.* Harcourt, Brace & Co.

Sandburg, Carl. *Abraham Lincoln, His Prairie Years.* Harcourt, Brace & Co.

Shakespeare. *Midsummer Night's Dream* (any edition). *Tales from Shakespeare*, ed. by Charles and Mary Lamb. E. P. Dutton & Co., Inc.

Sherwood, Merriam, ed. *The Tale of the Warrior Lord*, from the *Cantar de Mio Cid.* Longmans, Green & Co.

Spyri, Johanna. *Heidi.* Ginn & Company.

Stein, Evaline. *Gabriel and the Hour Book.* L. C. Page & Company.

Stevenson, R. L. *Child's Garden of Verses.* Chas. Scribner's Sons. *Treasure Island.* Chas. Scribner's Sons. *Black Arrow.* Chas. Scribner's Sons.

Swift. *Gulliver's Travels*, ed. by Colum. The Macmillan Company.

Thackeray, W. M. *The Rose and the Ring.* The Macmillan Company.

Twain, Mark. *Tom Sawyer.* Harper & Brothers. *Huckleberry Finn.* Harper & Brothers.

Untermeyer, Louis. *This Singing World* (poems). Harcourt, Brace & Company.

Wiggin, K. D. *Rebecca of Sunnybrook Farm.* Houghton Mifflin Co.

Wiggin and Smith. *Posy Ring* (poems). Doubleday, Doran & Co.

Wyss, J. D. *Swiss Family Robinson.* Macrae Smith.

Young, Ella. *The Tangle-coated Horse.* Longmans, Green & Co. *The Wonder Smith and His Son.* Longmans, Green & Co. Irish hero tales and legends.

Zwilgmeyer, Dikken. *What Happened to Inger Johanne.* Lothrop, Lee & Shepard.

Books on Story-telling

Bone, W. A. *Children's Stories and How to Tell Them.* Harcourt, Brace & Co. An analysis of types of stories—myths, legends and fairy tales, with a chapter on the technique of story-telling.

Bryant, Sara Cone. *How to Tell Stories to Children.* Houghton Mifflin Co. The author encourages the beginning story-teller and provides simplified versions of a number of stories for children below eight years of age.

Colum, Padraic. *The Fountain of Youth.* The Macmillan Company. Included for the essay on story-telling at the end of the book.

Hunt, Clara W. *What Shall We Read to the Children.* Houghton Mifflin Co. Methods of introducing literature to children.

Scott, Edna Lyman. *Story Telling.* A. C. McClurg & Co. Brief, practical little book which contains a chapter on the use of sagas and epics.

Shedlock, Marie. *The Art of Story-telling.* D. Appleton-Century Co., Inc. A first choice when one book only can be purchased.

Carnegie Library of Pittsburgh. *Stories to Tell to Children.* 5th ed. 1932. A selected list.

Davis, Mary Gould. *Stories: a List of Stories to Tell and Read Aloud.* New York Public Library, 1933.

Power, Effie. *List of Stories and Programs for Story Hours.* H. W. Wilson Co., 1925.

Miller, George T. *Story Telling to Live Wire Boys.* E. P. Dutton & Co., Inc.

Books on Children's Literature

Barry, Florence. *A Century of Children's Books.* 1923. Methuen & Company, London. Children's books in England between 1700 and 1825.

Beust, Nora, comp. *Graded List of Books for Children.* 1930. American Library Association. Annotated.

Darton, F. J. Harvey. *History of Children's Books in England.* 1933. Cambridge Press. A valuable summary to 1901. This is the only history of children's books in England covering so wide a period, that is now in print. American authors popular in England are considered.

Field, W. T. *Guide to Literature for Children.* 1928. Ginn & Company.

Green, J. L. *Reading for Fun.* 1925. Richard Badger. A teacher discusses pleasurable reading.

Hewins, Caroline M. *A Mid-Century Child and Her Books.* 1926. The Macmillan Company. A pioneer librarian in the Hartford, Conn. Public Library has written delightfully of her early associations with books.

Gardner, E. E. and Ramsey, Eloise. *Handbook of Children's Literature.* 1927. Scott Foresman & Co. Brief discussion of all classes of children's books. Many lists.

The Horn Book. Boston, Boys' and Girls' Bookshop (bi-monthly). Reviews of current books.

Hunt, Clara Whitehill. *What to Read to Children.* 1924. Houghton Mifflin Co. By the Superintendent of Work with Children in the Brooklyn Public Library.

Jordan, A. M. *Children's Interests in Reading.* 1926. University of North Carolina Press.

Lowe, Orton. *Literature for Children.* 1914. The Macmillan Company. Discussion for teachers and parents by a professor in the University of Miami, Florida.

Mahony, B. E. and Whitney, E. comps. *Contemporary Illustrators of Children's Books.* 1930. Woman's Educational & Industrial Union, Boston. Gives short biographical sketches of artists, a list of the books they have illustrated, their addresses and, in most cases, examples of their work.

Moore, Anne Carroll. *Roads to Childhood.* 1920. Doubleday, Doran & Co. *Cross-roads to Childhood.* 1926. Doubleday, Doran & Co. Literary criticisms which express the author's personal enthusiasms and intimate experiences in using books with children.

Moore, Anne Carroll. *Three Owls.* 1925. The Macmillan Company. *Three Owls; Second Book.* 1928. Coward-McCann, Inc. Critical reviews written in pleasing style.

FANCIFUL STORIES AND FAMILY BOOKS

Moses, Montrose J. *Children's Books and Reading.* 1907. Mitchell Kennerley. Of chief value for its summaries of historical periods in England and America.

Olcott, Frances Jenkins. *Children's Reading.* 1927. Houghton Mifflin Co. Discussion by an authority. Many lists.

Power, Effie. *Library Service for Children.* 1930. American Library Association. Contains four chapters on book selection.

Rawlinson, Eleanor. *Introduction to Literature for Children.* 1930. W. W. Norton & Co., Inc.

Terman, L. M. and Lima, Margaret. *Children's Reading; a Guide for Parents and Teachers.* Revised ed. 1931. D. Appleton-Century Co., Inc.

INDEX

INDEX

INDEX

INDEX

INDEX

INDEX

INDEX